ENGINEERING THERMODYNAMICS

ENGINEERING THERMODYNAMICS

Theory, worked examples and problems

G. Boxer

Senior Tutor, Department of Mechanical Engineering,
University of Aston in Birmingham

First published 1976 by
THE MACMILLAN PRESS LTD
London and Basingstoke

Associated companies in New York Dublin
Melbourne Johannesburg and Madras

ISBN 0 333 19226 5

Printed and bound in Great Britain by

UNWIN BROTHERS LTD
Old Woking, Surrey

CONTENTS

PREFACE

The difficulty in preparing a tutorial volume on a subject like engineering thermodynamics is to select problems covering an adequate range of material and to the right depth which can be contained in a published form which is economically acceptable to all.

The content of this book is based on material taught to all first year mechanical engineering undergraduates at Aston university and is offered as a reasonably self-contained basis of fundamental work essential to any more advanced study of the subject.

The greatest benefit can be obtained by the student in the use of this book only by the exercise of considerable self-discipline. He or she should first attempt the given questions unaided and refer to the solutions for comparison and clarification only if difficulty arises. It is all too easy to read the question and solution together and convince oneself that the whole is fully understood.

It is only by approaching all questions as though they were set in an examination (with no help available) that one discovers one's weaknesses. Then it is possible to do something about it by further reading and further practice. This is the very essence of learning.

The teaching of engineering thermodynamics has changed radically in the last twenty five years or so mainly through the beneficial influence of Professor Keenan at Massachusetts Institute of Technology. It is vital to define all terms as rigorously as possible and an attempt to do this is made in the following pages.

All units are in the Système International d'Unités, or SI for short. It is perhaps right to mention here the dual practice with regard to the unit for pressure. Some authorities favour the use of the pascal (Pa) i.e. 1 kN/m^2, others the bar i.e. 10^5 N/m^2 or 100 kN/m^2. In this volume both are used since there is no clear-cut all-round agreement.

I believe very firmly in the concept of one symbol for one physical idea and use T for all temperatures (and let the units display whether a scale or thermodynamic temperature is in use). Thus

(a) T = 20 °C is a scale temperature

(b) T = 293 K is a thermodynamic temperature.

However, a change in either a scale or a thermodynamic temperature is always given in degrees Kelvin.

The student must learn the vital importance of distinguishing between physical equations and numerical equations and in an effort to encourage this the Stroud convention is used throughout.

Anything multiplied by unity is unchanged and, for example, if a force of 1 N accelerates a mass of 1 kg by 1 m/s^2, then Newton says

$$\text{force} = \text{mass} \times \text{acceleration}$$

or $$\frac{1\ \text{N}}{1\ \text{kg} \times 1\ \text{m/s}^2} = \frac{[\text{N s}^2]}{[\text{kg m}]} = \text{UNITY}$$

This unity bracket can be used as a multiplier to rationalise the units in a numerical equation.

For example, to obtain the temperature equivalent of a fluid velocity of 600 m/s, the following calculation is appropriate to air with c_p = 1.005 kJ/(kg K).

$$\theta_u = \text{Temperature equivalent of } u = u^2/2c_p \quad \text{(physical equation)}$$

$$= \frac{600^2}{2 \times 1.005} \frac{m^2}{s^2} \frac{kg\ K}{kJ} \frac{[N\ s^2]}{[kg\ m]} \frac{[kJ\ ]}{[kNm]} \quad \text{(numerical equation)}$$

$$= \frac{600^2}{2000 \times 1.005} = 179.1\ K$$

Furthermore, for example, in calculating the power delivered from an engine which has a torque of 80 Nm at a speed of rotation of 2000 rev/min

$$\text{Power} = \text{rate of work transfer} = \text{torque} \times \text{angular velocity}$$

$$= \tau \times \omega \quad \text{(physical equation)}$$

$$= 80\ Nm \times 2000 \frac{rev}{min} \frac{[2\pi\ rad]}{[\ \ rev\ \ ]} \frac{[min\ ]}{[60\ s]} \frac{[\ \ kJ\ \ ]}{[1000\ Nm]}$$

$$= 16.76 \frac{kNm}{s} = 16.76\ kW \quad \text{(numerical equation)}$$

The last three terms in this numerical equation are unity brackets and can be used whenever convenient. The use of such brackets obviates the need to worry about homogeneous units since a physical equation is valid in any system of units.

I have endeavoured to grade the problems in each chapter to cover a range of work from the most elementary undergraduate calculations to those appropriate to a first-year examination at University. Occasionally I have borrowed questions from London University B.Sc. Part I degree papers and am grateful to that institution for permission to do so whilst accepting sole responsibility for the solutions which are presented in this book.

The whole of engineering thermodynamics is based on the three fundamental principles of conservation of mass, energy and momentum and the concept of energy degradation embodied in the second law of thermodynamics. It is vital in the solution of all problems to find out just how these principles are brought into use.

It is equally vital to avoid splitting up the subject into purely artificial compartments with labels e.g. reciprocating compressors, gas turbines etc. and to endeavour to bracket certain formulae with each section.

To assist the student in formulating a logical approach to the solution of all problems in the subject I have laid out a set of fundamental questions to be answered each and every time until the right habits have been formed. In order to answer these questions correctly he will have to understand the basic definitions and the associated principles in the subject but once these are mastered he will find his approach is consistent and much more readily applicable than any arbitrary sectioning of the material with its demands upon pure memory as distinct from any appeal to logic.

The figure numbers are associated directly with the questions in which they occur and are not chronologically placed as in other texts. Thus figure 14.3 refers to question 3 in chapter 14 and is not necessarily the third figure in chapter 14.

Throughout the book reference is made (in parentheses) to page numbers. The latter refer to tables of thermodynamic properties of fluids and other data by Y.R.Mayhew and G.F.C.Rogers published by Blackwell which should be used in conjunction with the solutions in this book.

I acknowledge with gratitude the help I have received from my colleagues at Aston over many years and particularly from Mr.F.R. Taylor who is responsible for a considerable proportion of the descriptive material at the start.

NOMENCLATURE

A	Non-flow availability or Area
a	Non-flow specific availability
B	Flow availability
b	Specific flow availability
C	Heat capacity
C_p	Molar isobaric heat capacity
C_v	Molar isochoric heat capacity
c_p	Mass isobaric specific heat capacity
c_v	Mass isochoric specific heat capacity
d	Change in a property (e.g. dv)
E	Internal energy
e	Specific internal energy
f	Saturated liquid state
g	Saturated vapour state or gravitational acceleration
H	Enthalpy
h	Specific enthalpy
i	Constituent gas
k	$(\gamma-1/\gamma)$
m	Mass
m_w	Molecular mass
$\dot{m}$	Mass flow rate
N	Rotational speed
n	Polytropic index OR number of mols
p	Pressure
Q	Heat transfer
$\dot{Q}$	Rate of heat transfer
q	Specific heat transfer
R	Gas constant for individual gas
R_0	Universal gas constant
r	Compression or expansion ratio
S	Entropy
s	Specific entropy
T	Temperature
t	Time
u	Velocity
V	Volume
$\dot{V}$	Volume flow rate
v	Specific volume
W	Work transfer
$\dot{W}$	Rate of work transfer (i.e. power)
w	Specific work transfer

x	Quality of liquid/vapour mixture OR mole fraction
$\bar{x}$	Mean value of x (e.g.)
z	Datum height
γ	$C_p/C_v = c_p/c_v$
δ	Change in a non-property (e.g. δQ)
θ	Angle OR change in temperature
π	Ratio of circumference to diameter of circle
ρ	Density
η	Efficiency
ε	Effectiveness
τ	Torque
ω	Angular Velocity
$\sum$	Sum of
$\oint$	Sum of - round a cycle

SOME USEFUL DEFINITIONS AND ANALOGIES

Historically, thermodynamics grew from the study of heat and temperature, which were often confused! Many of the terms and concepts used in thermodynamics, including *heat*, have been abstracted from common everyday usage where their meanings are very loosely defined. In the scientific study of thermodynamics precise definitions must be adopted and the thermodynamicist must accustom himself to using these terms in both contexts. Initially some self-discipline is necessary to adhere to the rigorous definitions used in thermodynamics.

Thermodynamics Thermodynamics may be described as the study of the equilibrium properties of large-scale systems in which temperature is an important variable.

System A prescribed and identifiable quantity of matter.

State The overall condition of a system at a given time.

Thermodynamic state That part of the overall condition of a system at rest which is dependent upon the state of motion and interaction of its component particles.

Property Any characteristic of a system which can be used to define its state i.e. which depends only upon the state of the system.

Extensive property A property whose magnitude is dependent upon the amount of matter considered e.g. volume.

Intensive property A property whose magnitude does not depend on the amount of matter considered. N.B. These are the potential properties e.g. pressure, temperature, electrical potential, etc. which tend to cause a change in state.

Specific property An extensive property expressed per unit quantity of matter. In the sense that this is independent of the mass in the system it may be regarded as an intensive property for the purpose of defining the state. Lower case letters are used for intensive properties and upper-case letters for extensive properties. e.g. a system of mass m and volume V has a specific volume $v = V/m$.

Equilibrium state A system is in equilibrium if its properties do not change in value when the system is isolated from its surroundings.

Thermodynamic equation of state Any mathematical relationship for the thermodynamic properties of a system in thermal equilibrium e.g. for a perfect gas the equation of state is $pv = RT$ where R is a constant depending on the particular gas.

Simple (or pure) substance A substance which is

(a) homogeneous in chemical composition
(b) homogeneous in chemical aggregation
(c) invariable in chemical aggregation.

N.B. such substances are important because the state of a system composed entirely of a pure substance may be completely defined by two independent, intensive properties.

Process A change of state of a system.

Cycle A process with identical initial and final states.

Phase of a substance The term *phase* is used to denote the molecular regime of a substance e.g. ice, water and steam are respectively the solid, liquid and vapour phases of H_2O.

Internal energy (E) The energy possessed by a system by virtue of the motion and arrangement of its molecules and the vibrations within the molecules. It is a property since its value depends only on the state of the system.

Work (W) Work is energy transferred across a system boundary by virtue of a potential property difference, other than temperature, across the boundary.

Both heat and work are fundamentally different from properties and are known as interactions because they are transient in nature. The nature of heat and work is dealt with in some detail in the following pages. However, the subject of thermodynamics is in essence the study of heat and work transfers upon the properties of a system and conversely the effect of a change in properties on the heat and work transfers.

It is vital to distinguish clearly between the properties of a fluid (p,v,T,etc.) and the interactions at the system boundary Q and W since the latter by their very nature can never be considered as properties. Q and W never exist IN a fluid - they occur at the boundary of a system and are transient in nature. To emphasise this point consider the following analogies.

Analogy 1 - Cloud/Lake

The figure depicts H_2O in three forms.

(a) As vapour in the cloud.
(b) As liquid in the lake.
(c) As liquid falling from the cloud to the lake.

Now we describe the H_2O in the cloud as WATER vapour, and that in the lake as WATER. However, we have a distinct name for the

H_2O in the act of passing between the two. We call it RAIN. The rain is not stored in the cloud nor in the lake - as soon as the rain reaches the lake it becomes just water. The analogy is that this corresponds to the transfer of HEAT from a hot body to a cold

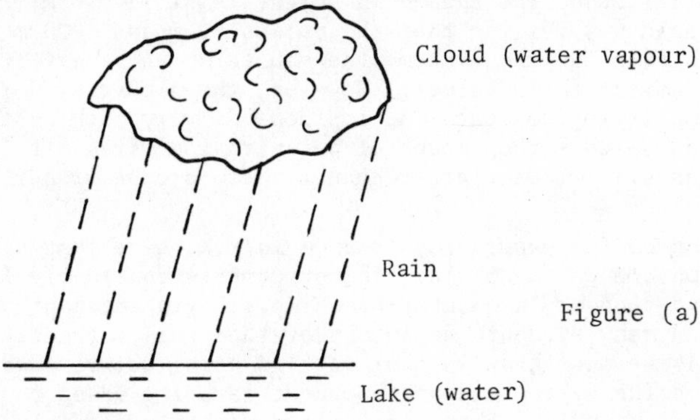

Figure (a)

body wherein the hot body has high internal energy (relatively) and the cold body a lower internal energy. The heat transfer is also energy - BUT the internal energies are properties - the heat transfer is not. The internal energies correspond to the water stored respectively in the cloud and the lake and the heat transfer corresponds to the rain.

Analogy 2 - The Mountain

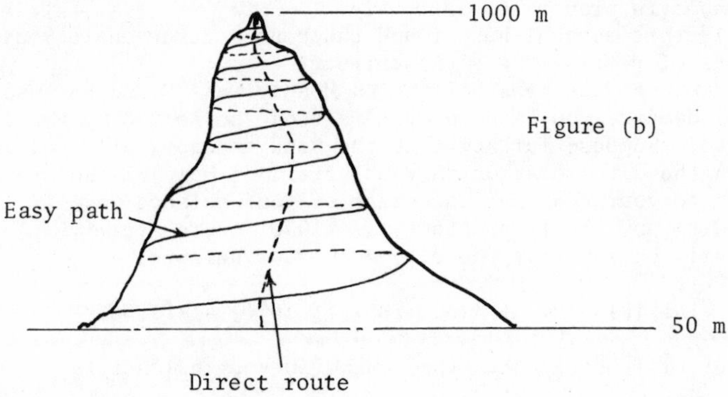

Figure (b)

The figure depicts a mountain with the customary hazards facing any would-be climber. Assuming that the area has been properly surveyed, the height of the mountain summit above sea-level will be known (say 1000 m) and let us suppose that a starting point for a climb is at say 50 m above sea-level.

Let us first assume that the climber is ambitious and attempts a climb by the most direct route. He will probably encounter scree slopes where he may slither around (we hope he is properly shod!) and if he knows what he is doing he will ultimately reach the top. The point is that when he gets there his overall change in height will be 1000 m - 50 m i.e. 950 m.

Let us now assume purely for the sake of argument that this is a mountain with a well-worn and measured path which follows very easy gradients so that it is possible to walk up all the way without the considerable effort required in real mountaineering. When the top is reached the change in height is still 950 m.

We should now realise that the values 50 m and 1000 m are PROPERTIES relating to the system (the mountain) and the PATH taken does not affect their values. However, the amount of work done by the person trying to reach the top depends very much on the path chosen and so does the amount of perspiration given off (i.e. the heat transfer). These latter cannot therefore be properties.

Digression on the expression 'change in' We have just used the expression *change in height*. The student is constantly involved in finding changes in quantities while studying mechanical engineering and many students do not understand this correctly.

Clearly we must know whether work is being delivered by a system or done on the system and whether heat is being added to a system or rejected from it. Thus *sense* plays a vital role. In other words Q and W have magnitude and sense (but not direction and are therefore not vectors).

Quite naturally as engineers we are interested in the production of work and it is logical to call work delivered positive work. Since we most commonly achieve positive work from a system by first of all supplying heat to it then heat supplied is also treated as positive. Conversely work in to a system or heat rejected from a system are treated as negative.

It is vital to adhere to this scheme of things by interpreting *changes in* properties correctly.

In this sense I have found the bank-balance analogy useful as a means of getting the signs correct.

Suppose your bank balance on Monday was £5 and because of various demands you have an overdraft on the following Friday of say £1000. Suppose further that the bank manager calls you in to discuss the deterioration in your affairs. How will he present the case to you? The initial state of your balance was +£5 (i.e. in credit) and the final state is -£1000 (overdraft).

Will he say that the *change in* your balance is

Initial - Final i.e. +£5 - £(-1000) = +£1005?

Or will he say that the *change in* your balance is

Final - Initial i.e. -£1000 - £(+5) = -£1005?

Clearly the latter is correct i.e.

change in means final - initial.

Thus for example the change in internal energy from state 1 to state 2 is $(E_2 - E_1)$.

Control surface and control volume It is vital in the study of thermodynamics to distinguish between two kinds of process.

(a) Non-flow process.
(b) Flow process.

To make this distinction we now define a *control volume* as any region in space having a *fixed* boundary and position. (Note that a system has a boundary which can change its shape and position but the mass contained therein is constant.)

We now define a non-flow process as one in which the system boundary change occurs wholly within the control volume under observation - i.e. no mass crosses the control surface which bounds the control volume.

Furthermore a flow process is one in which the system boundary change is such that mass does cross the control surface.

Note that Q and W can cross both system and control volume boundaries but by definition *mass* can only cross the latter.

Example of a non-flow process - expansion in a cylinder

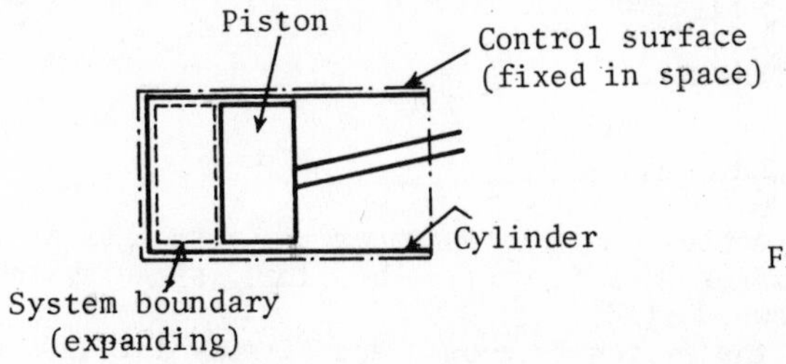

Figure (c)

In the expansion depicted in the figure there is work transfer across the system boundary due to a pressure difference, there may be a heat transfer across the system boundary due to a temperature difference, but there is no mass transfer across the system boundary.

The same remarks apply exactly to the control surface depicted.

Example of a flow process - flow through a nozzle

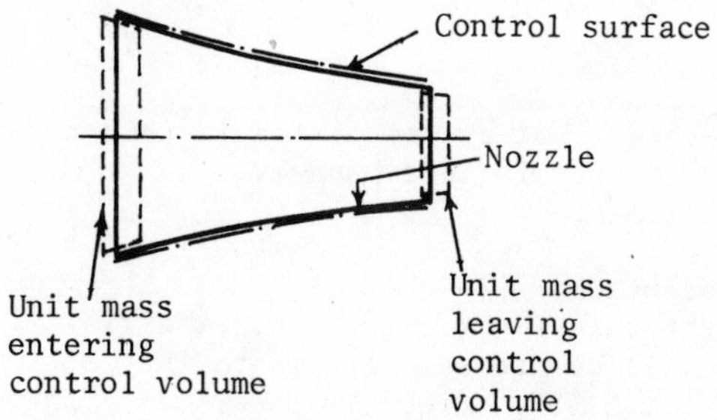

Figure (d)

In this case there is no work transfer or heat transfer to consider but mass does cross the control surface even though by definition it does not cross the system boundary where in this case the system is taken to be unit mass of fluid passing through the nozzle.

The nature of work transfer

Work was previously defined as energy transferred across a system boundary by virtue of a potential property difference, other than temperature, across the boundary.

For example, electric currents represent transfers of energy due to electric potential (voltage) differences across a boundary. More importantly for mechanical engineers, movement of some part of a system boundary due to a force (or pressure difference) across the boundary is a typical example of work transfer.

The force and motion may be either perpendicular to the system boundary or tangential to it. Energy will be transferred as mechanical work provided that some component part of both force and motion act in the same direction.

It is now necessary to discuss the difference between controlled streamline flow and free, turbulent flow.

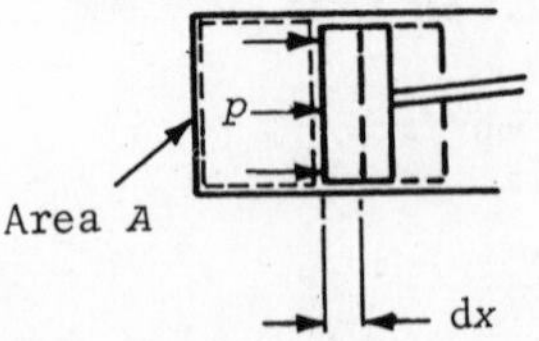

Figure (e)

Consider the expansion of a piston under the action of a fluid contained in a cylinder (see figure). The fluid is the system and its boundary is shown dotted.

Let the area of the piston face be A and firstly let us assume the expansion to be so controlled that at a given moment the pressure everywhere in the fluid is p. The force on the piston face due to the fluid will be pA.

Now assume that after an infinitesimal lapse of time the piston has moved a distance $\mathrm{d}x$ to the right and the flow is so controlled that although the pressure has changed infinitesimally it is everywhere the same at all points in the fluid.

The work done during this piston movement by the fluid on the piston is the product of force and the distance moved

$$\text{or} \quad \delta W = (pA) \times \mathrm{d}x$$
$$= p\,\mathrm{d}V$$

where $\mathrm{d}V$ is the volume swept out by the piston in this time.

Assuming the flow continues in this manner.

$$W_{\text{overall}} = \int_{\textit{initial state}}^{\textit{final state}} p\,\mathrm{d}V$$

Conversely, as is the case in practice, when the flow is turbulent and free, there will be pressure gradients in the fluid at a given time and p will not have a unique value at all points in the fluid at that time and nor will it be a unique function of V during expansion.

Under these circumstances

$$W \neq \int p\,\mathrm{d}V$$

The graphical interpretation of controlled, streamline flow is as shown in the figure.

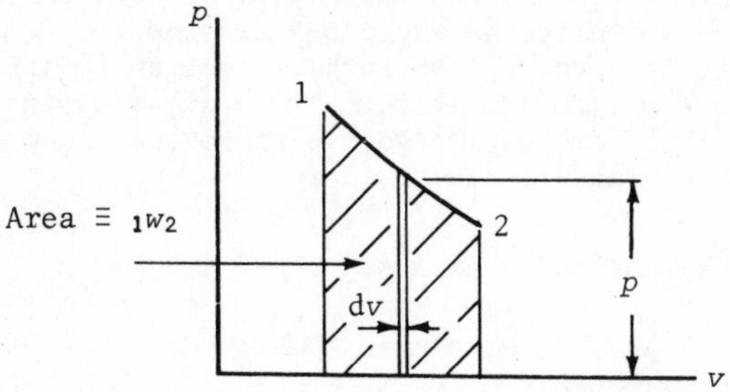

Figure (f)

$_1W_2$ ≡ Area under the curve 1-2 which represents the controlled expansion where p is some known function of V and all intermediate states between 1 and 2 are known.

Conversely free, turbulent flow must be represented as below.

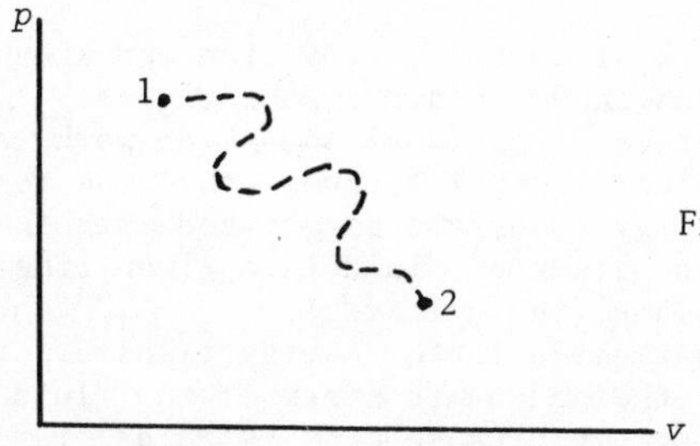

Figure (g)

No area under a curve can be found since there is no known curve between 1 and 2. A state cannot be found between these two states because the fluid is never in equilibrium. In order to calculate W in this case other information must be available. For example, from the first law of thermodynamics

$$_1Q_2 - {_1W_2} = E_2 - E_1$$

Provided that the initial and final states 1 and 2 are known and also $_1Q_2$ then $_1W_2$ is calculable.

The above arguments relate to a non-flow process if the control volume just embraces the entire cylinder.

However, many students cannot distinguish between this work transfer and that corresponding to a flow process made up of three distinct parts, namely suction, expansion and exhaust.

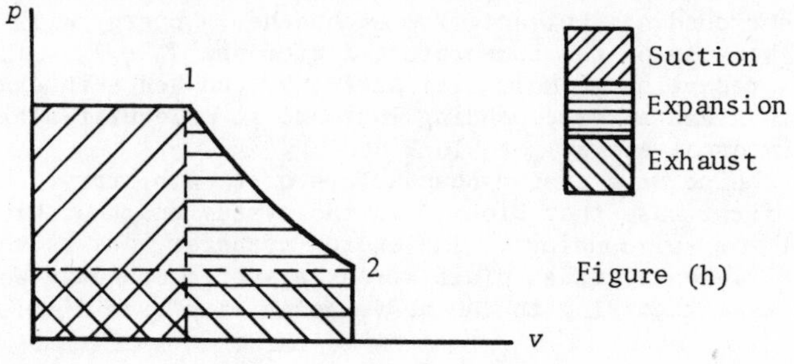

Figure (h)

Thus for the same cylinder but now assuming a constant pressure suction process to start with, the same expansion as before and a constant pressure exhaust process to finish with we have the configuration depicted as shown in the above p-V diagram.

The total work done is given by the work of suction (positive because fluid does work on the crank) plus the work of expansion as before plus the work of exhaust (negative since the crank does work on the fluid in this case).

Thus $W = W_{\text{suction}} + W_{\text{expansion}} + W_{\text{exhaust}}$

or $$W = p_1V_1 + \int_{V_1}^{V_2} p\, dV - p_1V_2$$

This work is clearly given by

$$W = \int_{p_2}^{p_1} V\, dp$$

which is the total work of suction, expansion and exhaust and is represented by the area shown shaded in the figure.

The distinction between $\int p\, dV$ work and $\int V\, dp$ work is very important and further consideration will reveal that the terms p_1V_1 and p_2V_2 represent the energy transfers associated with the movement of the system (a given packet of fluid in a given time) into and out of the control volume (the cylinder).

. One should note that these latter energy transfers take place with no change in the thermodynamic state of the fluid in the system - they are there simply because mass is being transferred into and out of the control volume. However, work transfer inevitably occurs with these mass transfers.

The thermodynamic state changes from 1 to 2 when a fixed packet of fluid contained within the control volume undergoes an expansion process.

The nature of heat transfer

Heat is energy transferred across a system boundary by virtue of a temperature difference across the boundary.

For example consider block A at a uniform temperature T_A and block B at another uniform temperature T_B (where $T_B < T_A$). Let the two be brought into contact and be thermally insulated from their surroundings but not from each other. Energy will flow from A to B because of the temperature difference $T_A - T_B$. This will cause a reduction in molecular activity (and hence internal energy) of block A and a corresponding increase in molecular activity (and hence internal energy) of block B.

The choice of a system boundary is quite arbitrary. Consider in the first case that block A is the system and that block B forms part of the surroundings. The energy transfer, due to the temperature difference, takes place across a system boundary and is thus termed *heat* according to the above definition (see figure)

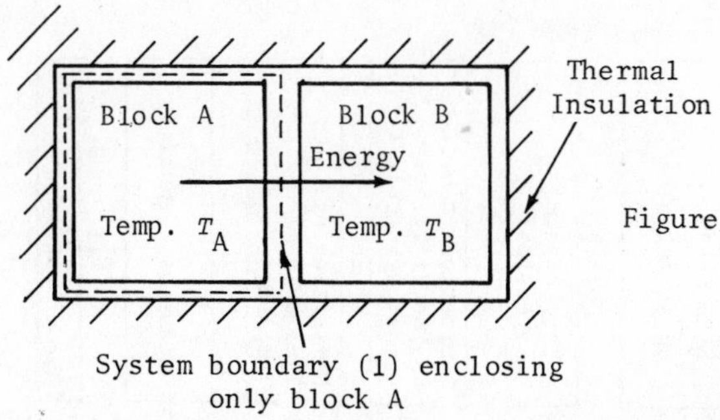

Figure (i)

By choosing the system boundary to include both blocks A and B the energy transfer no longer crosses a system boundary and would not be termed *heat* relative to the new system.

This second system is not in thermal equilibrium since it changes state by redistribution of its internal energy although it is isolated from its surroundings (see figure).

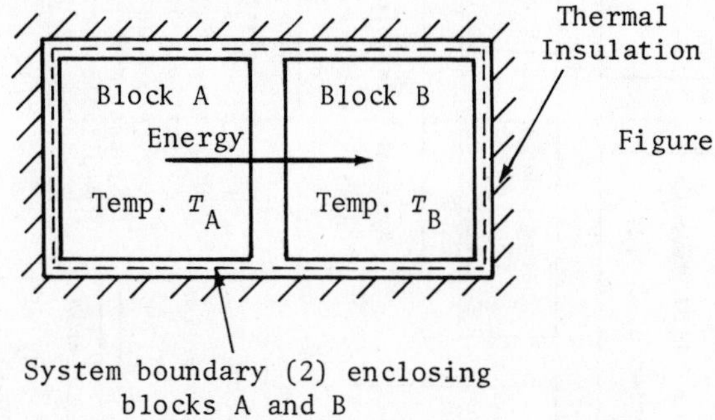

Figure (j)

Heat transfer is a subject in its own right and can occur in various modes, conduction, convection and radiation or a combination of one or more of these. We are only interested here in the numerical value of heat as predicted by the application of the laws of thermodynamics to systems and not in the detailed mechanism of the energy transfer.

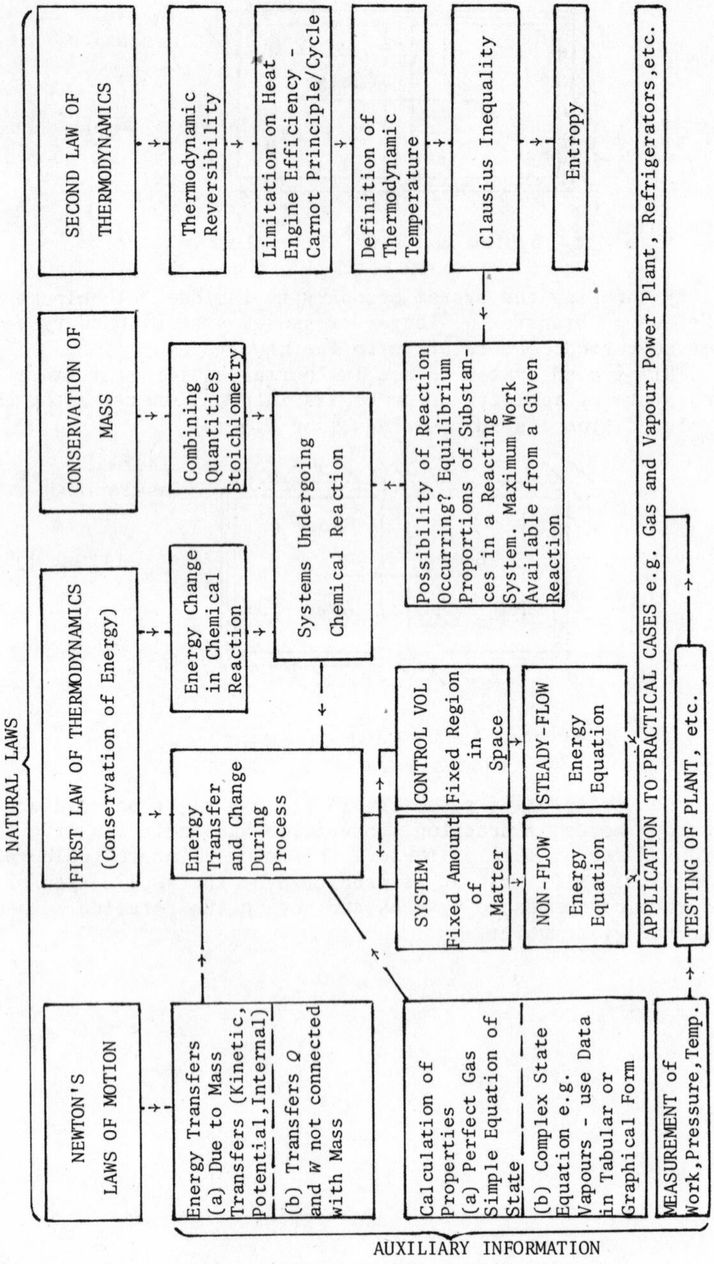

THE STRUCTURE OF ENGINEERING THERMODYNAMICS

This diagram is intended to show how the various topics in the subject are inter-related. Note that not all the topics shown are dealt with in a first year and some details are omitted.

A FUNDAMENTAL APPROACH TO THE SOLUTION OF THERMODYNAMICS PROBLEMS

The following is an attempt to assist students in adopting a rational approach to the solution of all problems in thermodynamics. If the following questions are correctly answered each and every time a problem is attempted there should be no fundamental difficulty in obtaining a solution.

1. What kind of *process*? (a) Flow or (b) Non-flow?

To answer this it is necessary to define the system boundary and/or the control surface and then decide whether mass crosses the latter.

2. What kind of *fluid*?

(a) Liquid?
(b) Liquid/Vapour Mixture?
(c) Saturated Vapour?
(d) Superheated Vapour?
(e) Perfect Gas?
(f) Semi-perfect Gas? (i.e. one with variable c_p and c_v)

3. Have you drawn a *state diagram(s)*?

It is vitally important to get a picture of events.

4. Which form of the *energy equation* is required?

(a) Non-flow?
(b) Steady-flow?
(c) Unsteady-flow?

5. Do you need to use the *mass continuity* equation?

$\dot{m}v = uA$

6. Do you need to use the *momentum* equation?

7. Have you used the *correct language*? e.g.

w in kJ/kg, W in kJ, $\dot{W}$ in kW, etc.

8. Always put in *dimensions* with the numbers in your reasoning.

Dimensions are a check on your arguments and are more important than the numbers in front. Use unity brackets to rationalise the dimensions.

9. Do not effect *numerical calculation* until you have to.

1 WORK AND HEAT TRANSFER

1. State the direction of the heat transfer Q and work W for each of the following processes. (The systems to be considered are underlined.)

(a) The air in a tyre and connected pump. The pump plunger is pushed down, forcing air into the tyre. Assume tyre, pump walls, plunger and connecting tube to be non-conducting.

(b) Steam in a closed rigid vessel at a temperature of 150 °C is left standing in an atmosphere which is at a temperature of 25 °C.

(c) Gas in an insulated cylinder expands as the piston is moved slowly outwards.

(d) The water and water vapour in a closed rigid metallic container. The container is set on a stove, and the pressure and temperature of its contents rise.

(e) The system in (d) bursts its container and explodes into a cold atmosphere.

(f) Liquid in a non-conducting vessel. The liquid comes to rest from an initial state of turbulent motion.

(g) A rigid vessel containing ammonia gas is connected through a valve to an evacuated rigid vessel. The vessels, valve and connecting pipe are insulated. The valve is opened and after a time conditions throughout the two vessels become uniform.

(h) One kilogram of air flows, so rapidly that heat transfer may be neglected, from the atmosphere into a previously evacuated bottle.

(a) Referring to figure 1.1a assuming the pump displacement is greater than the tyre expansion W is negative. Since all parts are non-conducting Q is zero.

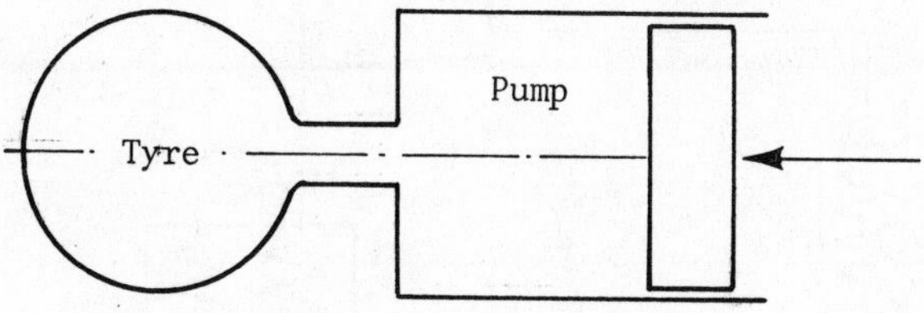

Figure 1.1a

(b) For a closed rigid vessel W is zero. Since the steam is at a higher temperature than the atmosphere Q is rejected to the atmosphere i.e. Q is negative.

(c) The system boundary expands so that the gas does work on the piston i.e. W is positive. For an insulated cylinder Q is zero.

(d) For a rigid container W is zero. For a metallic container with the pressure and temperature rising inside Q is into the system and is thus positive.

(e) The system boundary disintegrates due to the unresisted expansion and both water and water vapour receive unknown Q whilst W is zero.

(f) For a non-conducting vessel Q is zero. Because the system boundary is indeterminate there is no work i.e. W is zero. In this case random kinetic energy of the fluid molecules transforms into a change in the internal energy of these molecules.

(g) Since gas will diffuse to fill all the space offered to it and the system boundary may be considered to embrace both vessels at the start of the process both Q and W will be zero.

(h) Referring to figure 1.1h, at the start of the process the boundary encloses the air and vessel together and is reduced to be just the vessel only at the finish. Thus W is negative.

Note, however, that the fluid occupies volume V at pressure p before entering and possesses internal energy E. This last is transported into the vessel and since the surroundings have pushed in the fluid doing work pV *on* the system the net energy within the vessel is $E + pV$ i.e. H the enthalpy. This is the particular significance of this example.

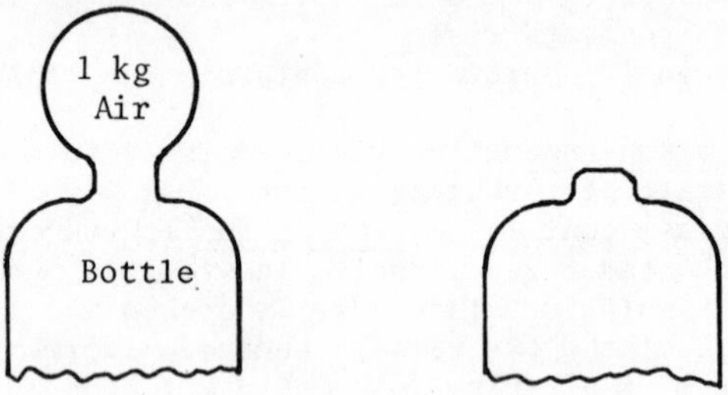

Figure 1.1h

2. The sketch (figure 1.2a) shows a steam power plant in which the turbine and feed pump operate adiabatically. The steam/water

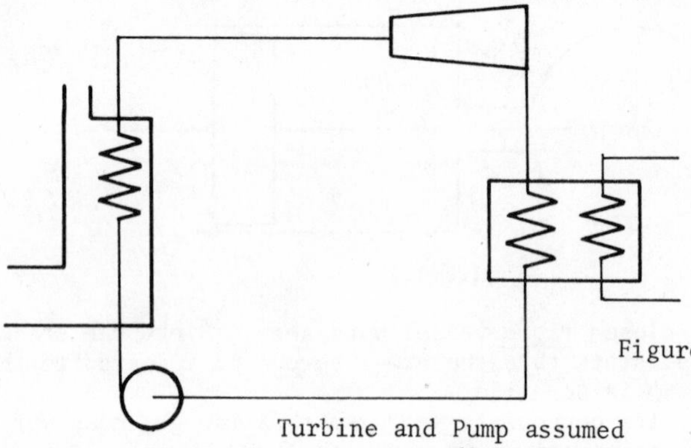

Figure 1.2a

Turbine and Pump assumed to operate adiabatically

circuit contains essentially a fixed quantity of fluid and can therefore be regarded as a system. Draw a boundary to enclose the system. Mark on the diagram the heat and work transfers which will occur, showing clearly which are positive and which negative.

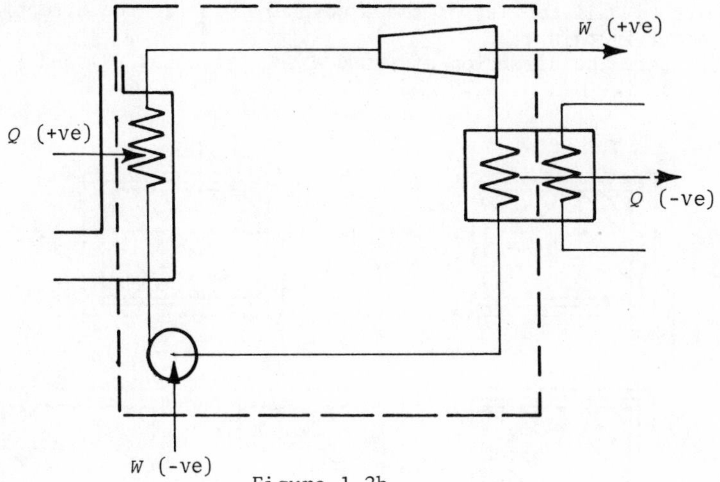

Figure 1.2b

3. Fuel is burned in the engine shown in figure 1.3a causing an increase in the pressure of the fluid contained therein. The piston is forced down and turns the crankshaft. The cylinder is uninsulated and runs at a temperature above atmospheric. Draw a boundary enclosing a system and indicate the heat and work transfers which are involved in the process.

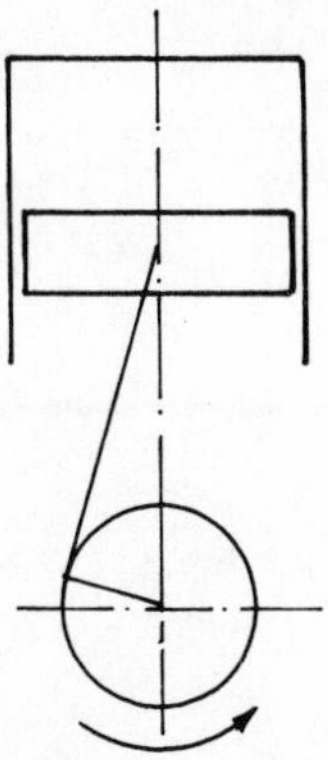

Figure 1.3a

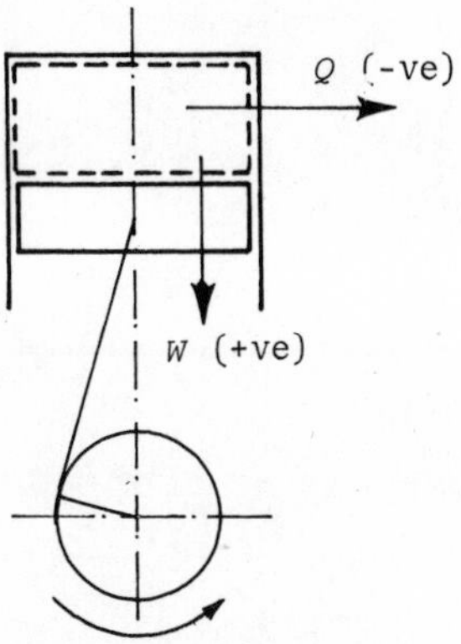

Figure 1.3b

4. A rigid insulated vessel is divided into two parts by a diaphragm. One part of the vessel contains sulphuric acid at a temperature of 18 °C and the other contains water at a temperature of 18 °C. The diaphragm is removed so allowing the two fluids to mix

freely, the pressure and temperature of the contents thereby rising.

(a) Considering the contents of the vessel as the system, state the direction of the heat transfer Q and that of the work transfer W.

(b) The insulation is removed allowing the temperature of the contents to fall to that of the atmosphere. State the direction of Q and W in this case.

(c) State the direction of Q and W for processes (a) and (b) together.

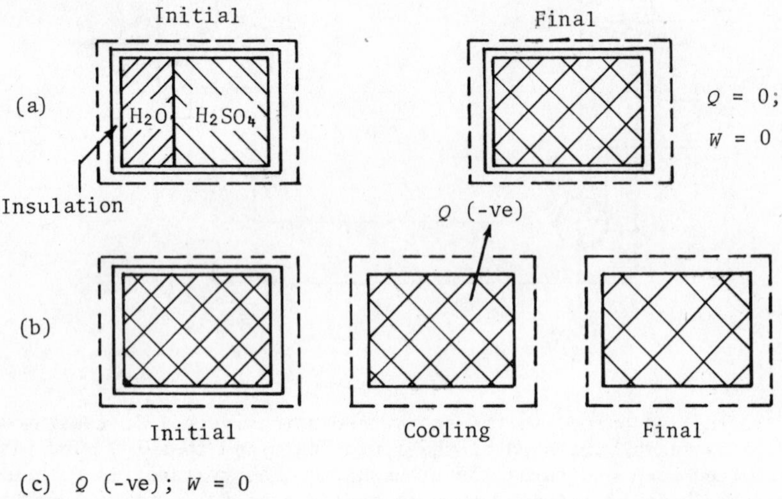

Figure 1.4

2 WORK TRANSFER (HARDER EXAMPLES)

1. An electrical generator is used to measure the torque available from the output shaft of a prime mover. The stator of the generator is carried on trunnion bearings and is restricted from rotating under the interaction of rotor and stator magnetic fields by means of a torque arm (see figure 2.1). (The torque arm must be horizontal during use so that the torque is the product of the net restraining force and the torque arm radius.) For a particular trial a torque arm of 0.5 m carries a fixed load of 120 N. This downward force is greater than can be supported by the torque transmitted from rotor to stator and the force difference required to restrain the stator is provided by a spring balance registering 15 N. Calculate the shaft power for a rotational speed of 3000 rev/min.

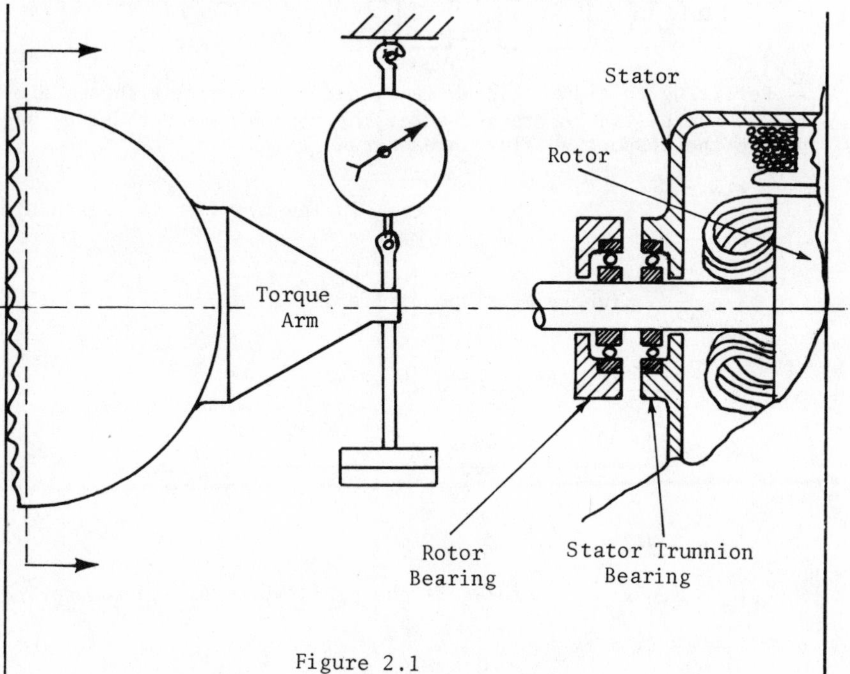

Figure 2.1

Work transfer W = torque × angle
and power, which is the rate of work transfer is given by

$$\dot{W} = \text{torque} \times \text{rate of angular displacement}$$

or $\dot{W} = (120 - 15)\ \text{N} \times 0.5\ \text{m} \times 3000\ \dfrac{\text{rev}}{\text{min}} \left[\dfrac{2\pi\ \text{rad}}{\text{rev}}\right]\left[\dfrac{\text{kW s}}{1000\ \text{Nm}}\right]\left[\dfrac{\text{min}}{60\ \text{s}}\right]$

or $\dot{W} = 16.5$ kW

2. A piston of 0.4 m diameter encloses fluid in one end of a cylinder and slides without friction. The other end of the cylinder is ventilated to atmosphere. The piston is connected to a coil spring of stiffness 40 kN/m. Initially the fluid pressure within the cylinder is 200 000 Pa and the atmospheric pressure is 1 bar. Find the distance through which the piston moves, the energy stored in the spring and the work transfer effected by the fluid as pressure rises slowly to 500 000 Pa.

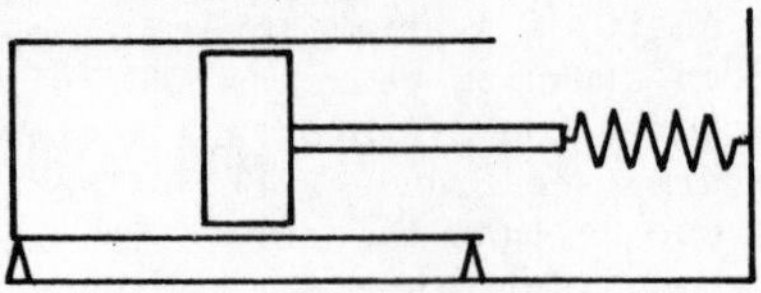

Figure 2.2

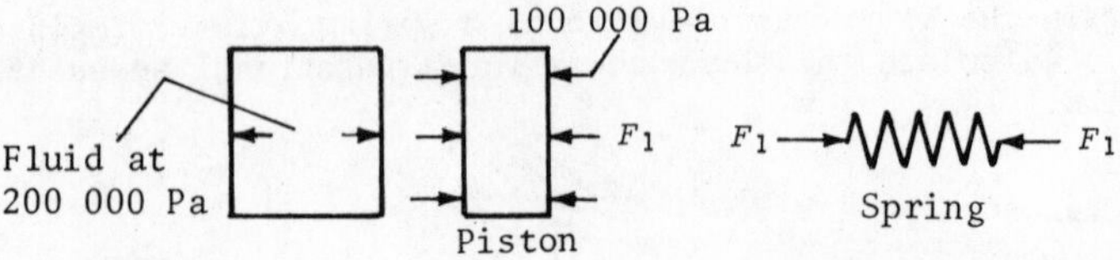

Referring to figure 2.2 where F_1 and F_2 are spring forces exerted on the piston before and after the piston movement and p_1 and p_2 are the respective fluid pressures

$$p_1A - p_aA - F_1 = 0$$

(where p_a is the atmospheric pressure)

$$p_2A - p_aA - F_2 = 0$$

$$K = \frac{dF}{dx} \quad \text{(where } K \text{ is the stiffness)}$$

Hence

$$\Delta x = \frac{F_2 - F_1}{K} = \frac{(p_2 - p_1)A}{K}$$

$$= \frac{(500\ 000 - 200\ 000)\ \text{Pa} \times \frac{\pi}{4} \times 0.4^2\ \text{m}^2}{40\ \frac{\text{kN}}{\text{m}}} \left[\frac{\text{Nm}^{-2}}{\text{Pa}}\right]$$

$\Delta x = 0.942$ m

$$W_s = \int F\, dx \quad \text{(where } W_s \text{ is the fluid work done on the spring)}$$

and $F = \int K\, dx = Kx + C$

Thus $W_s = Kx^2 + Cx + D$

Boundary conditions

$$F = 0 \text{ when } x = 0 \rightarrow C = 0$$

$$W_s = 0 \text{ when } x = 0 \rightarrow D = 0$$

Now $x_2 - x_1 = \Delta x = 0.942$ m

and $x_1 = \dfrac{(p_1 - p_a)A}{K} = \dfrac{100\ 000 \text{ Pa} \times \dfrac{\pi \times 0.4^2}{4} \text{ m}^2}{40 \dfrac{\text{kN}}{\text{m}}} \quad \dfrac{[\text{Nm}^{-2}]}{[\text{ Pa }]}$

$x_1 = 0.314$ m

Thus $x_2 = 0.314 + 0.942 = 1.256$ m

$$W_s = \int_{0.342}^{1.256} Kx \, dx = K\left[\frac{x^2}{2}\right]_{0.342}^{1.256} = 40 \frac{\text{kN}}{\text{m}}\left(\frac{1.578 - 0.117}{2}\right)\text{m}^2$$

$W_s = 29.5$ kJ

Also the work done on the atmosphere by the fluid is given by

$W_a = p_a A(x_2 - x_1)$

$= 100 \dfrac{\text{kN}}{\text{m}} \times 0.126 \text{ m}^2 \times 0.942 \text{ m} \quad \dfrac{[\text{kJ }]}{[\text{kNm}]}$

$W_a = 11.9$ kJ

Thus $\underline{W_F = W_s + W_a = 29.6 + 11.9 = 41.5 \text{ kJ}}$

3. A steam catapult is used to assist the acceleration of aircraft from standstill to flight speed in a very short distance. Steam is admitted to the cylinder and the steam pressure acts on one side of a piston sliding in the cylinder, the space on the other side being vented to atmosphere. The force produced is transmitted to the aircraft by means of a suitable linkage (see figure 2.3a).

(a) On a day when the atmospheric pressure is 980 mbar steam is admitted at 20 bar throughout the 25 m stroke of the piston. The piston diameter is 0.5 m and its motion is at all times resisted. What is the pressure difference across the piston and the total work transfer effected?

(b) Steam is now admitted during a part of the stroke only and thereafter the fixed mass of steam in the cylinder expands to a reduced pressure; due to the acceleration of the piston the air pressure acting on the ventilated side increases. Assuming the geometric details in (a) and that steam is now admitted at 20 bar for 60% of the stroke, the pressure falling linearly to 4 bar over the remainder of the stroke, sketch a diagram of steam pressure versus piston stroke. (This is called an *indicator diagram*.) On the same diagram show the air pressure acting on the ventilated side of the piston, assuming that it rises linearly from 1 bar to 8 bar. Estimate the net work transfer during the complete stroke of the piston.

(c) If the mass of the aircraft (i.e. airframe and engines), towing linkage and piston is 7000 kg and the turbojet engines produce a constant thrust of 44 kN during the launching what velocity does the aircraft reach at the end of the catapult in case (b)? Neglect all frictional effects.

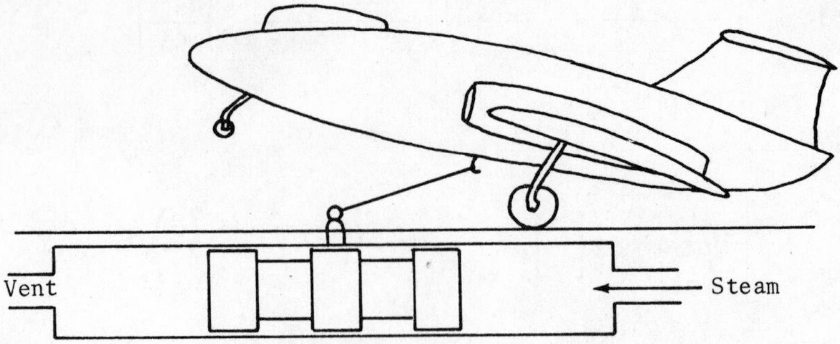

Figure 2.3

(a) $\Delta p = 20 \text{ bar} - 980 \text{ mbar}\left[\frac{\text{bar}}{1000 \text{ mbar}}\right] = \underline{19.02 \text{ bar}}$

$W = 19.02 \text{ bar}\left[\frac{100 \text{ kN}}{\text{bar m}^2}\right] \times \frac{\pi \times 0.5^2}{4} \text{ m}^2 \times 25 \text{ m}$

$\underline{W = 9.34 \times 10^6 \text{ Nm}}$

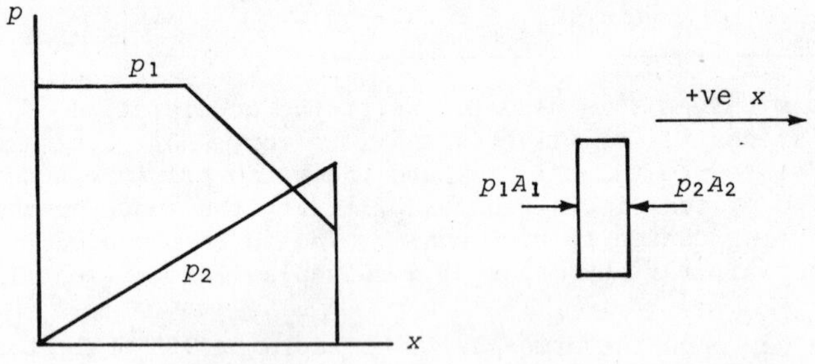

Figure 2.3a

(b) $W = \int_0^x F_{net} \, dx = \int_0^x (p_1 - p_2)A \, dx$

$W = 2000 \frac{\text{kN}}{\text{m}^2} \times 0.196 \text{ m}^2 \times 0.6 \times 25 \text{ m}$ (←constant p_1 = 20 bar)

$+ \frac{(2000 + 400)}{2} \frac{\text{kN}}{\text{m}^2} \times 0.196 \text{ m}^2 \times 0.4 \times 25 \text{ m}$ (←p_1 decreasing)

$- \frac{(100 + 800)}{2} \frac{\text{kN}}{\text{m}^2} \times 0.196 \text{ m}^2 \times 25 \text{ m}$ (←p_2 increasing)

$= \underline{6.03 \times 10^6 \text{ Nm}}$

(c) $\sum$energy transfers = 0

Aircraft + gear ≡ system

Kinetic energy change + work transfer from the system = 0

Total work transfer = $\frac{mu^2}{2}$

and $\frac{mu^2}{2} = \left(6.03 \times 10^6 \text{ Nm} \frac{[\text{ kN }]}{[1000 \text{ N}]}\right) + (44 \text{ kN} \times 25 \text{ m})$

$= 7130 \text{ kNm}$

or $u^2 = \frac{2 \times 7130 \text{ kNm}}{7000 \text{ kg}} \frac{[\text{kg m}]}{[\text{N s}^2]} \frac{[1000 \text{ N}]}{[\text{ kN }]}$

or $\underline{u = 45.1 \frac{\text{m}}{\text{s}}}$

4. A four cylinder four stroke petrol engine undergoes a test in which indicator diagrams are produced on a *p-V* field whose axes have scales

pressure scale $1 \text{ m} \equiv 10^{10} \text{ N/m}^2$

volume scale $1 \text{ m} \equiv 10^{-3} \text{ m}^3$

The average diagram area is $58.3 \times 10^{-6} \text{ m}^2$.

Find the indicated power of the engine in kilowatts if the crankshaft rotates at 3500 rev/min. The engine drives a brake on which the output torque is measured as a force of 308 N acting at a radius of 0.5 m. Find the output power of the engine. If the cylinder bore is 0.088 m and the stroke is 0.108 m find the brake mean effective pressure in bar.

Indicated power = rate of indicated work transfer

$= \frac{\text{work}}{\text{cycle}} \times \frac{\text{cycle}}{\text{time}} = \frac{\text{work}}{\text{cycle}} \times \frac{\text{cycle}}{\text{rev}} \times \frac{\text{rev}}{\text{time}}$

$1 \text{ m}^2 \text{ of diagram} \equiv 10^{10} \frac{\text{N}}{\text{m}^2} \times 10^{-3} \text{ m}^3 = 10^7 \text{ Nm}$

$\text{Indicated work} = 58.3 \times 10^{-6} \text{ m}^2 \frac{\text{diagram}}{\text{cycle}} \frac{[\quad 10^7 \text{ Nm} \quad]}{[\text{m}^2 \text{ diagram}]}$

$= 583 \frac{\text{Nm}}{\text{cycle}}$

$\text{Indicated power} = 583 \frac{\text{Nm}}{\text{cycle}} \times \frac{4 \text{ cycle}}{2 \text{ rev}} \times 3500 \frac{\text{rev}}{\text{min}} \times \frac{[\text{ kW s }]}{[1000 \text{ Nm}]} \frac{[\text{min}]}{[60 \text{ s}]}$

$= \underline{68 \text{ kW}}$

Brake power = torque × rate of angular displacement

$= 308 \text{ N} \times 0.5 \text{ m} \times 3500 \frac{\text{rev}}{\text{min}} \times \frac{[2\pi \text{ rad}]}{[\text{ rev }]} \frac{[\text{ kW s }]}{[1000 \text{ Nm}]} \frac{[\text{min}]}{[60 \text{ s}]}$

$= \underline{56.4 \text{ kW}}$

$$\text{Actual work per cycle} = \frac{\text{brake power}}{\frac{\text{cycle}}{\text{rev}} \times \frac{\text{rev}}{\text{min}}} = \frac{56.4 \text{ kW} \frac{[10 \quad \text{Nm}]}{[\text{ kW s }]}}{\frac{4 \text{ cycle}}{2 \text{ rev}} \times 3500 \frac{\text{rev}[\text{min}\ ]}{\text{min}[60 \text{ s}]}}$$

$$= 484 \frac{\text{Nm}}{\text{cycle}}$$

$$\text{Brake mean effective pressure} = \frac{\text{actual cyclic work}}{\text{swept volume}}$$

$$= \frac{484 \text{ Nm} \frac{[\text{bar m }]}{[100 \text{ kN}]}}{\frac{\pi}{4} \times 0.088^2 \text{ m}^2 \times 0.108 \text{ m}}$$

$$= \underline{7.37 \text{ bar}}$$

5. The device shown in figure 2.4a consists of a cylinder 0.25 m diameter fitted with a leak-tight frictionless piston coupled to a rack and pinion. The pitch circle diameter of the pinion teeth is 0.2 m. A drum fixed to the same shaft has a diameter of 1 m and carries a rope supporting masses which cause the fluid in the cylinder to be pressurised initially to 3 bar when the atmospheric pressure is 1 bar. Find the mass supported on the rope. Further masses are added slowly and the fluid compresses according to the law pV = constant until the pressure is finally 6 bar. If the initial volume of fluid was 0.01 m what is the total work transfer relative to the gas?

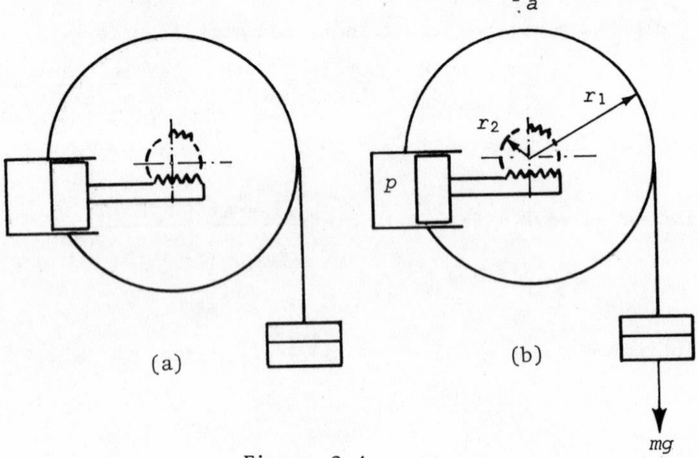

Figure 2.4

$\sum$Torque = 0 and taking clockwise torque as positive

$$m_1 g r_1 - (p - p_a)A r_2 = 0$$

$$m_1 = \frac{(p - p_a)A r_2}{g r_1} = \frac{(300 - 100)\frac{\text{kN}}{\text{m}^2} \times \frac{\pi}{4} \times 0.25^2 \text{ m}^2 \times 0.1 \text{ m} \frac{[\text{kg m}]}{[\text{N s}^2]}}{9.81 \frac{\text{m}}{\text{s}^2} \times 0.5 \text{ m}}$$

$$= \underline{200 \text{ kg}}$$

Work done by fluid on surroundings $W = \int p \, dv$ where pV = constant

$$W = p_1 V_1 \ln \frac{V_2}{V_1} = p_1 V_1 \ln \frac{p_1}{p_2} = 300 \frac{\text{kN}}{\text{m}^2} \times 0.01 \text{ m}^3 \times \ln \frac{1}{2}$$

$$= -2.08 \text{ kNm} = \underline{-2.08 \text{ kJ}}$$

3 FIRST LAW OF THERMODYNAMICS - SYSTEMS

1. The first law of thermodynamics may be expressed in the symbolic equation

$$ {}_1Q_2 - {}_1W_2 = E_2 - E_1 $$

Define the symbols and sign convention which give rise to the equation.

A fixed quantity of fluid is cooled and simultaneously compressed. If the heat rejected is 50 kJ and the work done in compression is 34 kJ, determine the change in internal energy.

The equation refers to a thermodynamic process starting with state 1 and finishing with state 2.

${}_1Q_2$ represents the heat transfer to or from the system during the process and if negative in value infers that heat is rejected and vice-versa.

${}_1W_2$ represents the work (positive if done by the system and vice-versa).

E_1 and E_2 are respectively the internal energies possessed by the system before and after the process.

$$ {}_1Q_2 - {}_1W_2 = E_2 - E_1 $$

or $\quad E_2 - E_1 = (-50 \text{ kJ}) - (-34 \text{ kJ}) = \underline{-16 \text{ kJ}}$

2. The tangential force on the cutting tool of a lathe when cutting a workpiece of 0.35 m diameter is 120 N. After 10 minutes the internal energy of the workpiece and chips has increased by 200 kJ. If the frequency of revolution of the workpiece is 200 rev/min estimate the heat transfer from the workpiece and chips in this time.

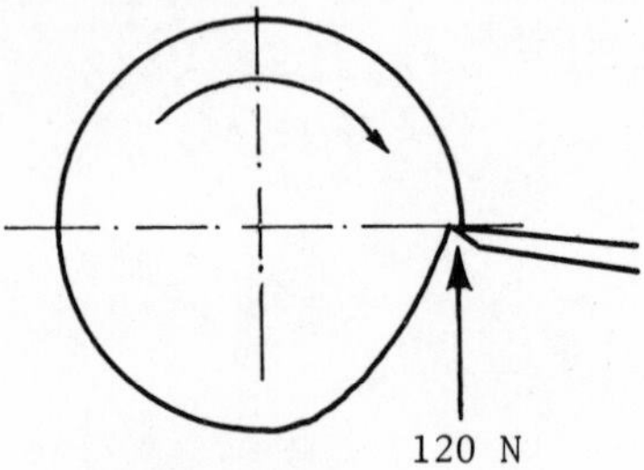

Figure 3.2

$$ {}_1Q_2 - {}_1W_2 = E_2 - E_1 $$

or $\quad {}_1Q_2 = (E_2 - E_1) + {}_1W_2$

where ${}_1W_2$ is the work done *on* the workpiece given by

$$_1W_2 = -(\text{torque} \times \text{angular displacement})$$

$$\text{Thus } _1Q_2 = 200 \text{ kJ} - (120 \text{ N} \times \frac{0.35}{2} \text{ m} \times 200 \frac{\text{rev}}{\text{min}} \times 10 \text{ min}) \times \left[\frac{2\pi \text{ rad}}{\text{rev}}\right]\left[\frac{\text{kJ}}{1000 \text{ Nm}}\right]$$

$$= 200 \text{ kJ} - 263.9 \text{ kJ} = \underline{-63.9 \text{ kJ}}$$

3. A system executes a cycle during which there are four heat transfers.

(a) A heat transfer of 210 kJ into the system.
(b) A heat transfer of 20 kJ out of the system.
(c) A heat transfer of 190 kJ out of the system.
(d) A heat transfer of 40 kJ into the system.

The above take place whilst there are three corresponding work transfers of 180 000 Nm, 200 000 Nm and 300 kJ respectively into, out of and into the system. There is a fourth work transfer which has to be calculated. What is it?

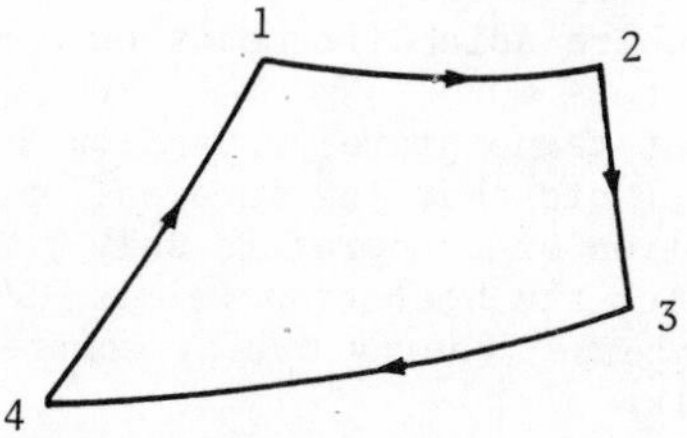

Figure 3.3

Let the four processes in the cycle be designated in order by the successive states 1-2, 2-3, 3-4 and 4-1.

Applying the first law of thermodynamics to each turn

$$_1Q_2 - {_1W_2} = E_2 - E_1$$

$$_2Q_3 - {_2W_3} = E_3 - E_2$$

$$_3Q_4 - {_3W_4} = E_4 - E_3$$

$$_4Q_1 - {_4W_1} = E_1 - E_4$$

Adding the above four equations algebraically

$$\oint Q - \oint W = 0$$

$$\text{Thus } \oint Q = (+210 - 20 - 190 + 40) \text{ kJ} = +40 \text{ kJ} = \oint W$$

$$\text{or} \quad 40 \text{ kJ} = -180 \text{ kJ} + 200 \text{ kJ} - 300 \text{ kJ} + {_4W_1}$$

$$\text{or} \quad \underline{_4W_1 = +320 \text{ kJ}}$$

4. A system receives 180 kJ by heat transfer at constant volume. Next it rejects 200 kJ by heat transfer as it receives 50 kJ of work at constant pressure.

(a) If a process can be found which will restore it to the initial state without a heat transfer to or from the system, how much work transfer is done by the system during the process?

(b) Taking the internal energy in the initial state as zero find the corresponding internal energies at the other two states.

(a) The three processes constitute a cycle if the initial state is restored, that is

$$\oint Q = \oint W$$

Thus $_1Q_2 - {_1W_2} = E_2 - E_1$ or $+180\text{ kJ} - (0) = E_2 - E_1$

$_2Q_3 - {_2W_3} = E_3 - E_2$ or $-200\text{ kJ} - (-50\text{ kJ}) = E_3 - E_2$

$_3Q_1 - {_3W_1} = E_1 - E_3$ or $(0) - {_3W_1} = E_1 - E_3$

$$(+180 - 200) - ({_3W_1} - 50) = 0$$

Thus $\underline{_3W_1 = +30\text{ kJ}}$

(b) if $E_1 = 0$, then

$E_2 - E_1 = +180\text{ kJ}$ or $\underline{E_2 = +180\text{ kJ}}$

$E_3 - E_2 = -150\text{ kJ}$ or $\underline{E_3 = +30\text{ kJ}}$

5. A gas in a cylinder undergoes a complete cycle consisting of the following operations in order.

(a) Adiabatic expansion (where adiabatic means no heat transfer) during which the work transfer is 40 000 Nm.

(b) Isothermal (or constant temperature) expansion during which the heat transfer is 45 kJ. (Note that the internal energy of a single-phase fluid is a function of temperature only.)

(c) Compression during which the heat transfer is -50 kJ.

Determine the change in internal energy during compression and the work done during the cycle.

$$_1Q_2 - {_1W_2} = E_2 - E_1$$

or $(0) - (+40\ 000\text{ Nm})\left[\dfrac{\text{kJ}}{1000\text{ Nm}}\right] = E_2 - E_1 = -40\text{ kJ}$

Also $(+45\text{ kJ}) - {_2W_3} = 0$ since $E = f(T)$ and $T_2 = T_3$

Also $(-50\text{ kJ}) - {_3W_1} = E_1 - E_3$

Since

$$\oint Q - \oint W = 0$$

then $E_1 - E_3 = -(E_2 - E_1) = -(-40)$

$= \underline{+40\text{ kJ}}$

From the above

$$_3W_1 = -(50) - (+40) = -90\text{ kJ}$$

Now $\oint Q = {_1Q_2} + {_2Q_3} + {_3Q_1} = 0 + 45\text{ kJ} - 50\text{ kJ} = -5\text{ kJ}$

But $\oint W = \oint Q = -5\text{ kJ} = [+40\text{ kJ} + (-90\text{ kJ}) + {_2W_3}]$

Thus $\underline{_2W_3 = -5 + 50 = +45\text{ kJ}}$

6. (a) A system consisting of a mixture of air and petrol vapour at an initial temperature of 20 °C is contained in a rigid vessel. The mixture undergoes the following processes in sequence.

(i) The mixture temperature is raised to 250 °C by a heat transfer of 3 kJ.

(ii) The mixture is ignited and burns completely; this process is adiabatic and the temperature is raised to 1500 °C.

(iii) The temperature of the products of combustion is reduced to 138 °C by a heat transfer of -35 kJ.

Evaluate the energy of the system after each process given that the initial internal energy of the system is 10 kJ.

(b) An equal mass of the SAME MIXTURE is contained in a cylinder closed by a piston. The mixture undergoes the following processes in sequence.

(i) Adiabatic compression to a temperature of 250 °C.

(ii) Adiabatic combustion at constant volume until burning is complete.

(iii) Expansion to a temperature of 138 °C during which the work done by the system is 30 000 Nm.

(iv) Cooling at constant volume until the temperature is again 20 °C.

On the assumption that the energy of the system depends only on its temperature and chemical aggregation (that is the way in which the elements are chemically combined), evaluate the work done during (b)(i) and the heat transfer during (b)(iii). Also state, with reasons, whether or not the system has executed a cyclic process.

(a) Rigid vessel

(i) ${}_1Q_2 - {}_1W_2 = E_2 - E_1$; thus 3 kJ + 0 = E_2 - 10 kJ

Thus $\underline{E_2 = 13 \text{ kJ}}$

(ii) ${}_2Q_3 - {}_2W_3 = E_3 - E_2$; thus $0 + 0 = E_3 - E_2$;

Thus $\underline{E_3 = 13 \text{ kJ}}$

(iii) ${}_3Q_4 - {}_3W_4 = E_4 - E_3$; thus -35 kJ - 0 = $E_4 - E_3$;

Thus $\underline{E_4 = -22 \text{ kJ}}$

(b) Cylinder and piston

$E = f(T)$ only: or E_b (250 °C) = E_a (250 °C)

(i) ${}_1Q_2 - {}_1W_2 = E_2 - E_1$ and E_2 = +13 kJ as in (a)

Thus $0 - {}_1W_2 = 13 - 10$ or $\underline{{}_1W_2 = -3 \text{ kJ}}$

(ii) ${}_2Q_3 - {}_2W_3 = E_3 - E_2 = 0$ since ${}_2Q_3 = {}_2W_3 = 0$

Thus $E_3 = E_2$ = +13 kJ

(iii) ${}_3Q_4 - {}_3W_4 = E_4 - E_3$; ${E_4}_b = {E_4}_a$ = -22 kJ

Thus ${}_3Q_4$ - (+30 kJ) = -22 kJ - 13 kJ

or $\underline{{}_3Q_4 = -5 \text{ kJ}}$

There is no cycle since the final aggregation is not the same as the initial.

Further Examples

7. A fixed quantity of fluid can be expanded in two different ways between the same initial and final states.

(a) In the first expansion the heat transfer received is 42 kJ and the work done by the fluid is 53 kJ. What is the change in internal energy? (-11 kJ)

(b) In the second expansion the heat received is only 30 kJ. What is the work transfer produced? (41 kJ)

8. A system consisting of fuel and air in a cylinder undergoes the following processes

(a) adiabatic compression during which the work transfer is 50 kJ in to the fluid,

(b) combustion at constant volume accompanied by a heat transfer of 15 kJ out,

(c) expansion to the initial volume during which the work out is 60 kJ and the heat transfer is 5 kJ in,

(d) cooling to the initial pressure, the heat transfer being 10 kJ.

Calculate the internal energy at each state relative to the initial internal energy and determine the net work transfer during these processes. (+50 kJ, +35 kJ, +90 kJ, +10 kJ)

9. The working fluid in an engine continuously executes a cyclic process. During one cycle the fluid engages in two work transfers: 11 kJ to the working fluid and 32 kJ from the working fluid. Also during the cycle there are three heat transfers, two of which are known: 74 kJ to the working fluid and 39 kJ from the working fluid.

Determine the magnitude and sense of the third heat transfer. (14 kJ out).

4 FLUID PROPERTIES (EXCLUDING ENTROPY)

Throughout this volume all tabulated fluid properties are taken from 'Thermodynamic and Transport Properties of Fluids' by Y.R. Mayhew and G.F.C. Rogers published by Basil Blackwell, hereafter referred to as 'tables'.

Entropy is not treated at this stage and its calculation and use are left until a later chapter.

Two departures from the nomenclature of the tables should be noted.

(a) Tables use symbol U for internal energy and this book uses E.
(b) Tables use t_s for saturation temperature and this book uses T_{sat}.

Figure 4a,b gives sketches of the temperature-specific volume and temperature-specific enthalpy fields for a typical fluid.

It is imperative always to know in which area(s) of these fields the necessary calculations have to be made. For example, in the gas region the relationship $pV = RT$ may be held to be reasonably valid, whereas in the liquid-vapour region recourse must be made to tables of properties such as the one quoted above since no characteristic equation between properties holds true.

Two salient states should be noted and are designated f (for saturated liquid) and g (for saturated vapour) (see figure 4a,b)

The tables also refer to values at the critical point c (for example see at the foot of page 8 v_c, h_c, s_c).

By definition $h = e + pv$ and one of the first calculations demonstrates that the values of e and h listed in the tables are consistent with each other according to this relationship. Later on when entropy (S) is covered it will be shown that the relationships between S and the other properties also hold good by use of some of the listed values.

1. Calculate the specific enthalpy of ammonia at 6.585 bar and 75 degrees of superheat.

This calculation is for a superheated vapour and the data may be found on page 12 of tables.

For a saturation pressure of 6.585 bar,
At 50 K degrees of superheat h = 1586 kJ/kg
At 100 K degrees of superheat h = 1705.7 kJ/kg.

Assuming, as we may, that the values quoted allow of linear interpolation

At 75 degrees of superheat $h = \dfrac{1586 + 1705.7}{2} = \underline{1645.9 \text{ kJ/kg}}$

2. Show that the quoted values of e_f and e_g are consistent with

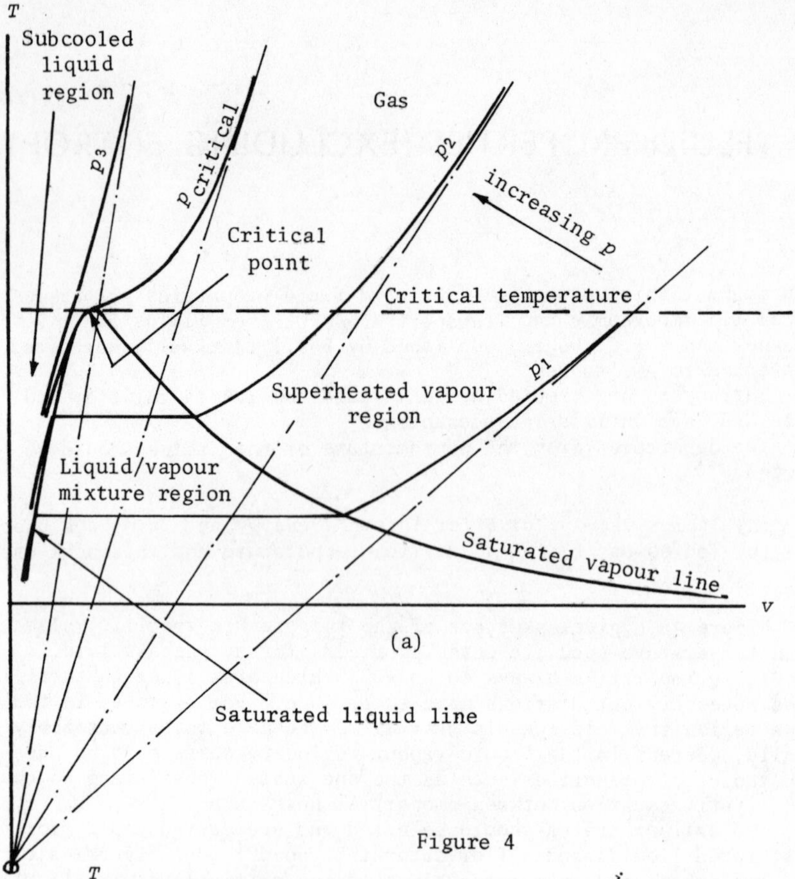
T
Subcooled liquid region
Gas
p3
p critical
p2
increasing p
Critical point
Critical temperature
p1
Superheated vapour region
Liquid/vapour mixture region
Saturated vapour line
v
Saturated liquid line

(a)

Figure 4

(b)

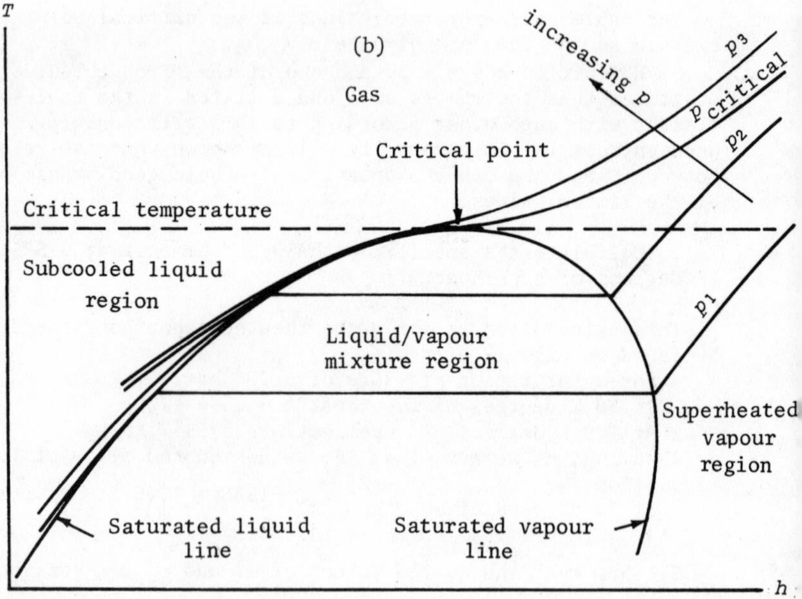
T
increasing p
p3
p critical
p2
Gas
Critical point
Critical temperature
Subcooled liquid region
p1
Liquid/vapour mixture region
Superheated vapour region
Saturated liquid line
Saturated vapour line
h

the quoted values of h_f and h_g in tables (page 5) for the case when the pressure is 55 bar.

At 55 bar $h_f = e_f + p_f v_f$ and from pages 5 and 10

$$h_f = 1178 \frac{\text{kJ}}{\text{kg}} + \left(5500 \text{ kN m}^{-2} \times 0.001303 \frac{\text{m}^3}{\text{kg}} \frac{[\text{ kJ}]}{[\text{kNm}]}\right)$$

$$= 1178 + 7.2 = \underline{1185.2 \frac{\text{kJ}}{\text{kg}}}$$

Notes:

(a) the value for v_f is taken from page 10 at the appropriate value of T_{sat} (269.9 °C); this is because pressure has little effect on specific volume for a liquid,

(b) the value obtained is close to the listed value of 1185 kJ/kg.

3. Calculate the specific internal energy for saturated Freon-12 vapour at 5 °C.

Tables page 13 for Freon-12.
By definition

$$e_g = h_g - p_g v_g = 189.66 \frac{\text{kJ}}{\text{kg}} - \left(3.626 \text{ bar} \times 0.0475 \frac{\text{m}^3}{\text{kg}}\right) \times \frac{[100 \text{ kN}]}{[\text{bar m}^2]}$$

$$= 189.66 - 17.22 = \underline{172.44 \frac{\text{kJ}}{\text{kg}}}$$

4. Complete the following table in which the fluid is H_2O.

	p (bar)	v $\left(\frac{\text{m}^3}{\text{kg}}\right)$	T (°C)	x	e $\left(\frac{\text{kJ}}{\text{kg}}\right)$	h $\left(\frac{\text{kJ}}{\text{kg}}\right)$
(a)	0.12	12.36				
(b)	30		450			
(c)	70			0.5		
(d)	14				1534	
(e)	1.7					483
(f)		0.0481	500			
(g)		103.05		0.5	1188	
(h)		0.02944				2990
(i)			400			3187

The complete table is given here with explanatory notes below.

(a)	0.12	12.36	49.4	1.0	207	2590	page 3
(b)	30	0.1078	450	NA	3020	3343	page 7
(c)	70	0.01369	285.8	0.5	1919.5	2019.5	page 5
(d)	14	0.04192	195.0	0.4	1534	1614	page 4
(e)	1.7	1.031	115.2	0	483	483	page 4
(f)	70	0.0481	500	NA	3073	3410	page 7
(g)	0.006112	103.05	0.01	0.5	1187.5	1250.5	page 3
(h)	80	0.02994	350	NA	2750.5	2990	page 8
(i)	55	0.052	400	NA	2900	3187	pages 7/11

(a) Saturated vapour, $v = v_g$

(b) Superheated vapour since $T > T_{sat}$ at 30 bar

(c) Liquid/vapour mixture (neglect v_f here as being very small)

(d) $e_f < e < e_g$ i.e. liquid/vapour mixture

$$x = \frac{e - e_f}{e_g - e_f} = \frac{1534 - 828}{2593 - 828} = 0.4 \quad \text{(neglect } v_f \text{ again)}$$

(e) $h = h_f$, i.e. saturated liquid

(f) Superheated vapour (note that $v = 0.0481 \frac{m^3}{kg}$ at 500 °C, 70 bar)

(g) Liquid/vapour mixture since $x = 0.5$

$v_g = 2 \times 103.05 = 206.1 \frac{m^3}{kg}$ gives 0.006112 bar as the pressure if v_f is neglected

(h) Given data is for $p = 80$ bar, $T = 350$ °C

$$e = h - pv = 2990 \frac{kJ}{kg} - \left(8000 \frac{kN}{m^2} \times 0.02994 \frac{m^3}{kg}\right) = 2750.5 \frac{kJ}{kg}$$

(i) h is halfway between 3196 kJ/kg at 50 bar, 400 °C and 3177 kJ/kg at 60 bar, 400 °C. Thus since vertical interpolation is not advisable for v when the pressure is on the low side (see Question 5), from the foot of page 11

$$v = \frac{0.3}{1.3} \frac{(3187 - 1943)}{5500} = 0.052 \frac{m^3}{kg}$$

and $e = \frac{(2907 + 2893)}{2} = 2900 \frac{kJ}{kg}$ directly from page 7.

5. As intimated in the previous question the values of v for superheated steam do not vary linearly even approximately in some parts of the tables for steam and the errors involved in such an assumption are progressively greater as the pressure is lowered. This example is intended to bring this point out.

Calculate values of specific volume for steam

(a) by interpolation using the product pv linearly and dividing by p (which is, in effect, using the relationship at the foot of page 11),

(b) by interpolating linearly for v in each of the following cases.

$T = 500$ °C, $p = 0.03$, 9.5, 375 bar and
$T = 250$ °C, $p = 0.03$ bar.

<u>$T = 500$ °C, $p = 0.03$ bar</u>

For $T = 500$ °C, $p = 0.01$ bar, $v = 356.8 \frac{m^3}{kg}$ (page 6)

For $T = 500$ °C, $p = 0.05$ bar, $v = 71.36 \frac{m^3}{kg}$

Thus at 0.01 bar, 500 °C, $pv = 3.568 \frac{bar\ m^3}{kg}$

And at 0.05 bar, 500 °C, $pv = 3.568 \frac{bar\ m^3}{kg}$

Interpolating, therefore at 0.03 bar, 500 °C, $pv = 3.568 \ \frac{\text{bar m}^3}{\text{kg}}$

$$\text{or } v_{0.03,500} = \frac{(pv)_{0.03,500}}{p} = \frac{3.568}{0.03} = 118.9 \ \frac{\text{m}^3}{\text{kg}}$$

$$\text{Also } (pv)_{9,500} = 9 \times 0.3937 = 3.543 \ \frac{\text{bar m}^3}{\text{kg}} \quad \text{(page 7)}$$

$$(pv)_{10,500} = 10 \times 0.354 = 3.540 \ \frac{\text{bar m}^3}{\text{kg}}$$

$$\text{Thus } v_{9.5,500} = \frac{3.543 + 3.540}{2 \times 9.5} = 0.373 \ \frac{\text{m}^3}{\text{kg}}$$

$$\text{Also } (pv)_{350,500} = 350 \times 0.00693 = 2.426 \ \frac{\text{bar m}^3}{\text{kg}} \quad \text{(page 9)}$$

$$(pv)_{400,500} = 400 \times 0.00562 = 2.248 \ \frac{\text{bar m}^3}{\text{kg}}$$

$$\text{Thus } v_{375,500} = \frac{2.426 + 2.248}{2 \times 375} = 0.00623 \ \frac{\text{m}^3}{\text{kg}}$$

$$\text{Also } (pv)_{0.01,250} = 0.01 \times 241.4 = 2.414 \ \frac{\text{bar m}^3}{\text{kg}} \quad \text{(page 7)}$$

$$(pv)_{0.05,250} = 0.05 \times 48.28 = 2.414 \ \frac{\text{bar m}^3}{\text{kg}}$$

$$\text{Thus } v_{0.03,250} = \frac{2.414 + 2.414}{2 \times 0.03} = 80.5 \ \frac{\text{m}^3}{\text{kg}}$$

Direct linear interpolation for v

$$v_{0.03,500} = \frac{356.8 + 71.36}{2} = 214.1 \ \frac{\text{m}^3}{\text{kg}} \quad \text{(page 6)}$$

(Compare this with 118.9 previously!)

$$v_{9.5,500} = \frac{0.3937 + 0.354}{2} = 0.374 \ \frac{\text{m}^3}{\text{kg}} \quad \text{(page 7)}$$

(Compare this with 0.373 previously)

$$v_{375,500} = \frac{0.00693 + 0.00562}{2} = 0.00628 \ \frac{\text{m}^3}{\text{kg}} \quad \text{(page 9)}$$

(Compare this with 0.00623 previously)

$$v_{0.03,250} = \frac{241.4 + 48.28}{2} = 144.8 \ \frac{\text{m}^3}{\text{kg}} \quad \text{(page 6)}$$

(Compare this with 80.5 previously!)

Clearly linear interpolation is subject to gross error at low values of pressure and becomes progressively more accurate as the pressure is raised. However, complete accuracy is always assured by interpolating for pv first and then dividing by p (or by use of the expression at the foot of page 11 - which is the same thing).

6. Mercury has a specific enthalpy of 312 kJ/kg. Determine the

fluid quality and the specific volume if the pressure is 1 bar.

$$x = \frac{h - h_f}{h_g - h_f} = \frac{312 - 48.45}{341 - 48.45} = \frac{263.55}{292.55} = \underline{0.901} \text{ (page 14)}$$

$v = xv_g$ (neglecting v_f, since from page 15 for liquid mercury v_f is approximately 1/13 400)

Thus $v = 0.901 \times 0.2581 = \underline{0.2325 \ \frac{m^3}{kg}}$

7. Determine the specific enthalpy for Freon-12 at 5 bar, 25 °C.

This calculation requires a double interpolation on page 13 of tables and is best illustrated by the use of similar triangles.

The scheme is to interpolate horizontally just below and then just above 5 bar at 25 °C and find values of specific enthalpy in each case.

The final calculation is then performed by interpolating vertically to get the specific enthalpy at <u>5</u> bar and 25 °C.

<u>First interpolation</u> $p = 4.914$ bar, $T = 25$ °C

$\underline{h_{4.914,25}}$ Here $T_{sat} = 15$ °C and the degree of superheat is (25 - 10) = 10 K.

Thus h lies between h_g and h at 15 K superheat as listed.

or $$h_{4.914,25} = 193.78 + \frac{10}{15}(204.1 - 193.78) = 200.66 \ \frac{kJ}{kg}$$

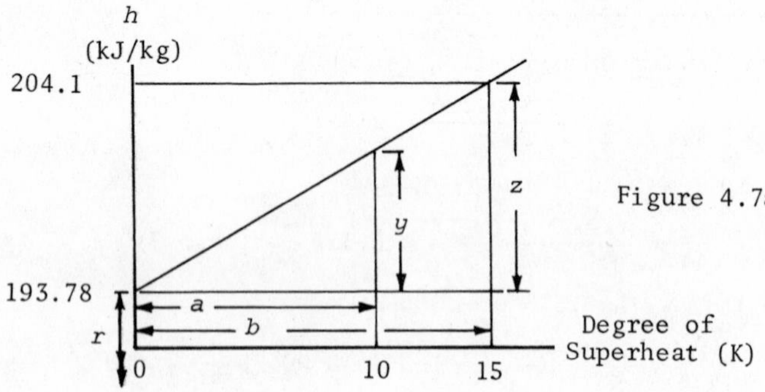

Figure 4.7a

Figure 4.7a shows the above interpolation schematically. From the similar triangles in this figure

$$h_{4.914,25} = r + y = r + \frac{az}{b}$$

$$= 193.78 + \frac{(10 - 0)}{(15 - 0)}(204.1 - 193.78)$$

$$= 200.66 \ \frac{kJ}{kg}$$

Similarly

$$h_{5.673,25} = 195.78 + \frac{10}{15}(206.32 - 195.68) = 202.81 \ \frac{kJ}{kg}$$

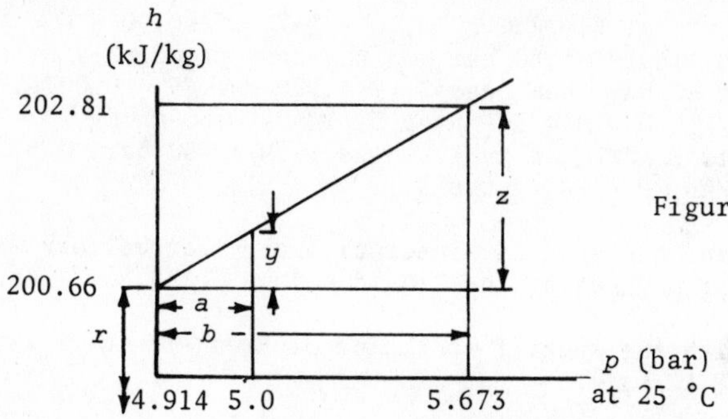

Figure 4.7b

Thus as shown in figure 4.7b we now have a second similar triangles calculation to perform, this time from the plot of h against p. Thus

$$h_{5,25} = r + \frac{az}{b} = 200.66 + \frac{(5 - 4.914)(202.81 - 200.66)}{(5.673 - 4.914)}$$

$$= 200.90 \ \frac{\text{kJ}}{\text{kg}}$$

All interpolations follow a similar pattern to this.

Calculations for a perfect gas are very easily performed by use of the standard gas equation $pv = RT$ where T is the absolute thermodynamic temperature. Since many of these calculations and the dependent calculations of specific heat capacity, etc. appear in the following chapters and are self-explanatory none appears here.

Further Examples

8. (a) Make a sketch of the T-v field for H_2O showing the saturated liquid and saturated vapour boundaries. Indicate on your diagram the liquid, liquid/vapour and superheated vapour regions. Mark the critical point and add to your sketch a typical constant pressure line.

(b) Complete the following table of properties of H_2O.

	p (bar)	v (m^3/kg)	T (°C)	e (kJ/kg)	h (kJ/kg)	x
(i)	10	0.18	A	B	C	D
(ii)	E	F	369	G	H	0.5
(iii)	90	I	475	J	K	L

(A = 179.9 °C, B = 2449.2 kJ/kg, C = 2628.9 kJ/kg, D = 0.926, E = 208 bar, F = 0.00353 m^3/kg where v_f is not negligible, G = 2037 kJ/kg, H = 2113.5 kJ/kg, I = 0.0353 m^3/kg, J = 3002.6 kJ/kg, K = 3320.5 kJ/kg, L = NA.)

9. Complete the following table of properties of water and steam.

	p (bar)	v (m^3/kg)	T (°C)	e (kJ/kg)	h (kJ/kg)	x
(i)	80	A	B	C	1185	D
(ii)	E	F	357	2000	G	H
(iii)	135	I	375	J	K	L
(iv)	M	0.0016	N	O	1729	P

(A = 0.001302 m^3/kg, B = 269.9 °C, C = 1178 kJ/kg, D = 0 - Note that subcooled liquid at 80 bar has the same properties as saturated liquid at 55 bar, see page 5, E = 180 bar, F = 0.00431 m^3/kg, G = 2078.2 kJ/kg, H = 0.445 - page 5, I = 0.0166 m^3/kg, J = 2688.8 kJ/kg, K = 2912.5 kJ/kg, L = NA - page 8, M = 450 bar, N = 375 °C, O = 1657.0 kJ/kg, P = NA - page 9.)

10. Determine the specific internal energy for mercury when x is 0.5 at 6 bar neglecting the liquid volume. (193.81 kJ/kg).

11. Determine the specific enthalpy of Freon-12 at 15.26 bar, 83 °C. (222.88 kJ/kg).

5 SYSTEMS - MORE ADVANCED CALCULATIONS

1. A mass of 0.5 kg of water at a temperature of 130 °C and a pressure of 1 000 000 Pa is heated isobarically until the final temperature of 200 °C is reached. Calculate the heat transfer, the change of volume and the work transfer. It is now cooled isochorically to a final pressure of 200 000 Pa. Determine the heat transfer.

T_{sat} at 1 000 000 Pa (10 bar) is 179.9 °C (tables page 4)

State 1 is thus subcooled liquid (10 bar, 130 °C)

State 2 is superheated vapour (10 bar, 200 °C)

Also $v_2 = 0.2061 \frac{\text{m}^3}{\text{kg}}$ (= v_3) (tables page 7)

But v_{g_2} at 200 000 Pa (i.e. 2 bar) is $0.8856 \frac{\text{m}^3}{\text{kg}}$ (tables page 4)

Thus state 3 is a liquid/vapour mixture wherein

$$x_3 \simeq \frac{v_3}{v_{g_3}} = \frac{0.2061}{0.8856} = 0.233$$

We are now in a position to draw clear sketches of the two processes involved in the problem.

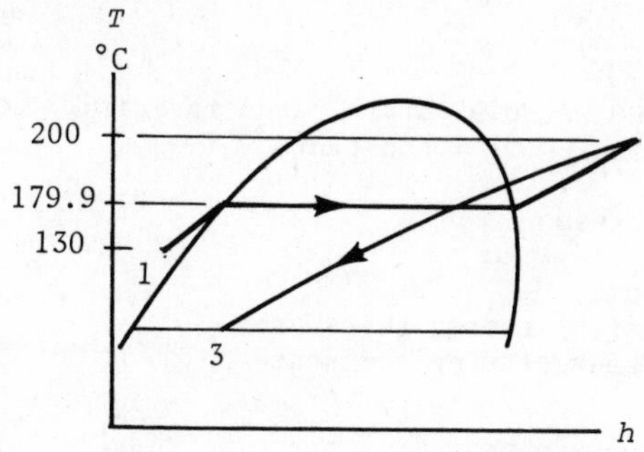

Figure 5.1a

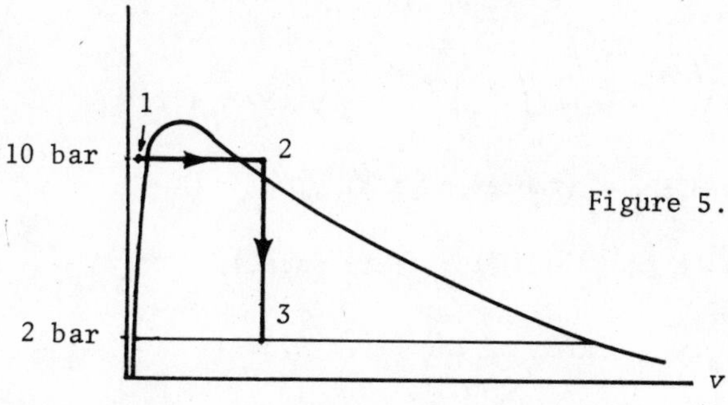

Figure 5.1b

1-2 First Law

$$_1Q_2 - {_1W_2} = E_2 - E_1 = m(e_2 - e_1)$$

Now $_1w_2 = p_1(v_2 - v_1) = 1000 \frac{\text{kN}}{\text{m}^2} (0.2061 - 0.00107) \frac{\text{m}^3}{\text{kg}}$

$= 205 \frac{\text{kJ}}{\text{kg}}$ (since $v_1 = 0.00107 \frac{\text{m}^3}{\text{kg}}$ at 130 °C - page 10)

Thus $_1W_2 = m(_1w_2) = 0.5 \text{ kg} \times 205 \frac{\text{kJ}}{\text{kg}} = \underline{102.5 \text{ kJ}}$

Also $m(e_2 - e_1) = 0.5 \text{ kg} \left(2623 \frac{\text{kJ}}{\text{kg}} - 546 \frac{\text{kJ}}{\text{kg}}\right) = 1038.5 \text{ kJ}$

(using pages 7 and 4 respectively)

Thus $_1Q_2 = 102.5 + 1038.5 = \underline{1142 \text{ kJ}}$

Also $V_2 - V_1 = m(v_2 - v_1) = 0.5 \text{ kg } (0.2061 - 0.00107) \frac{\text{m}^3}{\text{kg}}$

$= \underline{0.103 \text{ m}^3}$

2-3 First Law

$$_2Q_3 - {_2W_3} = E_3 - E_2$$

But $_2W_3 = 0$ (since this process is isochoric)

Thus $_2Q_3 = m(e_3 - e_2) = m(e_{f_3} + x_3 e_{fg_3} - e_2)$

$= 0.5 \text{ kg}[505 + 0.233(2530 - 505) - 2623] \frac{\text{kJ}}{\text{kg}}$

$= \underline{823.1 \text{ kJ}}$

2. Steam at 400 000 Pa, 0.95 dry expands reversibly to 130 000 Pa according to the law $pv^{1 \cdot 1}$ = constant.

Determine per kg steam

(a) the final volume,
(b) the work transfer stating the sense,
(c) the heat transfer stating the sense.

$v_1 \simeq x_1 v_{g_1} = 0.95 \times 0.4623 \frac{\text{m}^3}{\text{kg}} = 0.439 \frac{\text{m}^3}{\text{kg}}$ (page 4 neglecting v_{f_1})

$$v_2 = \left(\frac{p_1}{p_2}\right)^{1/n} \times v_1 = \left(\frac{4}{1.3}\right)^{0.909} \times 0.439 = 1.218 \frac{\text{m}^3}{\text{kg}}$$

Now $v_{g_2} = 1.325 \frac{\text{m}^3}{\text{kg}}$ (tables page 4)

Thus $x_2 \simeq \frac{v_2}{v_{g_2}} = \frac{1.218}{1.325} = 0.919$ (from page 4)

We can now draw a sketch of the p-v field.

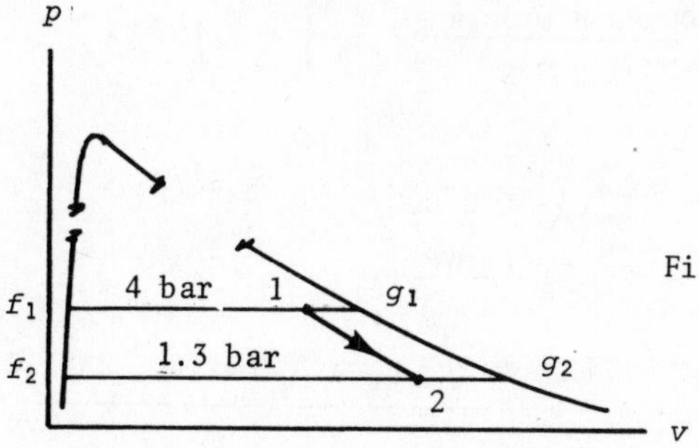

Figure 5.2

$$_1w_2 = \int_{v_1}^{v_2} p\, dv = \frac{p_1v_1 - p_2v_2}{n - 1} \text{ (when } p_1v_1{}^n = p_2v_2{}^n\text{)}$$

$$_1w_2 = \frac{1}{0.1}\left(4 \times 10^5 \text{ Pa} \times 0.439 \frac{\text{m}^3}{\text{kg}} - 1.3 \times 10^5 \text{ Pa} \times 1.218 \frac{\text{m}^3}{\text{kg}}\right)$$

$$\times \frac{[\text{Nm}^{-2}]}{[\text{ Pa }]}$$

$$\underline{_1w_2 = 173 \frac{\text{kJ}}{\text{kg}}}$$

From the first law of thermodynamics for a system

$$_1q_2 = {_1w_2} + e_2 - e_1 = {_1w_2} + (h_2 - p_2v_2) - (h_1 - p_1v_1)$$

$$_1q_2 = {_1w_2} + (h_{f_2} + x_2h_{fg_2} - p_2v_2) - (h_{f_1} + x_1h_{fg_1} - p_1v_1)$$

$$= 173 \frac{\text{kJ}}{\text{kg}} + [449 + (0.919 \times 2238) - 158.3] \frac{\text{kJ}}{\text{kg}}$$

$$- [605 + (0.95 \times 2134) - 175.6] \frac{\text{kJ}}{\text{kg}} \quad \text{(using tables page 4)}$$

$$\underline{_1q_2 = 63.7 \frac{\text{kJ}}{\text{kg}}}$$

3. A volume of 0.36 m^3 of a gas at 15 °C and 103 000 Pa is compressed reversibly and adiabatically to 1 000 000 Pa. It is then cooled at constant pressure to its original temperature after which it expands isothermally at constant pressure. Find the heat transfer at constant pressure, the heat transfer during expansion and the work transfer during the cycle, [γ = 1.41, R = 0.287 kJ/kg K]

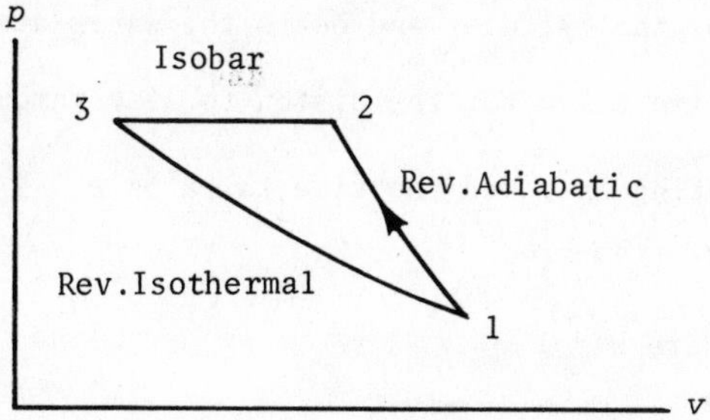

Figure 5.3

$$m = \frac{pV}{RT} = \frac{103\ 000\ \text{Pa} \times 0.36\ \text{m}}{0.287\ \frac{\text{kJ}}{\text{kg}} \times 287\ \text{K}} \frac{[\text{N m}^{-2}]}{[\ \text{Pa}\ ]} = 0.449\ \text{kg}$$

$$T_2 = T_1\left(\frac{p_2}{p_1}\right)^k = 288\ \text{K}\left(\frac{1\ 000\ 000}{1\ 030\ 000}\right)^{0.291} = 557.8\ \text{K} = T_3$$

$${}_2Q_3 = -mc_p(T_2 - T_3) = -\frac{m\gamma R}{\gamma - 1}(T_2 - T_3)$$

$$= \frac{0.448\ \text{kg} \times 1.41 \times 0.287\ \frac{\text{kJ}}{\text{kg K}} \times (557.8 - 288)\ \text{K}}{0.41}$$

$${}_2Q_3 = 119.3\ \text{kJ}$$

$${}_3Q_1 = {}_3W_1 + E_1 - E_3 = {}_3W_1 \quad (\text{since } T_3 = T_1)$$

$${}_3Q_1 = \int_{V_3}^{V_1} p\ \text{d}V = \int_{V_3}^{V_1} \frac{RT}{V}\ \text{d}V = mRT_3 \ln\frac{V_1}{V_3} = mRT_3 \ln\frac{p_3}{p_1}$$

$$= 0.449\ \text{kg} \times 0.287\ \frac{\text{kJ}}{\text{kg K}} \times 288\ \text{K} \times \ln\frac{10}{1.03}$$

$${}_3Q_1 = 84.4\ \text{kJ}$$

$${}_1W_2 = \frac{p_1V_1 - p_2V_2}{\gamma - 1} = \frac{mR(T_1 - T_2)}{\gamma - 1}$$

$$= \frac{1}{0.41}\left[0.449\ \text{kg} \times 0.287\ \frac{\text{kJ}}{\text{kg K}} \times (-269.8\ \text{K})\right]$$

$${}_1W_2 = -84.8\ \text{kJ}$$

$${}_2W_3 = p_2(V_3 - V_2) = mR(T_3 - T_2)$$

$$= 0.449\ \text{kg} \times 0.287\ \frac{\text{kJ}}{\text{kg K}} \times (-269.8\ \text{K})$$

$${}_2W_3 = -34.8\ \text{kJ}$$

Thus $\oint W = {}_1W_2 + {}_2W_3 + {}_3W_1 = {}_1W_2 + {}_2W_3 + {}_3Q_1$

$$= -84.8 + (-34.8) + 84.4$$

$$\oint W = -35.2\ \text{kJ}$$

4. A vertical insulated cylinder with a cross-sectional area of 0.1 m^2 contains 1 kg water at 15 °C, and a piston resting on the water exerts a constant pressure of 7 bar. An electric heater forms the bottom of the cylinder and heats the water at the rate of 500 W.

Calculate the time taken for the piston to rise through a distance of 1 m.

If the rate of heating is $\dot{Q}$ and the time taken is t

$$\dot{Q}t = {}_1Q_2 = {}_1W_2 + E_2 - E_1$$

where

$${}_1W_2 = pAx \ (\text{where } x = 1\ \text{m})$$

Also $E_2 = H_2 - p_2V_2$; $E_1 = H_1 - p_1V_1$

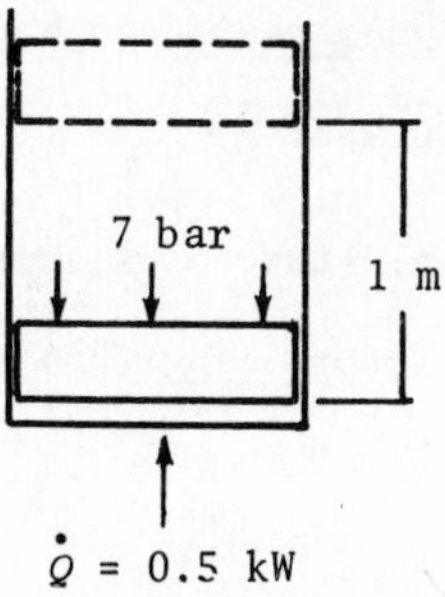

Figure 5.4

$V_1 = mv_1 = mv_{f_1}$ (water at 15 °C page 10)

$$V_1 = 1 \text{ kg} \times 0.001001 \frac{\text{m}^3}{\text{kg}} \simeq 0.001 \text{ m}^3$$

$$H_1 = mh_1 = mh_{f_1} = 1 \text{ kg} \times 62.9 \frac{\text{kJ}}{\text{kg}} \quad \text{(page 2)}$$

$$H_1 = 62.9 \text{ kJ}$$

$$V_2 \simeq V_1 + \Delta V = 0.001 \text{ m}^3 + (0.1 \text{ m}^2 \times 1 \text{ m}) = 0.1001 \text{ m}^3$$

$$V_{g_2} = mv_{g_2} = 1 \text{ kg} \times 0.2728 \frac{\text{m}^3}{\text{kg}} \text{ (page 4)} = 0.2728 \text{ m}^3$$

Thus $x_2 = \dfrac{V_2}{V_{g_2}} \simeq \dfrac{0.1001}{0.2728} = 0.367$

Also $H_2 = mh_2 = m(h_{f_2} + x_2 h_{fg_2})$ and from page 4 at 7 bar

$$H_2 = 1 \text{ kg}\left[697 \frac{\text{kJ}}{\text{kg}} + 0.367\left(2067 \frac{\text{kJ}}{\text{kg}}\right)\right] = 1455.6 \text{ kJ}$$

Then $E_2 = 1455.6 \text{ kJ} - (700 \text{ kN m}^{-2} \times 0.1001 \text{ m}^3) = 1385.6 \text{ kJ}$

and $E_1 = 62.9 \text{ kJ} - (700 \text{ kN m}^{-2} \times 0.001 \text{ m}^3) = 62.2 \text{ kJ}$

Also ${}_1W_2 = pAx = 700 \text{ kN m}^{-2} \times 0.1 \text{ m}^2 \times 1 \text{ m} = 70.0 \text{ kJ}$

Thus ${}_1Q_2 = 70 + 1385.5 - 62.2 = 1393.4 \text{ kJ}$

and $t = \dfrac{{}_1Q_2}{\dot{Q}} = \dfrac{1393.4 \text{ kJ}}{0.5 \dfrac{\text{kJ}}{\text{s}} \dfrac{[60 \text{ s}]}{[\text{min}]}} = 45.6 \text{ min}$

---

5. One kg of water and steam at a pressure of 3.5 bar and 0.52 dry is heated isochorically to 7 bar. The steam is then expanded according to the law pV = constant until the pressure is 2.0 bar.
For the above series of changes calculate
(a) the state of the fluid after heating
(b) the heat transfer during isochoric heating
(c) the temperature of the steam after expansion.

$$v_1 = x_1 v_{g_1} = 0.52 \times 0.5241 \frac{\text{m}^3}{\text{kg}} = 0.2725 \frac{\text{m}^3}{\text{kg}} \text{ (page 4)} = v_2$$

and v_g at 7 bar $= 0.2728 \dfrac{\text{m}^3}{\text{kg}}$ (page 4)

Thus state 2 is saturated vapour near enough (a)

Also $v_3 = \dfrac{p_2 v_2}{p_3} = \dfrac{7}{2} \times 0.2725 \ \dfrac{\text{m}^3}{\text{kg}} = 0.9538 \ \dfrac{\text{m}^3}{\text{kg}}$

and $v_{g_3} = 0.8856 \ \dfrac{\text{m}^3}{\text{kg}}$ (page 4) i.e. state 3 is superheated

We can now draw a reasonable picture of events as in the figure.

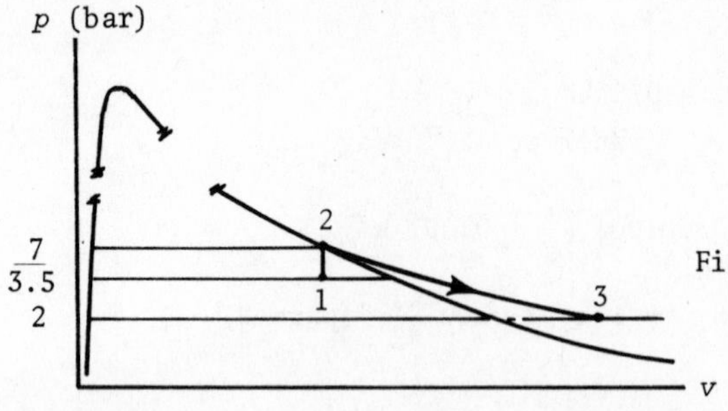

Figure 5.5

Now $_1q_2 = {_1w_2} + e_2 - e_1 = e_2 - e_1 \quad (_1w_2 = 0)$

$$_1q_2 = (h_2 - p_2v_2) - (h_1 - p_1v_1) = h_2 - h_1 - v_1(p_2 - p_1)$$

$$_1q_2 = [h_{g_2} - (h_{f_1} + x_1 h_{fg_1})] - v_1(p_2 - p_1)$$

$$= [2764 - (584 + \{0.52 \times 2184\})] \ \frac{\text{kJ}}{\text{kg}} \quad \text{(page 4)}$$

$$- \ 0.2725 \ \frac{\text{m}^3}{\text{kg}} \ (700 - 350) \ \frac{\text{kN}}{\text{m}^2}$$

$$_1q_2 = 968 \ \frac{\text{kJ}}{\text{kg}} \quad \text{(b)}$$

$$h_3 = \left(p_3 v_3 \times \frac{1.3}{0.3}\right) + 1943 = \frac{(200 \times 0.9538 \times 1.3)}{0.3} + 1943$$

$$= 2769.6 \ \frac{\text{kJ}}{\text{kg}}$$

Thus $T_3 = 120.2 \ ^\circ\text{C} + \dfrac{(2769.6 - 2707)}{(2770.0 - 2707)}(150 - 120.2) \ \text{K}$ (from page 6)

$T_3 = 149.8 \ ^\circ\text{C}$ (c) (since $T_{sat} = 120.2 \ ^\circ\text{C}$)

6. A mass of 2 kg of gas expands reversibly and polytropically to three times its original volume, its temperature falling from 300 °C to 60 °C. During the expansion, the work transfer is 100 kJ while the heat transfer is 20 kJ. What are the specific heat capacities of the gas by mass?

$$_1Q_2 = {_1W_2} + E_2 - E_1 = \frac{p_1V_1 - p_2V_2}{n - 1} + mc_v(T_2 - T_1)$$

for the reversible polytropic expansion of a perfect gas.

Thus $_1Q_2 = \dfrac{mR(T_1 - T_2)}{n - 1} + \dfrac{mR(T_2 - T_1)}{\gamma - 1} \quad \left(c_v = \dfrac{R}{\gamma - 1}\right)$

$$= mR(T_1 - T_2)\left(\frac{1}{n - 1} - \frac{1}{\gamma - 1}\right)$$

$$= mR(T_1 - T_2)\left[\frac{(\gamma - 1) - (n - 1)}{(\gamma - 1)(n - 1)}\right]$$

$$= \frac{\gamma - n}{\gamma - 1}\left[\frac{mR(T_1 - T_2)}{n - 1}\right]$$

or $\quad {}_1Q_2 = \dfrac{(\gamma - n)}{(\gamma - 1)}\,{}_1W_2$

Thus $\dfrac{\gamma - n}{\gamma - 1} = \dfrac{{}_1Q_2}{{}_1W_2} = \dfrac{20}{100} = 0.2$

For the reversible polytropic expansion of a gas wherein $pv^n = K$

$$\frac{T_2}{T_1} = \left(\frac{V_1}{V_2}\right)^{n-1}$$

or $\quad n - 1 = \dfrac{\ln (T_2/T_1)}{\ln (V_1/V_2)} = \dfrac{\ln (333/573)}{\ln (1/3)} = 0.495$

Thus $n = 1.495$

and $\gamma - 1.495 = 0.2(\gamma - 1)$

or $\quad \gamma = c_p/c_v = 1.619$

Also $c_v = \dfrac{E_2 - E_1}{m(T_2 - T_1)} = \dfrac{{}_1Q_2 - {}_1W_2}{m(T_2 - T_1)} = \dfrac{(20 - 100)\text{ kJ}}{2\text{ kg}(-240\text{ K})} = \underline{0.167 \dfrac{\text{kJ}}{\text{kg K}}}$

and $c_p = \gamma c_v = 1.619 \times 0.167 = \underline{0.27 \dfrac{\text{kJ}}{\text{kg K}}}$

7. One kg of air at 213 °C and 1 bar is contained in a closed insulated vessel A. Vessel B which is also insulated has a volume of 0.2 m^3 and contains air at 6 bar and 412 °C. Find the final temperature and pressure when vessels A and B are interconnected.

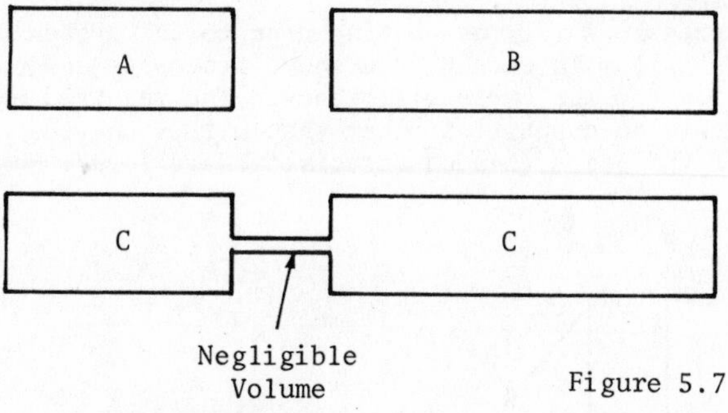

Figure 5.7

From the first law of thermodynamics since $Q = W = 0$

$$E_A = E_B = E_C$$

From the mass continuity equation

$$m_A = m_B = m_C$$

Thus $m_A e_A + m_B e_B = (m_A + m_B) e_C$

and $T_C = \dfrac{m_A c_v T_A + m_B c_v T_B}{(m_A + m_B) c_v}$ (since $E = mc_v T$)

Now $V_A = \left(\dfrac{mRT}{p}\right)_A = \dfrac{1\ \text{kg} \times 0.287\ \dfrac{\text{kJ}}{\text{kg K}} \times 486\ \text{K}}{1\ \text{bar}} \dfrac{[\text{bar m}^2]\,[\text{kNm}]}{[100\ \text{kN}]\,[\text{kJ}\ ]}$

$= 1.395\ \text{m}^3$

Thus $V_A + V_B = V_C = 1.395 + 0.2 = 1.595\ \text{m}^3$

Also $m_B = \left(\dfrac{pV}{RT}\right)_B = \dfrac{600\ \text{kN m}^{-2} \times 0.2\ \text{m}^3}{0.287\ \dfrac{\text{kJ}}{\text{kg K}} \times 685\ \text{K}} = 0.61\ \text{kg}$

Thus $m_C = m_A + m_B = 1.61\ \text{kg}$

and $T_C = \dfrac{(1 \times 486) + (0.61 \times 685)}{1.61} = \underline{561.4\ \text{K (or } 288.4\ ^\circ\text{C)}}$

Also $p_C = \left(\dfrac{mRT}{V}\right)_C = \dfrac{1.61\ \text{kg} \times 0.287\ \dfrac{\text{kJ}}{\text{kg K}} \times 561.4\ \text{K}\ \dfrac{[\text{bar m}^2]}{[100\ \text{kN}]}}{1.595\ \text{m}^3}$

or $\underline{p_C = 1.626\ \text{bar}}$

8. A system, comprising an amount of a perfect gas of mass m and initially at a temperature T_1, undergoes the following sequence of reversible processes

(a) an adiabatic expansion, for which the ratio of the final to the initial pressure is r,

(b) a constant pressure process, and

(c) a constant volume process which returns the system to the initial state.

Find expressions for the heating done *to* the system and the work done *by* the system in each of the above processes and hence obtain an expression for the cycle efficiency. The required expressions should contain no quantities other than m, T_1, r and the properties c_v and γ of the gas. (London University Part I 1971 No 6)

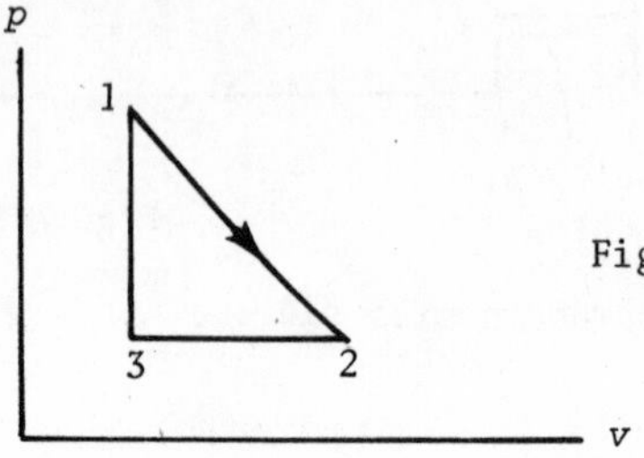

Figure 5.8

The figure shows the cycle of operations on the p-V field.

$_1Q_2 = 0$ since the process 1-2 is a reversible adiabatic

$$_1W_2 = \int_1^2 p\,dV = \frac{p_1V_1 - p_2V_2}{\gamma - 1} = \frac{mR(T_1 - T_2)}{\gamma - 1}$$

$$= \frac{mRT_1}{\gamma - 1}\left(1 - \frac{T_2}{T_1}\right) = \frac{mRT_1}{\gamma - 1}\left(1 - \frac{p_2}{p_1}\right)^k \quad \text{where } k = \frac{\gamma - 1}{\gamma}$$

$$\underline{_1W_2 = \frac{mRT_1}{\gamma - 1}(1 - r^k)} \text{ which is positive since } r < 1$$

$$_2Q_3 = {_2W_3} + E_3 - E_2 = p_2(V_3 - V_2) = mc_V(T_3 - T_2)$$

$$= mR(T_3 - T_2) + mc_V(T_3 - T_2)$$

$$= mT_2\left[R\left(\frac{T_3}{T_2} - 1\right) + c_V\left(\frac{T_3}{T_2} - 1\right)\right] = mT_2(R + c_V)\left(\frac{T_3}{T_2} - 1\right)$$

Now $\frac{T_3}{T_2} = \frac{V_3}{V_2} = \frac{V_1}{V_2} = \left(\frac{p_2}{p_1}\right)^{1-k} = r^{1-k}$ since $\frac{1}{\gamma} = 1 - k$

Thus $\underline{_2Q_3 = m(r^{1-k} - 1)T_1r^k(R + c_V)}$ which is negative since $r < 1$

Also $\underline{_2W_3 = mRT_2\left(\frac{T_3}{T_2} - 1\right) = mRT_1r^k(r^{1-k} - 1)}$ which is negative

$\underline{_3W_1 = 0}$ since $dV = 0$

$$_3Q_1 = E_1 - E_3 = mc_V(T_1 - T_3) = mc_VT_1\left(1 - \frac{T_3}{T_1}\right)$$

$$_3Q_1 = mc_VT_1\left[1 - \left(\frac{T_3}{T_2} \times \frac{T_2}{T_1}\right)\right]$$

$$= mc_VT_1[1 - r^{1-k}r^k]$$

$$\underline{_3Q_1 = mc_VT_1(1 - r)} \text{ which is positive since } r < 1$$

Cycle efficiency $\eta = \frac{\text{net work done}}{\text{heat supplied}} = \frac{_2Q_3 + {_3Q_1}}{_3Q_1}$ (since $\oint W = \oint Q$)

$$\text{or} \quad \eta = \frac{[mT_1(R + c_V)r^k(r^{1-k} - 1)] + [mc_VT_1(1 - r)]}{mc_VT_1(1 - r)}$$

$$= \frac{(\gamma + 1)r^k(r^{1-k} - 1) + (1 - r)}{(1 - r)}$$

$$\text{or} \quad \underline{\eta = 1 - \frac{(1 - r^{1-k})r^k(\gamma + 1)}{1 - r}}$$

Further Examples

9. Show that the work transfer per unit mass in a reversible non-flow process obeying the law pV^n = constant is

$$_1W_2 = (p_1V_1 - p_2V_2)/(n - 1)$$

Saturated steam in the cylinder of a traction engine expands from 6 bar to 1.5 bar according to the law pV^n = constant where n is 1.135. Find

(a) the final specific volume and quality,
(b) the final specific internal energy,
(c) the heat transfer per unit mass during the process.
(1.07 m^3/kg, 0.924, 2362.3 kJ/kg, 8.1 kJ/kg)

10. A mass of 0.1 kg of steam at 100 bar and 350 °C expands reversibly to 1 bar according to the law pV = constant. Determine the work and heat transfers stating the sense in each case. Sketch the process on a p-V field. (103.2 kJ out, 101.1 kJ in)

11. A perfect gas undergoes a cycle comprised of three processes. It is first compressed isothermally from 1 bar, 27 °C to one-eighth of its initial volume. Energy is then added at constant pressure, increasing the temperature of the gas, and the cycle is completed by a reversible adiabatic expansion to the original conditions.

The isobaric specific heat capacity is 1.25 kJ/(kg K) and the characteristic gas constant is 0.5 kJ/(kg K).

Sketch the cycle on a p-V field, calculate the maximum cycle temperature and pressure and find the net work transfer per kg.
(416.4 °C, 8 bar, +174.3 kJ/kg)

6 STEADY FLOW PROCESSES - VAPOURS

1. The nozzles of a steam turbine receive steam at 3 bar and 150 °C with negligible velocity. The steam expands adiabatically through the nozzles and leaves at 1 bar with a dryness fraction of 0.96. Calculate
   (a) the exit velocity,
   (b) the total exit area for a mass flow rate of 10 kg/s.

Referring to figure 6.1

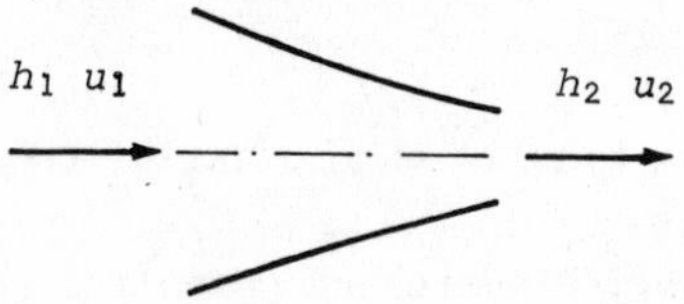

Figure 6.1

Energy Equation

$${}_1\dot{Q}_2 - {}_1\dot{W}_2 = \dot{m}\left[h_2 - h_1 + \frac{1}{2}(u_2{}^2 - u_1{}^2) + g(z_2 - z_1)\right]$$

Now ${}_1\dot{Q}_2 = 0;\ {}_1\dot{W}_2 = 0;\ u_1 = 0;\ g(z_2 - z_1) = 0.$

Thus $u_2{}^2 = 2(h_1 - h_2)$

Now $h_1 = 2762\ \frac{\text{kJ}}{\text{kg}}$ (page 6)

Also $h_2 = h_{f_2} + x_2 h_{fg_2} = 417 + 0.96(2258) = 2584.7\ \frac{\text{kJ}}{\text{kg}}$ (page 4)

Thus $u_2 = \sqrt{2(2762 - 2584.7)\ \frac{\text{kJ}}{\text{kg}}\ \frac{[10^3\ \text{Nm}]}{[\ \text{kJ}\ ]}\ \frac{[\text{kg m}]}{[\text{N s}^2]}}$

$u_2 = 595\ \frac{\text{m}}{\text{s}}$ (a)

Mass Continuity Equation

$$A_2 = \frac{\dot{m}v_2}{u_2} = \frac{\dot{m}x_2 v_{g2}}{u_2} \quad \text{(neglecting the liquid volume)}$$

$$A_2 = \frac{10\ \frac{\text{kg}}{\text{s}} \times 0.96 \times 1.694\ \frac{\text{m}^3}{\text{kg}}}{595\ \frac{\text{m}}{\text{s}}} = 0.0273\ \text{m}^2 \quad \text{(b)}$$

2. Steam at 8 bar and 250 °C, flowing at the rate of 4 kg/s, flows into a pipe carrying steam which is 0.9 dry at 8 bar. After

mixing adiabatically at this pressure the flow rate is 10.5 kg/s. Determine the quality of the mixture.

If the mixture is now expanded in a nozzle to a pressure of 5 bar and 0.95 dry determine the velocity of the steam leaving the nozzle.

Referring to figure 6.2a

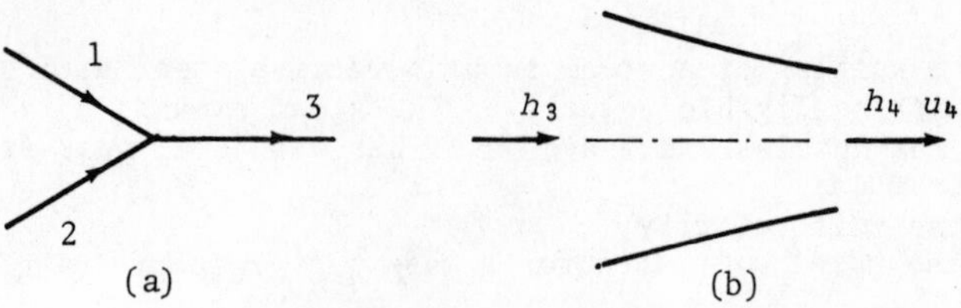

Figure 6.2

Energy Equation

$$\dot{Q} - \dot{W} = \sum_{\text{IN}}(\text{flow of enthalpy, kinetic and potential energies}) - \sum_{\text{OUT}}(\text{flow of enthalpy, kinetic and potential energies})$$

Now $\dot{Q} = \dot{W} = 0$ and K.E. and P.E. terms are negligible.

Thus $\sum \dot{H}_{\text{IN}} = \sum \dot{H}_{\text{OUT}}$

or $\quad \dot{m}_1 h_1 + \dot{m}_2 h_2 = \dot{m}_3 h_3$

Mass Continuity Equation

$$\dot{m}_1 + \dot{m}_2 = \dot{m}_3$$

Thus $h_3 = \dfrac{\dot{m}_1 h_1 + \dot{m}_2 h_2}{\dot{m}_3} = \dfrac{\dot{m}_1 h_1 + \dot{m}_2 h_2}{\dot{m}_1 + \dot{m}_2}$

$$= \frac{4\ \frac{\text{kg}}{\text{s}}\left(2951\ \frac{\text{kJ}}{\text{kg}}\right) + 6.5\ \frac{\text{kg}}{\text{s}}\left[721 + 0.9(2048)\ \frac{\text{kJ}}{\text{kg}}\right]}{10.5\ \frac{\text{kg}}{\text{s}}}$$ (pages 7 and 4 respectively)

$$h_3 = 2711.6\ \frac{\text{kJ}}{\text{kg}}$$

Thus $x_3 = \dfrac{h_3 - h_{f3}}{h_{fg3}} = \dfrac{2711.6 - 721}{2048} = 0.972$ (from page 4)

Referring to figure 6.2b

Energy Equation

$$_3\dot{Q}_4 - {_3\dot{W}_4} = \dot{m}\left[h_4 - h_3 + \frac{1}{2}(u_4^2 - u_3^2)\right]$$

Now $_3\dot{Q}_4 = {_3\dot{W}_4} = u_3 = 0.$

Thus $u_4 = 2(h_3 - h_4)$

and $h_4 = h_{f_4} + x_4 h_{fg_4} = 640 + 0.95(2109) = 2643.6 \frac{kJ}{kg}$

Thus $u_4 = \sqrt{2(2711.6 - 2643.6)\frac{kJ}{kg}\frac{[10^3 \text{ Nm}]}{[\text{ kJ }]}\frac{[kg\ m]}{[N\ s^2]}}$

$u_4 = 369 \frac{m}{s}$

3. Saturated Freon-12 vapour at -20 °C is drawn into a rotary compressor at the rate of 0.12 kg/s and compressed to 7.45 bar at 45 °C.

The power input to the compressor is 4.5 kW.

Calculate the heat transfer rate for this process, stating the sense.

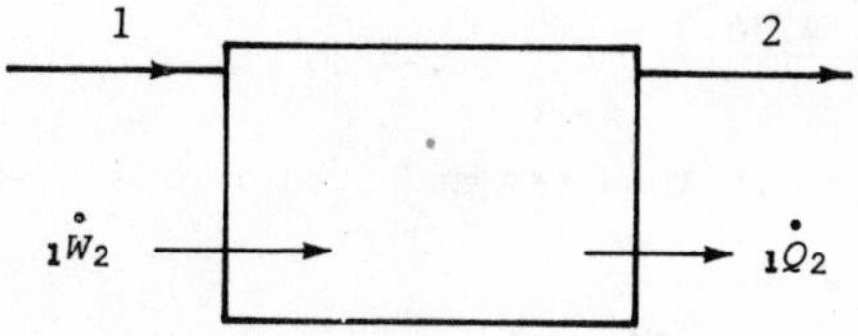

Figure 6.3

Energy Equation

$$_1\dot{Q}_2 - {_1\dot{W}_2} = \dot{m}(h_2 - h_1) \quad \text{(all other terms zero)}$$

$$_1\dot{Q}_2 = (-4.5 \text{ kW}) + 0.12 \frac{kg}{s}(210.63 - 178.73)\frac{kJ}{kg}\frac{[kW\ s]}{[\ kJ\ ]} \quad \text{(p.13)}$$

$$_1\dot{Q}_2 = -4.5 \text{ kW} + 3.828 \text{ kW}$$

$$_1\dot{Q}_2 = -0.672 \text{ kW}$$

4. Steam flows along a main at the rate of 20 g/s and at a particular point its pressure and temperature are 6 bar and 160 °C respectively.

Further downstream, where the pressure is 5 bar, a sampling pipe takes the steam to a separating and throttling calorimeter from which the following results were taken:-

Mass of water separated	15 g
Mass of condensate from throttling calorimeter	0.5 kg
Pressure after throttling	1 bar
Temperature after throttling	115 °C

Calculate

(a) the dryness fraction of the steam in the main at 5 bar,

(b) the heat transfer rate between the first point and the sampling point.

Referring to figure 6.4

$$h_4 = 2676 + \frac{15}{30}(2777 - 2676) = 2706.3 \frac{kJ}{kg} \quad \text{(page 6)}$$

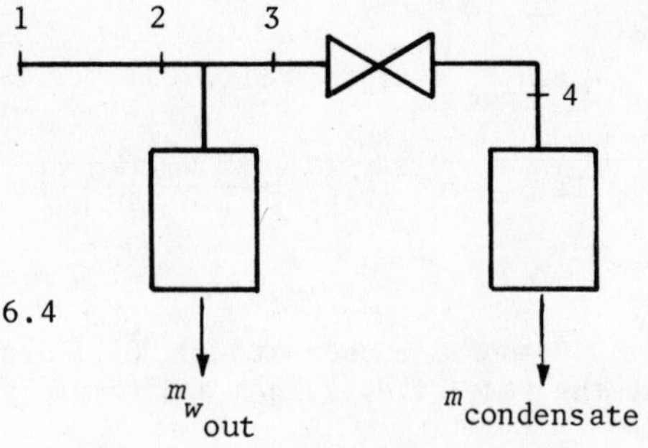

Figure 6.4

Thus $h_3 = h_4 = 2706.3 \ \frac{\text{kJ}}{\text{kg}}$ (since the process 3-4 is a throttling process)

Thus $x_3 = \frac{h_3 - h_{f_3}}{h_{fg_3}} = \frac{2706.3 - 640}{2109} = 0.98$

Now if subscript w refers to water and subscript s to steam

$$x_3 = \frac{m_{s_3}}{m_{w_3} + m_{s_3}} = \frac{1}{1 + \frac{m_{w_3}}{m_{s_3}}}$$

from which

$$\frac{m_{w_3}}{m_{s_3}} = \frac{1}{x_3} - 1 = 0.0204$$

Also $m_{w_3} + m_{s_3} = m_{condensate} = 0.5$ kg

From these last two equations

$$0.0204 m_{s_3} + m_{s_3} = 0.5 \text{ kg}$$

or $\quad m_{s_3} = 0.49$ kg; $m_{w_3} = 0.01$ kg

Now $m_{w_2} = m_{w_3} + m_{w_{out}} = 0.01 + 0.015 = 0.025$ kg

and $m_{s_2} = m_{s_3} = 0.49$ kg

Thus $x_2 = \frac{m_{s_2}}{m_{total}} = \frac{m_{s_2}}{m_{w_{out}} + m_{condensate}} = \frac{0.49}{0.015 + 0.5} = 0.951$

Energy Equation

$$_1\dot{Q}_2 - {}_1\dot{W}_2 = \dot{m}\left[(h_2 - h_1) + \frac{1}{2}(u_2{}^2 - u_1{}^2) + g(z_2 - z_1)\right]$$

Now $\quad {}_1\dot{W}_2 = \Delta u^2 = \Delta gz = 0$

$$h_2 = 640 + 0.951(2109) = 2645.7 \ \frac{\text{kJ}}{\text{kg}} \quad \text{(page 4 at 5 bar)}$$

and $\quad h_1 = 2757 + \frac{160 - 158.8}{200 - 158.8}(2851 - 2757) = 2759.7 \ \frac{\text{kJ}}{\text{kg}}$ (p.7, 6 bar)

$$ {}_1\dot{Q}_2 = 20\ \frac{kg}{s}(2645.7 - 2759.7)\ \frac{kJ}{kg}\left[\frac{kg}{10^3\ g}\right] = -2.28\ kW $$

5. Steam flows steadily through a small adiabatic turbine with a mass flow rate of 0.5 kg/s. The pressure and temperature at the inlet are 10 bar and 380 °C respectively. The velocity of the steam at exit is 38 m/s and the cross-sectional area of the exit duct is 0.2 m^2. The power developed by the turbine is 310 kW. Determine the pressure and temperature at exit from the turbine when operating under the above conditions. Neglect those terms in the steady flow energy equation which relate to velocity and gravity. (London University Part I 1970 recast)

Energy Equation

$$ h_1 - h_2 = \frac{{}_1\dot{W}_2}{\dot{m}} \quad (\text{neglecting } \Delta KE,\ \Delta PE,\ {}_1\dot{Q}_2) $$

$$ = \frac{310\ \frac{kJ}{s}}{0.5\ \frac{kg}{s}} = 620\ \frac{kJ}{kg} $$

$$ h_1 = 3158 + \frac{30}{50}(3264 - 3158) = 3221.6\ \frac{kJ}{kg} \quad \text{(page 7)} $$

Thus $h_2 = 3221.6 - 620 = 2601.6\ \frac{kJ}{kg}$

Mass Continuity Equation

$$ v_2 = \frac{u_2 A_2}{\dot{m}} = \frac{38\ \frac{m}{s} \times 0.2\ m^2}{0.5\ \frac{kg}{s}} = 15.2\ \frac{m^3}{kg} $$

Thus $p_2 = \frac{0.3}{1.3}\frac{(h_2 - 1943)}{100 \times v_2} = \frac{0.3}{1.3}\frac{(2601.6 - 1943)}{100 \times 15.2} = 0.10$ bar (page 11)

and $T_2 = (45.8 + 50)\ °C + \frac{(2601.6 - 2592)}{(2688 - 2592)}(100 - 50)\ K$ (page 6)

$T_2 = 100.8\ °C$

6. Saturated steam at 1.4 bar is used as the heating fluid in an air heater in which air enters at 60 °F at the rate of 1.5 lb/s. If all the steam condenses without being subcooled, determine the greatest flow rate that will be required. What will be the result of supplying more than this amount of steam? Assume that the steam condenses at constant pressure and take c_p for air as 0.24 Btu/lb R.

Referring to figure 6.6

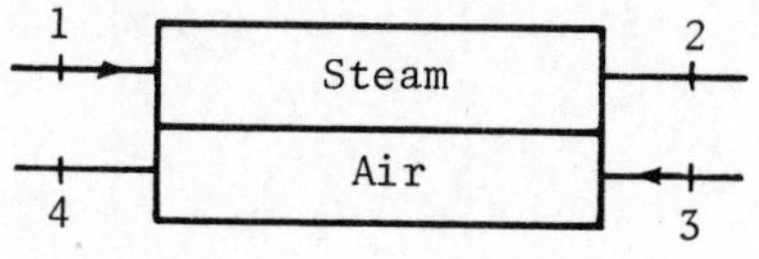

Figure 6.6

$$Q - W = \sum H_{out} - \sum H_{in}$$

$W = Q = 0$ in this instance

Thus $\dot{m}_s h_1 + \dot{m}_a h_3 = \dot{m}_s h_2 + \dot{m}_a h_4$

Maximum temperature of the air is given by

$T_{sat} = 109.3$ °C (page 4 at 1.4 bar)

Now $\dot{m}_s(h_1 - h_2) = \dot{m}_a(h_4 - h_3)$

And $h_1 = h_g$, $h_2 = h_f$;

Thus $h_1 - h_2 = h_g - h_f = h_{fg} = 2232 \frac{\text{kJ}}{\text{kg}}$ (page 4)

$$\dot{m}_s \times 2232 \frac{\text{kJ}}{\text{kg}} = \dot{m}_a c_p \left[109.3 - \frac{5}{9}(60 - 32)\right] \text{K}$$

$$\dot{m}_s = \frac{1.5 \times 0.24}{2232} \frac{\text{lb Btu kg}}{\text{s lb °R kJ}} \left(109.3 - \frac{5 \times 28}{9}\right) \text{K} \times \left[\frac{9\ \text{R}}{5\ \text{K}}\right] \left[\frac{\text{kJ}}{0.9478\ \text{Btu}}\right]$$

$$\underline{\dot{m}_s = 0.028 \frac{\text{kg}}{\text{s}}}$$

If more steam is supplied then the steam is a liquid/vapour mixture at exit.

Further Examples

7. A steam boiler operating under steady conditions receives feed water at 13 °C and delivers saturated steam at 2.2 bar. Calculate the heat transfer rate required for a boiler steam output of 100 kg/s. (265.64 MW)

8. Steam is supplied to a turbine at 100 bar, 500 °C. The casing of the turbine is thermally insulated and the heat transfer to surroundings per unit mass of steam flowing through the turbine is negligible. The steam flow rate is 100 000 kg/h, entering the turbine at negligible velocity and leaving through a duct of cross-section 3 m^2 in area with quality 0.89 at a pressure of 0.89 bar. Calculate

(a) the velocity of steam in the exhaust duct (169 m/s)

(b) the power output of the turbine (29.2 MW)

9. A steam turbine is supplied with steam at the rate of 2.2 million kg/h. The state of the steam at entry is 150 bar, 500°C with negligible velocity and the exhaust steam is at 0.08 bar and 0.94 dry. The cross-sectional area of the exhaust duct is 60 m^2. Calculate the power output if the heat transfer rate from the turbine to the surroundings is 5% of the power output. (554.6 MW)

7 STEADY FLOW PROCESSES - GASES

1. A reciprocating compressor raises air from atmospheric conditions of 100 kN/m^2 and 15 °C to 1000 kN/m^2 at a rate of 2 kg per min. The air in the delivery pipe is at 155 °C and the internal diameter of the pipe is 50 mm. The inlet velocity is negligible. Calculate the heat transfer between the compressor and its surroundings when the power input to the compressor is 6 kW.

Mass Continuity Equation

$$\dot{m}v = Au$$

Characteristic Gas Equation

$$pv = RT$$

$$\text{Thus } u_2 = \frac{\dot{m}v_2}{A_2} = \frac{\dot{m}RT_2}{p_2A_2} = \frac{2\ \frac{\text{kg}}{\text{min}} \times 0.287\ \frac{\text{kJ}}{\text{kg K}} \times 428\ \text{K}}{10^6\ \frac{\text{N}}{\text{m}^2} \times \frac{\pi}{4} \times 0.05^2\ \text{m}^2} \left[\frac{\text{min}}{60\ \text{s}}\right]\left[\frac{10^3\ \text{Nm}}{\text{kJ}}\right]$$

$$= 2.1\ \frac{\text{m}}{\text{s}}$$

Energy Equation

$${}_1\dot{Q}_2 - {}_1\dot{W}_2 = \dot{m}\left(h_2 - h_1 + \frac{u_2^2 - u_1^2}{2}\right) \quad (\text{and } u_1 = 0)$$

$$\text{or} \quad {}_1\dot{Q}_2 - {}_1\dot{W}_2 = \dot{m}\left[c_p(T_2 - T_1) + \frac{u_2^2}{2}\right]$$

$$\text{or} \quad {}_1\dot{Q}_2 - (-6\ \text{kW}) = 2\ \frac{\text{kg}}{\text{min}}\left[\frac{\text{min}}{60\ \text{s}}\right]\left[1.005\ \frac{\text{kJ}}{\text{kg K}}\ (155 - 15)\ \text{K} + \frac{2.1^2}{2}\ \frac{\text{m}^2}{\text{s}^2}\left[\frac{\text{N s}^2}{\text{kg m}}\right]\left[\frac{\text{kJ}}{10^3\ \text{Nm}}\right]\right]$$

$$\text{or} \quad \underline{{}_1\dot{Q}_2 = -1.31\ \text{kW}}$$

2. An uncooled rotary compressor raises air from atmospheric conditions of 100 kN/m^2 and 15 °C to a pressure of 1000 kN/m^2 at a rate of 2 kg/s. The temperature at delivery, after adiabatic compression, is 315 °C and the internal diameter of the delivery pipe is 75 mm. Calculate the power required to drive the compressor neglecting the inlet kinetic energy.

From the Mass Continuity and the Characteristic Gas Equations

$$u_2 = \frac{\dot{m}v_2}{A_2} = \frac{\dot{m}RT_2}{p_2A_2} = \frac{2\ \frac{\text{kg}}{\text{s}} \times 0.287\ \frac{\text{kJ}}{\text{kg K}} \times 588\ \text{K}}{10^6\ \frac{\text{N}}{\text{m}^2} \times \frac{\pi}{4} \times 0.075^2\ \text{m}^2} = 76.4\ \frac{\text{m}}{\text{s}}$$

Energy Equation

$$_1\dot{Q}_2 - {_1\dot{W}_2} = \dot{m}\left(h_2 - h_1 + \frac{u_2^2 - u_1^2}{2}\right) \text{ where } {_1\dot{Q}_2} = 0;\ u_1 = 0.$$

Thus $-{_1\dot{W}_2} = \dot{m}\left[c_p(T_2 - T_1) + \frac{u_2^2}{2}\right]$

$$= 2\ \frac{\text{kg}}{\text{s}}\left[1.005\ \frac{\text{kJ}}{\text{kg K}}\ (315 - 15)\ \text{K} + \frac{76.4^2}{2}\ \frac{\text{m}^2}{\text{s}^2}\ \frac{[\text{N s}^2]}{[\text{kg m}]}\frac{[\text{kJ}]}{[10^3\ \text{Nm}]}\right]$$

$$= 608.8\ \text{kW}$$

or $\underline{{_1\dot{W}_2} = -608.8\ \text{kW}}$

3. A compressor takes in 500 kg/min of air at 0.98 bar and 18 °C and delivers it at 5.5 bar and 68 °C. The diameters of the intake and delivery pipes are respectively 450 mm and 200 mm and the compressor is driven by a motor of 1000 kW. Determine the air velocities in the intake and delivery pipes and assuming that all the energy from the motor is transmitted to the air estimate the rate at which heat is transferred to or from the air during compression.

From the Mass Continuity and the Characteristic Gas Equations

$$u_1 = \frac{\dot{m}RT_1}{p_1A_1} = \frac{500\ \frac{\text{kg}}{\text{min}}\ \frac{[\text{min}]}{[60\ \text{s}]} \times 0.287\ \frac{\text{kJ}}{\text{kg K}} \times 291\ \text{K}}{0.98\ \text{bar} \times \frac{\pi}{4} \times 0.45^2\ \text{m}^2}\ \frac{[\text{bar m}^3]}{[10^2\ \text{kJ}]}$$

$$\underline{u_1 = 44.7\ \frac{\text{m}}{\text{s}}}$$

Similarly

$$u_2 = \frac{\dot{m}RT_2}{p_2A_2} = \frac{500 \times 0.287 \times 341}{60 \times 5.5 \times 0.25\pi \times 0.2^2 \times 100}$$

$$\underline{u_2 = 47.2\ \frac{\text{m}}{\text{s}}}$$

Energy Equation

$$_1\dot{Q}_2 - {_1\dot{W}_2} = \dot{m}\left[c_p(T_2 - T_1) + \frac{u_2^2 - u_1^2}{2}\right]$$

or

$$_1\dot{Q}_2 - (-1000)\text{kW} = 500\ \frac{\text{kg}}{\text{min}}\frac{[\text{min}]}{[60\ \text{s}]}\left[1.005\ \frac{\text{kJ}}{\text{kg K}}\ (50)\ \text{K} + \frac{44.7^2 - 44.7^2}{2}\ \frac{\text{m}^2}{\text{s}^2}\ \frac{[\text{N s}^2]}{[\text{kg m}]}\frac{[\text{kJ}]}{[10^3\ \text{Nm}]}\right]$$

or $\underline{{_1\dot{Q}_2} = -580\ \text{kW}}$

4. 6 kg/s of air at 200 °C flowing through a pipe at 100 m/s are mixed adiabatically with 1 kg/s of air at 100 °C which is flow-

ing through another pipe at 50 m/s. The resulting mixture flows at a pressure of 4 bar in a pipe of 100 mm diameter. Estimate the temperature and velocity of the mixture.

Referring to figure 7.4

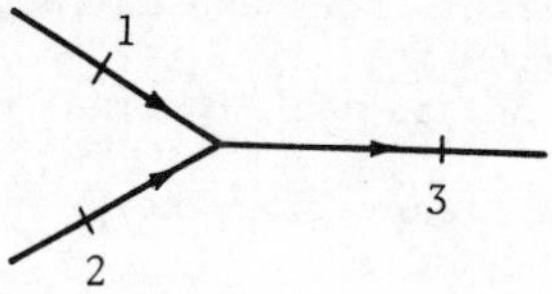

Figure 7.4

Energy Equation

$$\dot{Q} - \dot{W} = \sum(\dot{H} + \text{K.E.} + \text{P.E.})_{\text{OUT}} - \sum(\dot{H} + \text{K.E.} + \text{P.E.})_{\text{IN}}$$

Now $\dot{Q} = 0$; $\dot{W} = 0$; and P.E. is negligible.

Thus $\sum(\dot{H} + \text{K.E.})_{\text{IN}} = \sum(\dot{H} + \text{K.E.})_{\text{OUT}}$

or $$\dot{m}_1\left(h_1 + \frac{u_1^2}{2}\right) + \dot{m}_2\left(h_2 + \frac{u_2^2}{2}\right) = \dot{m}_3\left(h_3 + \frac{u_3^2}{2}\right)$$

Thus $$6\ \frac{\text{kg}}{\text{s}}\left[1.005\ \frac{\text{kJ}}{\text{kg K}}\ (473 - T_\text{d})\ \text{K} + \frac{100^2}{2}\ \frac{\text{m}^2}{\text{s}^2}\ \frac{[\text{N s}^2]}{[\text{kg m}]}\frac{[\text{kJ}]}{[10^3\ \text{Nm}]}\right]$$

$$+ 1\ \frac{\text{kg}}{\text{s}}\left[1.005\ \frac{\text{kJ}}{\text{kg K}}\ (373 - T_\text{d})\ \text{K} + \frac{50^2}{2}\ \frac{\text{m}^2}{\text{s}^2}\ \frac{[\text{N s}^2]}{[\text{kg m}]}\frac{[\text{kJ}]}{[10^3\ \text{Nm}]}\right]$$

$$= 7\ \frac{\text{kg}}{\text{s}}\left[1.005\ \frac{\text{kJ}}{\text{kg K}}\ (T_3 - T_\text{d}) + \frac{u_3^2}{2}\right]$$ (where T_d is a datum and cancels out)

From the Mass Continuity and Characteristic Gas Equations

$$u_3 = \frac{\dot{m}RT_3}{p_3A_3} = \frac{7\ \frac{\text{kg}}{\text{s}} \times 0.287\ \frac{\text{kJ}}{\text{kg K}} \times T_3}{4\ \text{bar} \times \pi \times 0.1^2\ \text{m}^2}\ \frac{[\text{bar m}^3]}{[10^2\ \text{kJ}]}$$

or $$u_3 = 0.639\ T_3\ \frac{\text{m}}{\text{sK}}$$

Thus substituting in the original energy equation

$$\frac{6}{7}\left(473 + \frac{10\ 000}{2 \times 10^3 \times 1.005}\right)\frac{\text{kJ}}{\text{kg}} + \frac{1}{7}\left(373 + \frac{2500}{2 \times 10^3 \times 1.005}\right)\frac{\text{kJ}}{\text{kg}}$$

$$= T_3\ \frac{\text{kJ}}{\text{kg K}} + \frac{0.639^2}{2 \times 1.005}\ T_3^2\ \frac{\text{m}^2}{\text{s}^2\text{K}^2}\ \frac{[\text{N s}^2]}{[\text{kg m}]}\frac{[\text{kJ}]}{[10^3\ \text{Nm}]}$$

or $$T_3 = \frac{463.2}{(1 + 0.0002T_3)}$$

or $\underline{T_3 = 426.8\ \text{K}}$

and $\underline{u_3 = 0.639 \times 426.8 = 273\ \frac{\text{m}}{\text{s}}}$

5. Air flows steadily through a heat exchanger. The temperature and pressure are 125 °C and 200 kN/m^2 at inlet, and 10 °C and 140 kN/m^2 at exit respectively. The mass flow rate is 1 kg/s. The cross-sectional areas of the inlet and exit pipes are each 0.1 m^2. Determine

(a) the velocities of the air at inlet and outlet,

(b) the heat transfer rate from the air,

(c) the difference between the specific internal energies of the air inlet and outlet.

Neglect gravity terms in the steady-flow energy equation.

(London University 1969 Part I No 3)

Referring to figure 7.5

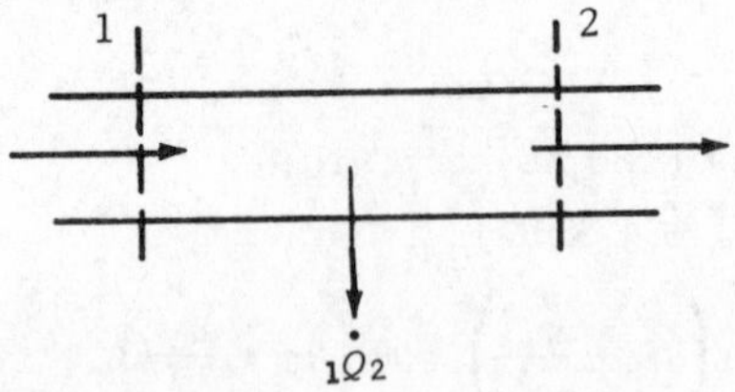

Figure 7.5

Energy Equation

$$\dot{m}\left(h_1 + \frac{u_1^2}{2} + gz_1\right) + {}_1\dot{Q}_2 = \dot{m}\left(h_2 + \frac{u_2^2}{2} + gz_2\right) + {}_1\dot{W}_2$$

Mass Continuity Equation

$$\dot{m} = \frac{A_1 u_1}{v_1} = \frac{A_1 u_1 p_1}{RT_1}$$

$$\text{Thus } u_1 = \frac{\dot{m}RT_1}{A_1 p_1} = \frac{1\ \frac{\text{kg}}{\text{s}} \times 0.287\ \frac{\text{kJ}}{\text{kg K}} \times 398\ \text{K}}{0.1\ \text{m}^2 \times 200\ \frac{\text{kN}}{\text{m}^2}}$$

$$\underline{u_1 = 5.71\ \frac{\text{m}}{\text{s}}}$$

$$\text{Also } u_2 = \frac{\dot{m}RT_2}{A_2 p_2} = \frac{1 \times 0.287 \times 413}{0.1 \times 140} = \underline{8.47\ \frac{\text{m}}{\text{s}}}$$

Thus in the energy equation with gravity terms zero and substituting for $(h_2 - h_1)$ assuming the fluid is a perfect gas

$${}_1\dot{Q}_2 = \dot{m}\left[(h_2 - h_1) + \frac{u_2^2 - u_1^2}{2}\right] = \dot{m}\left[c_p(T_2 - T_1) + \frac{u_2^2 - u_1^2}{2}\right]$$

$$= 1\ \frac{\text{kg}}{\text{s}}\left[1.005\ \frac{\text{kJ}}{\text{kg K}}\ (10 - 125)\ \text{K} + \frac{8.47^2 - 5.71^2}{2}\ \frac{\text{m}^2}{\text{s}^2}\ \left[\frac{\text{N s}^2}{\text{kg m}}\right]\left[\frac{\text{kJ}}{10^3\ \text{Nm}}\right]\right]$$

$$\underline{{}_1\dot{Q}_2 = -115.6\ \text{kW}}$$

$$e_1 - e_2 = c_v(T_1 - T_2) = (c_p - R)(T_1 - T_2)$$

$$= (1.005 - 0.287)\ \frac{\text{kJ}}{\text{kg K}}\ (125 - 10)\ \text{K}$$

$$e_1 - e_2 = 82.6\ \frac{\text{kJ}}{\text{kg}}$$

Further Examples

6. Air is expanded in a group of nozzles from a temperature of 650 °C at inlet to 500 °C and 1 bar at exit. The velocity of approach and the heat transfer per unit mass during the expansion are both negligible. Find the total nozzle exit area required for a mass flow of 30 kg/s. (0.1212 m^2)

7. The conditions at entry to a gas turbine are 5 bar and 1000 K with negligible velocity. The exhaust duct has an area of 0.1 m^2 and the gas flows uniformly therein with a purely axial velocity of 150 m/s at 1 bar and 670 K. Calculate the shaft power assuming that the heat transfer from the turbine amounts to 5% of the shaft work. For the gas c_p = 1.15 kJ/(kg K), R = 0.29 kJ/(kg K). (493.7 kW)

8 STEADY FLOW PROCESSES - ENERGY AND MOMENTUM

In this chapter a new fundamental concept appears - namely momentum - and in addition to the principles of conservation of mass and energy previously encountered we have to use the third principle - conservation of momentum which is embodied in Newton's laws of motion.

Students should be aware that the examples treated here are only first year in standard but nevertheless serve to show how momentum fits into the general picture.

1. The combustion chamber and propulsion nozzle of a rocket engine are represented in figure 8.1. During the test bed firing the combustion gases expand exactly to atmospheric pressure at exit from the nozzle and leave with a velocity of 10 000 ft/s. Calculate the static thrust developed by the engine if the mass flow rate is 200 lb/s.

The conditions within the engine remain constant during flight - i.e. the velocity of the gases leaving the nozzle is still 10 000 ft/s relative to the nozzle. If the pressure of the gases in the exit plane of the nozzle is 14.2 lbf/in^2 extimate the net thrust when the rocket is travelling at an altitude of 100 miles (where the atmospheric pressure is 6×10^{-10} lbf/in^2). The nozzle exit area is 6 ft^2.

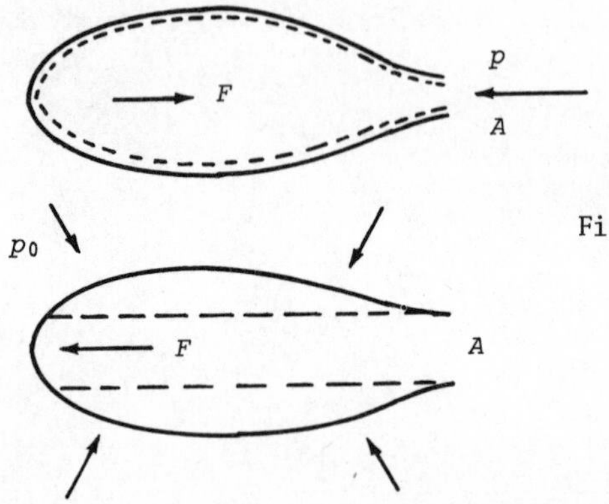

Figure 8.1

Let F = reaction between the fluid and the inside of the rocket

then $F - pA = \dot{m}u$ (since net force is rate of change of momentum)

Thus static thrust is given by

$$\dot{m}u = 200\ \frac{\text{lb}}{\text{s}} \times 10\ 000\ \frac{\text{ft}}{\text{s}} \left[\frac{\text{kg}}{2.205\ \text{lb}}\right]\left[\frac{\text{m}}{3.281\ \text{ft}}\right]\left[\frac{\text{kN}}{10^3\ \text{N}}\right]$$

$$= \underline{276.4\ \text{kN}}$$

Net thrust in flight is given by

$$F - p_0 A = \dot{m}u + A(p - p_0)$$

$$= 276.4\ \text{kN} + 6\ \text{ft}^2 \left[\frac{\text{m}^2}{3.281^2\ \text{ft}^2}\right] \left[14.2 - (6 \times 10^{-10})\right] \frac{\text{lbf}}{\text{in}^2}$$

$$\times \left[\frac{10^5\ \text{Nm}^{-2}}{14.5\ \text{lbf in}^{-2}}\right] \left[\frac{\text{kN}}{10^3\ \text{N}}\right]$$

$$= 276.4\ \text{kN} + 54.6\ \text{kN}$$

$$\underline{F - p_0 A = 331\ \text{kN}}$$

2. Figure 8.2 shows a jet pump (or ejector) in which a primary stream of high velocity fluid at section (1) entrains a secondary stream of the same fluid with low velocity at section (2). At the end of the constant diameter mixing tube, section (3) the streams are thoroughly mixed and the velocity is uniform. Note that A_3 is equal to the sum of A_1 and A_2.

For the purpose of elementary analysis assume that at sections (1) and (2) both streams have the same pressure; also neglect friction at the walls of the mixing tube.

If $A_1 = 0.01\ \text{m}^2$; $A_3 = 0.1\ \text{m}^2$; $u_1 = 30$ m/s; $u_2 = 3$ m/s and the density of the fluid is $10^3\ \text{kg/m}^3$ calculate

(a) the velocity at section (3),

(b) the pressure difference between sections (1) and (3).

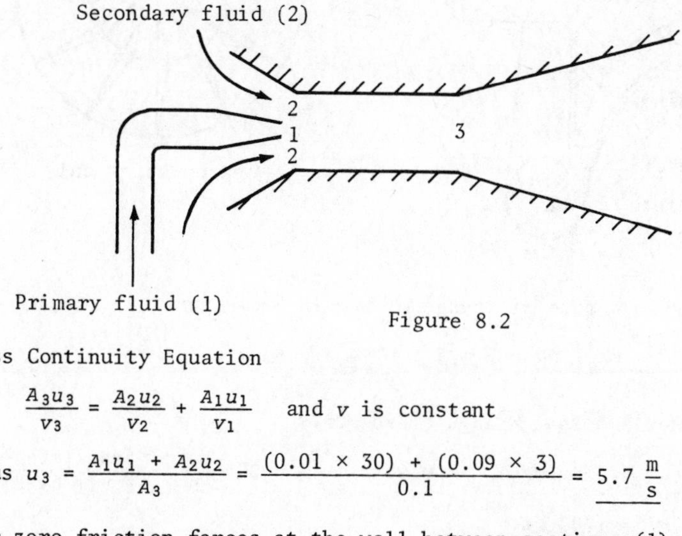

Figure 8.2

Mass Continuity Equation

$$\frac{A_3 u_3}{v_3} = \frac{A_2 u_2}{v_2} + \frac{A_1 u_1}{v_1} \quad \text{and } v \text{ is constant}$$

$$\text{Thus } u_3 = \frac{A_1 u_1 + A_2 u_2}{A_3} = \frac{(0.01 \times 30) + (0.09 \times 3)}{0.1} = \underline{5.7\ \frac{\text{m}}{\text{s}}}$$

For zero friction forces at the wall between sections (1) and (3)

$$p_1 A_1 + p_2 A_2 - p_3 A_3 = \dot{m}_3 u_3 - \dot{m}_2 u_2 - \dot{m}_1 u_1 \text{ and } p_1 = p_2$$

$$p_1(A_1 + A_2) - p_3 A_3 = (\dot{m}_2 + \dot{m}_1)u_3 - \dot{m}_2 u_2 - \dot{m}_1 u_1.$$

$$(p_1 - p_3)A_3 = \dot{m}_2(u_3 - u_2) + \dot{m}_1(u_3 - u_1)$$

$$= \frac{A_2 u_2}{v_2}(u_3 - u_2) + \frac{A_1 u_1}{v_1}(u_3 - u_1)$$

$$p_1 - p_3 = \frac{10^3\ \text{kg}}{\text{m}^3}\left[0.09 \times 3(5.7 - 3) + 0.01 \times 30(5.7 - 30)\right] \times \text{m}^2\ \frac{\text{m}^2}{\text{s}^2}\ \frac{[\text{N s}^2]}{[\text{kg m}]}\frac{[\text{bar m}^2]}{[10^5\ \text{N}]}$$

$$\underline{p_1 - p_3 = 0.656\ \text{bar}}$$

3. Figure 8.3 shows a centrifugal compressor with an impeller (rotor) diameter of 1.3 m driven at 4000 rev/min by a motor of 1200 kW. Air is drawn into the eye of the impeller in a purely axial direction - i.e. there is no angular motion of the air entering the rotor - and leaves with the velocity indicated in the figure. If friction and windage losses are negligible estimate the rate of mass flow through the compressor.

If the diameter of the eye is 0.5 m calculate the axial thrust on the impeller for air entering at 0.96 bar and 20 °C.

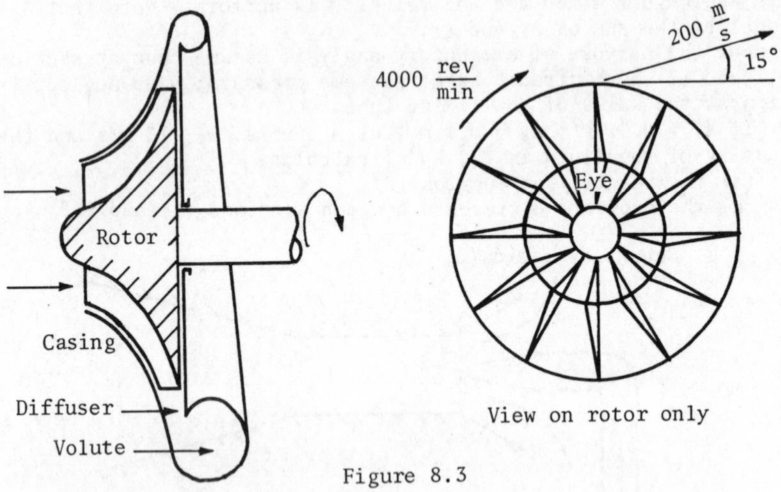

Figure 8.3

Torque = rate of change of angular momentum

$$= \dot{m}(200\cos 15° - 0)\ \frac{\text{m}}{\text{s}} \times 0.65\ \text{m}$$

Power = torque × angular velocity

$$= 200\cos 15° \times 0.65\ \dot{m}\ \frac{\text{m}^2}{\text{s}^2} \times 4000\ \frac{\text{rev}}{\text{min}}\ \frac{[2\pi\ \text{rad}]}{[\text{rev}]}\frac{[\text{min}]}{[60\ \text{s}]}$$

$$= 1200\ \text{kW}$$

Thus $$\dot{m} = \frac{1200 \times 60}{400\pi \times 4000 \times 0.65\cos 15°}\ \frac{\text{kW s}^2}{\text{m}^2}\ \frac{[\text{kJ}]}{[\text{kW s}]}\frac{[10^3\ \text{Nm}]}{[\text{kJ}]}\frac{[\text{kg m}]}{[\text{N s}^2]}$$

$$\underline{\dot{m} = 22.81\ \frac{\text{kg}}{\text{s}}}$$

Axial thrust = change in axial momentum and is given by

$$\dot{m}\Delta u_f = \frac{\dot{m}^2 RT}{pA}$$

$$= \frac{22.81^2 \dfrac{kg^2}{s^2} \times 0.287 \dfrac{kJ}{kg\ K} \times 293\ K}{0.96\ bar \times \pi \times 0.25^2\ m^2} \frac{[bar\ m^3]}{[10^2\ kJ]}\frac{[N\ s^2]}{[kg\ m]}$$

$$\underline{\dot{m}\Delta u_f = 2.32\ kN}$$

4. Air flows through a duct of constant cross-section 0.1 m² and at a given station (1) its velocity is 100 m/s, its pressure 1.5 bar and its temperature 100 °C. At a subsequent station (2) its pressure is 1.4 bar.

(A) Assuming the flow to be frictionless, calculate
   (a) the mass flow rate,
   (b) the velocity at station (2),
   (c) the heat transfer between stations (1) and (2).

(B) Assuming adiabatic flow with friction, calculate
   (a) the mass flow rate,
   (b) the temperature and velocity at station (2),
   (c) the frictional drag of the duct walls.

From the Mass Continuity and Characteristic Gas Equations

$$\dot{m} = \frac{A_1 u_1}{v_1} = \frac{p_1 A_1 u_1}{RT_1}$$

$$= \frac{1.5\ bar \times 0.1\ m^2 \times 100\ \dfrac{m}{s}}{0.287\ \dfrac{kJ}{kg\ K} \times 375\ K} \frac{[10^2\ kJ]}{[bar\ m^3]}$$

$$\underline{\dot{m} = 14.01\ \frac{kg}{s}} \quad \text{(A)(a)}$$

From the conservation of momentum and in the absence of friction

$$A(p_1 - p_2) = \dot{m}(u_2 - u_1)$$

or $$0.1\ m^2 \times 0.1\ bar = 14.01\ \frac{kg}{s}\left(u_2 - 100\ \frac{m}{s}\right) \frac{[bar\ m^2]}{[10^5\ N\ ]}\frac{[N\ s^2]}{[kg\ m]}$$

or $$\underline{u_2 = 171.4\ \frac{m}{s}} \quad \text{(A)(b)}$$

$$T_2 = \frac{p_2 A_2 u_2}{\dot{m}R} = \frac{1.4\ bar \times 0.1\ m^2 \times 171.4\ \dfrac{m}{s}}{0.287\ \dfrac{kJ}{kg\ K} \times 14.01\ \dfrac{kg}{s}} = 597\ K$$

Energy Equation

$${}_1\dot{Q}_2 - {}_1\dot{W}_2 = \dot{m}\left[c_p(T_2 - T_1) + \frac{u_2{}^2 - u_1{}^2}{2}\right] \quad (W = 0)$$

$${}_1\dot{Q}_2 = 14.01\left[\frac{kg}{s}\ 1.005\ \frac{kJ}{kg\ K}\ (597 - 373)\ K + \frac{171.4^2 - 100^2}{2}\ \frac{m^2}{s^2}\ \frac{[N\ s^2]}{[kg\ m]}\frac{[\ kJ\ ]}{[10^3\ Nm]}\right]$$

$\underline{{}_1\dot{Q}_2 = 3.289 \text{ MW}}$ (A)(c)

Adiabatic flow with friction

$\underline{\dot{m} = 14.01 \frac{\text{kg}}{\text{s}} \text{ as before}}$ (B)(a)

Energy Equation

$${}_1\dot{Q}_2 - {}_1\dot{W}_2 = \dot{m}\left[c_p(T_2 - T_1) + \frac{u_2^2 - u_1^2}{2}\right] \qquad ({}_1\dot{Q}_2 = {}_1\dot{W}_2 = 0)$$

$$c_p(T_1 - T_2) = \frac{u_2^2 - u_1^2}{2}$$

Also $T_2 = \dfrac{p_2 A_2 u_2}{\dot{m}R}$

and substituting this into the previous line

$$1.005 \frac{\text{kJ}}{\text{kg K}}\left(373 \text{ K} - \frac{1.4 \text{ bar} \times 0.1 \text{ m}^2 \times u_2}{14.01 \frac{\text{kg}}{\text{s}} \times 0.287 \frac{\text{kJ}}{\text{kg K}}} \frac{[10^2 \text{ kJ}]}{[\text{bar m}^3]}\right)$$

$$= \frac{u_2^2}{2} - \frac{100^2}{2} \frac{\text{m}^2}{\text{s}^2}$$

$$\text{Thus } 373 - \frac{1.4 \times 10}{14.01 \times 0.287} \frac{u_2}{(\text{m/s})} = \frac{u_2^2}{2.01} \frac{\text{kg}}{\text{kJ}} \frac{[\text{N s}^2]}{[\text{kg m}]} \left[\frac{\text{kJ}}{10^3 \text{ Nm}}\right]$$

$$- \frac{100}{2.01} \frac{\text{m}^2}{\text{s}^2} \frac{\text{kg}}{\text{kJ}} \frac{[\text{N s}^2]}{[\text{kg m}]} \left[\frac{\text{kJ}}{10^3 \text{ Nm}}\right]$$

or $\quad u_2 = \dfrac{759730}{u_2 + 6999}$

or $\quad \underline{u_2 = 106.9 \frac{\text{m}}{\text{s}}}$ (B)(b)

$$T_2 = \frac{p_2 A_2 u_2}{\dot{m}R} = \frac{1.4 \text{ bar} \times 0.1 \text{ m}^2 \times 106.9 \text{ m s}^{-1}}{0.287 \frac{\text{kJ}}{\text{kg K}} \times 14.01 \frac{\text{kg}}{\text{s}}} \frac{[10^2 \text{ kJ}]}{[\text{bar m}^3]}$$

$\underline{T_2 = 372.2 \text{ K}}$ (B)(b)

Momentum equation

$$p_1 A_1 + F - p_2 A_2 = \dot{m}(u_2 - u_1)$$

or $\quad F = 14.01 \dfrac{\text{kg}}{\text{s}} \times 6.7 \dfrac{\text{m}}{\text{s}} \dfrac{[\text{N s}^2]}{[\text{kg m}]} + 0.1 \text{ m}^2 \; (1.4 - 1.5) \text{ bar} \dfrac{[10^5 \text{ N}]}{[\text{bar m}^2]}$

$\underline{F = 93.9 - 1000 = -906 \text{ N}}$ (B)(c)

5. In order to improve the ground running performance of the air intake to the turbojet engine of a supersonic aircraft it is customary to attach a 'Borda mouthpiece'. Figure 8.5 shows such a device in cross-section. Air enters at the rate of 30 kg/s under the conditions given in the figure.

If the flow of air through the Borda mouthpiece may be assumed to be frictionless and adiabatic, estimate the pressure at the intake face , section (2). What is the magnitude and direction of any axial force on the mouthpiece resulting from the acceleration of the air? Take atmospheric pressure to be 1 bar.

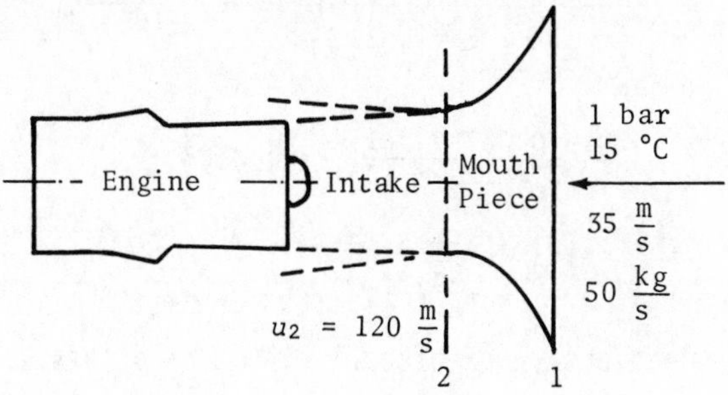

Figure 8.5

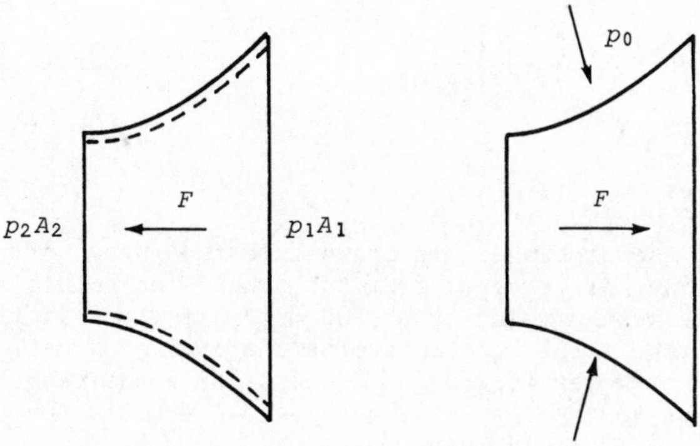

Figure 8.5a

Energy Equation

$$c_p(T_1 - T_2) = \frac{u_2^2 - u_1^2}{2} = \frac{155 \times 85}{2 \times 1005}\ \frac{m^2}{s^2}$$

$$T_2 = T_1 - \frac{155 \times 85}{2 \times 1.005}\ \frac{m^2}{s^2}\ \frac{kg\ K}{kJ}\ \frac{[N\ s^2]}{[kg\ m]}\left[\frac{kJ}{10^3\ Nm}\right]$$

$$T_2 = 288\ K - \frac{155 \times 85}{2 \times 1005}\ K = 281.5\ K$$

For frictionless, adiabatic flow of a perfect gas:

$$\frac{p_2}{p_1} = \left(\frac{T_2}{T_1}\right)^{1/k} = \left(\frac{281.5}{288}\right)^{3.5} = 0.923$$

$$\underline{p_2 = 1\ bar \times 0.923 = 0.923\ bar}$$

Let F be the reaction between the fluid and the duct (figure 8.5a).

Momentum Equation

$$p_1A_1 + F - p_2A_2 = \dot{m}(u_2 - u_1)$$

From the Mass Continuity and Characteristic Gas Equations

$$A_1 = \frac{\dot{m}RT_1}{p_1u_1} = \frac{30\ \frac{\text{kg}}{\text{s}} \times 0.287\ \frac{\text{kJ}}{\text{kg K}} \times 288\ \text{K}}{1\ \text{bar} \times 35\ \frac{\text{m}}{\text{s}}} \frac{[\text{bar m}^3]}{[10^2\ \text{kJ}]}$$

$$A_1 = 0.7085\ \text{m}^2$$

Also $A_2 = \dfrac{\dot{m}RT_2}{p_2u_2} = \dfrac{30 \times 0.287 \times 281.5}{0.923 \times 120 \times 100} = 0.2188\ \text{m}^2$

$$\text{Thrust} = F + p_0(A_1 - A_2)$$

$$= p_2A_2 - p_1A_1 + \dot{m}(u_2 - u_1) + p_0(A_1 - A_2)$$

$$= 0.923\ \text{bar} \times 0.2188\ \text{m}^2 - 1\ \text{bar} \times 0.7085\ \text{m}^2$$

$$+ 30\ \frac{\text{kg}}{\text{s}} \times 85\ \frac{\text{m}}{\text{s}} + 1\ \text{bar}(0.7085 - 0.2188)\ \text{m}^2$$

$$\text{Thrust} = 30 \times 85\ \frac{\text{kg m}}{\text{s}} \frac{[\text{N s}^2]}{[\text{kg m}]} - 0.2188 \times 0.077\ \text{bar m}^2 \frac{[10^5\ \text{N}]}{[\text{bar m}^2]}$$

$$\underline{\text{Thrust} = 865\ \text{N}}$$

Further Examples

6. Air from the atmosphere is drawn into the intake of a stationary jet engine. It emerges from the propulsion nozzle at atmospheric pressure with a velocity of 500 m/s. If the mass flow rate through the engine is 50 kg/s determine the engine thrust.

The engine now moves forward at 200 m/s while the velocity of the jet relative to the engine is unchanged. What is the new value of thrust? (25 kN, 15 kN)

7. An axial flow fan is mounted in a duct of cross-sectional area 2 ft^2. The fluid flowing in the duct is air and the flow may be assumed to be adiabatic. At section (1) immediately before the fan the pressure and temperature of the air are 14.7 lbf/in^2 and 60 °F respectively and the velocity is 100 ft/s. The power input to the fan is 24 hp and the pressure at station (2) is 15.2 lbf/in^2.

Neglecting the presence of the driving shaft calculate

(a) the fluid velocity at station (2),

(b) the axial thrust on the fan, stating its direction.

(29.7 m/s, 635.7 N)

8. Air enters a 20 mm diameter pipe from the atmosphere at 1 bar and 20 °C. At a particular section downstream the pressure and temperature are found to be 0.9 bar and 19 °C. Calculate the velocities at entry and exit and the mass flow rate assuming that the flow is frictionless. (280 m/s, 310 m/s, 0.105 kg/s)

9 UNSTEADY FLOW PROCESSES

In this chapter some elementary examples of unsteady flow are given and the energy equation needs to be recast to meet the changed situation.

In the general case we must again define a system and its boundary, prescribe the initial and final states, note any inflows and/or outflows of mass (and therefore energy) and calculate the heat and work transfers.

Thus the energy equation will appear as follows

$$ {}_1Q_2 + \sum_i (\delta m \times h) + m_1 e_1 = {}_1W_2 + \sum_e (\delta m \times h) + m_2 e_2 $$

where ${}_1Q_2$ and ${}_1W_2$ are the heat and work transfers respectively,
m_1, m_2 are the initial and final masses in the system,
e_1, e_2 are the initial and final specific internal energies,
$\sum_i (\delta m \times h)$ is the sum of all the inflows of energy to the system during the process due to mass transfer,
$\sum_e (\delta m \times h)$ is the sum of the outflows of energy from the system during the process due to mass transfer.

The manner in which these last two summation terms are handled depends on the problem and in a first-year book of this kind only simple examples are given. Note that terms involve the product of mass and specific enthalpy because mass is transferring across the system boundary.

1. A vessel of constant volume 0.3 m^3 contains air at 1.5 bar and is connected, via a valve, to a large main carrying air at a temperature of 38 °C and high pressure.

The valve is opened, allowing air to enter the vessel and raising the pressure therein to 7.5 bar. Assuming the vessel and valve to be thermally insulated, find the mass of air entering the vessel.

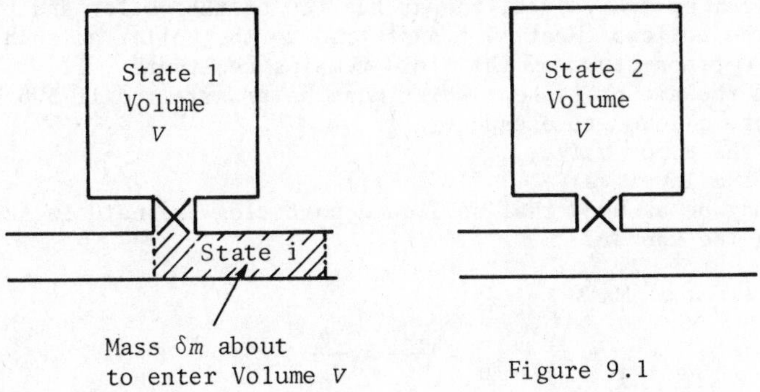

Figure 9.1

Energy Equation

$$ {}_1Q_2 + \sum_{i}(\delta m \times h) + m_1e_1 = {}_1W_2 + \sum_{e}(\delta m \times h) + m_2e_2 $$

in which in this case

$$ h_i\sum\delta m = m_2e_2 - m_1e_1 \quad \text{(A)} $$ (since h_i is constant and the other terms are all zero)

Conservation of Mass

$$ m_2 - m_1 = \sum_{i}\delta m \quad \text{(B)} $$

From (A) and (B)

$$ m_2e_2 - m_1e_1 = h_i(m_2 - m_1) = (e_i + RT_i)(m_2 - m_1) $$ for a perfect gas

or $$ m_2c_v(T_2 - T_0) - m_1c_v(T_1 - T_0) = (m_2 - m_1)c_v(T_i - T_0) + (m_2 - m_1)RT_i $$ (T_0 is a datum)

Thus $c_v(m_2T_2 - m_1T_1) = (m_2 - m_1)c_pT_i$ (since $c_v + R = c_p$)

Thus mass entering the system is given by

$$ m_2 - m_1 = \frac{c_v}{c_pT_i}(m_2T_2 - m_1T_1) = \frac{c_v}{c_pT_i}\left(\frac{p_2V}{R} - \frac{p_1V}{R}\right) = \frac{V}{\gamma RT_i}(p_2 - p_1) $$

$$ = \frac{0.3\ \text{m}^3 \times (7.5 - 1.5)\ \text{bar}}{1.4 \times 0.287\ \dfrac{\text{kJ}}{\text{kg K}} \times (38 + 273)\ \text{K}} \frac{[10^2\ \text{kJ}]}{[\text{bar m}^3]} $$

$$ \underline{m_2 - m_1 = 1.44\ \text{kg}} $$

2. A boiler has a volume of 10 m^3 and contains water in the liquid and vapour phases at 20 bar. Initially, the liquid phase occupies half the total volume. Fluid may be allowed to escape from the boiler by two valves, one at the top of the boiler and the other at the bottom. Heat is transferred to the boiler at such a rate that the temperature of the fluid remains constant.

Find the amount of heat which must be transferred if 300 kg of fluid are allowed to escape via

(a) the upper valve,

(b) the lower valve.

It may be assumed that no liquid particles are held in suspension in the vapour.

Conservation of Mass

$$ m_1 = m_{water_1} + m_{steam_1} = \frac{V}{v_{f_1}} + \frac{V}{v_{g_1}} $$

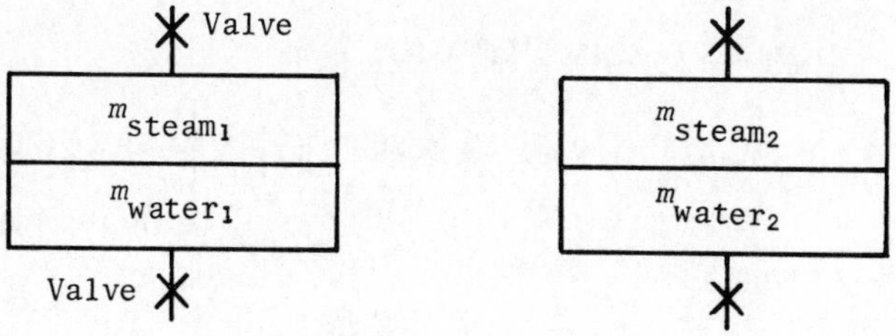

Figure 9.2

At 212.4 °C from page 10

$$v_{f_1} = 0.001173 + \frac{2.4}{10}(0.00119 - 0.001173) = 0.001177\ \frac{\text{m}^3}{\text{kg}}$$

$$v_{g_1} = 0.09957\ \frac{\text{m}^3}{\text{kg}} \quad \text{(page 4)}$$

Thus $m_{water_1} = \dfrac{V}{v_{f_1}} = \dfrac{5\ \text{m}^3}{0.001177\ \frac{\text{m}^3}{\text{kg}}} = 4248.1$ kg

$$m_{steam_1} = \frac{V}{v_{g_1}} = \frac{5}{0.09957} = 50.2\ \text{kg}$$

Thus $m_1 = 4248.1 + 50.2 = 4298.3$ kg

Thus $m_2 = m_1 - \sum_e(\delta m) = 4298.3 - 300 = 3998.3$ kg

Also $x_2 = \dfrac{v_2 - v_{f_2}}{v_{g_2} - v_{f_2}}$ where $v_{g_2} = v_{g_1}$; $v_{f_2} = v_{f_1}$; $v_2 = \dfrac{V}{m_2}$

$$x_2 = \frac{\left(\frac{10}{3998.3} - 0.001177\right)}{0.09957 - 0.001177} = \frac{0.001324}{0.098393} = 0.0135$$

Thus $m_{steam_2} = x_2 m_2 = 0.0135 \times 3998.3 = 53.8$ kg

and $m_{water_2} = m_2 - m_{steam_2} = 3998.3 - 53.8 = 3944.5$ kg

Conservation of Energy

(a) $\quad {}_1Q_2 + \sum_i(\delta m \times h) + m_1e_1 = {}_1W_2 + \sum_e(\delta m \times h) + m_2e_2$

from which

$${}_1Q_2 = m_2e_2 - m_1e_1 + \sum_e(\delta m \times h) \quad \text{(all other terms zero)}$$

$$h_2 = h_g = 2799\ \frac{\text{kJ}}{\text{kg}} \ \text{constant (page 4)}$$

$$\delta m = m_1 - m_2$$

Thus ${}_1Q_2 = (m_{water_2} - m_{water_1})e_{water} + (m_{steam_2} - m_{steam_1})e_{steam}$

$$+ h_{steam}(m_1 - m_2)$$

$$= \left[(3944.5 - 4248.1)\text{kg} \times 907 \frac{\text{kJ}}{\text{kg}}\right] + \left[(53.8 - 50.2)\text{ kg} \times 2600 \frac{\text{kJ}}{\text{kg}}\right] + \left[2799 \frac{\text{kJ}}{\text{kg}}(300\text{ kg})\right]$$

(using page 4)

$${}_1Q_2 = 573700\text{ kJ}$$

(b) Here h_2 is constant at h_f $\left(909 \frac{\text{kJ}}{\text{kg}}\right)$

$$\text{Thus } {}_1Q_2 = \left[(3944.5 - 4248.1) \times 907\right] + \left[(53.8 - 50.2) \times 2600\right] + (909 \times 300)$$

$${}_1Q_2 = 6700\text{ kJ}$$

3. A vessel containing a perfect gas at an initial pressure of 20 bar and a temperature of 115 °C is connected through a valve to a vertical cylinder closed at its upper end by a piston. The mass of the piston is such that a pressure of 7 bar is required to support it.

Initially the piston rests on the bottom of the cylinder and the volume between the valve and the piston is negligible.

The valve is opened slowly so that the gas flows into the cylinder until the pressures on each side of the valve are equal. The temperature of the gas in the vessel is then found to be 19 °C.

Find the temperature of the gas in the cylinder, assuming no heat transfer from gas to walls or from the vessel to the cylinder. Take $\gamma = 1.4$.

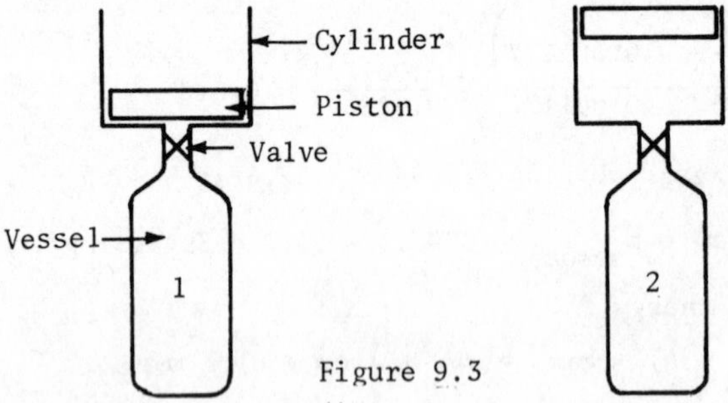

Figure 9.3

Conservation of Energy

$${}_1Q_2 + \sum_i(\delta m \times h) + m_1e_1 = {}_1W_2 + \sum_e(\delta m \times h) + m_2e_2$$

For a system comprising the cylinder + vessel this reduces to

$$m_1e_1 = {}_1W_2 + m_2e_2 \quad \text{(all other terms being zero)}$$

Let the cylinder volume be V_c at the end of the process,

the cylinder pressure be p_c (constant),

the cylinder temperature be T_c at the end of the process,

the vessel volume be V_v,

the pressure be p_{v1}, p_{v2} at the start and end of the process,

Let the vessel temperatures be T_{v1}, T_{v2} at the start and end of the process,

the masses in the vessel be m_{v1}, m_{v2} at the start and end of the process.

Now $m_{c1} = 0$; $m_{c2} = m_{v1} - m_{v2}$.

Thus $-{}_1W_2 = m_2e_2 - m_1e_1 = (m_{c2}e_{c2} + m_{v2}e_{v2}) - m_{v1}e_{v1}$

or $-p_cV_c = m_{c2}c_v(T_c - T_0) + m_{v2}c_v(T_{v2} - T_0) - m_{v1}c_v(T_{v1} - T_0)$

$$= \frac{p_cV_c}{RT_c}c_vT_c + \frac{p_{v2}V_v}{RT_{v2}}c_vT_{v2} - \frac{p_{v1}V_v}{RT_{v1}}c_vT_{v1}$$

Now $m_c = m_{v1} - m_{v2}$

or $$\frac{p_cV_c}{RT_c} = \left(\frac{p_{v1}V_v}{RT_{v1}} - \frac{p_{v2}V_v}{RT_{v2}}\right)$$

or $$V_c = \frac{T_cV_v}{p_c}\left(\frac{p_{v1}}{T_{v1}} - \frac{p_{v2}}{T_{v2}}\right)$$ and substituting in the energy equation

$$-p_c\frac{T_cV_v}{p_c}\left(\frac{p_{v1}}{T_{v1}} - \frac{p_{v2}}{T_{v2}}\right) = p_c\frac{c_vT_c}{Rp_c}V_v\left(\frac{p_{v1}}{T_{v1}} - \frac{p_{v2}}{T_{v2}}\right) + \frac{p_{v2}V_vc_v}{R} - \frac{p_{v1}V_vc_v}{R}$$

or $$T_c\left(\frac{p_{v1}}{T_{v1}} - \frac{p_{v2}}{T_{v2}}\right)\left(1 + \frac{c_v}{R}\right) = \frac{c_v}{R}(p_{v1} - p_{v2})$$

or $$T_c\left(\frac{p_{v1}}{T_{v1}} - \frac{p_{v2}}{T_{v2}}\right)\left(1 + \frac{1}{\gamma - 1}\right) = \frac{1}{\gamma - 1}(p_{v1} - p_{v2})$$

i.e. $$T_c\left(\frac{20}{388} - \frac{7}{292}\right)\left(1 + \frac{1}{0.4}\right) = \frac{1}{0.4}(20 - 7)$$

or $$T_c = \frac{2.5 \times 13}{3.5 \times (0.0515 - 0.0240)} = 337.3\ \text{K} = 64.3\ °\text{C}$$

4. A compressed air bottle, containing air at 35 bar and 16 °C, is to be used to drive a small turbine as an emergency starter for an engine. The turbine is required to produce an average output of 4 kW for a period of 30 seconds. Assuming the expansion is adiabatic and frictionless, that the pressure in the bottle is allowed to fall to 3.5 bar during the process and that the turbine ex-

hausts to atmosphere at 1 bar find the necessary capacity of the bottle.

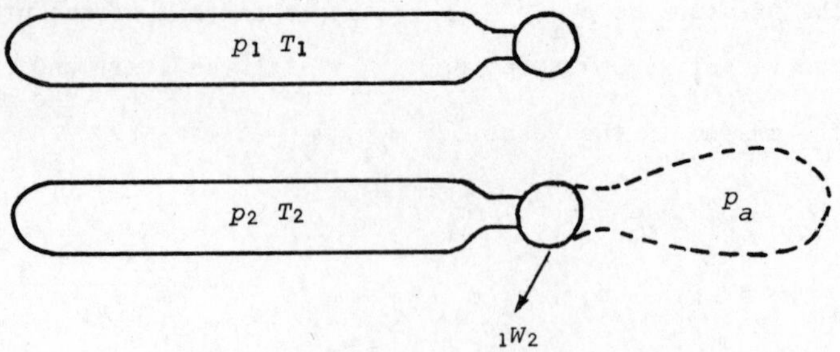

Figure 9.4

Conservation of energy

$$_1Q_2 + \sum_i(\delta m \times h) + m_1e_1 = {}_1W_2 + \sum_e(\delta m \times h) + m_2e_2$$

for the system comprising the cylinder plus the turbine.

Now $\sum(\delta m \times h) = {}_1Q_2 = 0$

and $_1W_2 = \dot{W} \times t = 4\ \text{kW} \dfrac{[\text{kJ}]}{[\text{kW s}]} \times 30\ \text{s} = 120\ \text{kJ}$

Consider the air mass left behind in the cylinder after the leaving air has expanded through the turbine. This remaining air can be treated as a system originally occupying only a fraction of the cylinder volume and finally occupying the whole of the cylinder volume and expanding according to frictionless, adiabatic laws of a perfect gas.

Let p_1, T_1 be the initial pressure and temperature in the bottle,
p_2, T_2 be the final pressure and temperature in the bottle,
p, T be the pressure and temperature at some intermediate step,
p_a be atmospheric pressure.

Then $\dfrac{T}{T_1} = \left(\dfrac{p}{p_1}\right)^k$ where p and T are also the turbine inlet conditions.

If T_e is the turbine exit temperature and the turbine expansion is also frictionless and adiabatic

$$\frac{T_e}{T} = \left(\frac{p_a}{p}\right)^k$$

thus $\dfrac{T_e}{T} \times \dfrac{T}{T_1} = \left(\dfrac{p_a}{p}\right)^k \times \left(\dfrac{p}{p_1}\right)^k = \left(\dfrac{p_a}{p_1}\right)^k$

Now p_a is constant at 1 bar and p_1 and T_1 are the given cylinder initial conditions. Also γ and therefore $k = (\gamma - 1/\gamma)$ is constant.

Thus the energy equation now becomes

$$ {}_1W_2 = (m_1e_1 - m_2e_2) - h_e\sum_e \delta m \quad \text{since } T_e \text{ and thus } h_e \text{ is constant.} $$

Conservation of Mass

$$ \sum_e \delta m = m_1 - m_2 $$

Thus
$$ {}_1W_2 = c_v\left[m_1(T_1 - T_0) - m_2(T_2 - T_0)\right] - (e_e + RT_e)(m_1 - m_2) $$

$$ = c_v\left[m_1(T_1 - T_0) - m_2(T_2 - T_0)\right] - (m_1 - m_2)c_v(T_e - T_0) - (m_1 - m_2)RT_e $$

$$ = c_v(m_1T_1 - m_2T_2) - (m_1 - m_2)(c_v + R)T_e $$

$$ {}_1W_2 = c_v(m_1T_1 - m_2T_2) - (m_1 - m_2)c_pT_e $$

Now
$$ T_e = T_1\left(\frac{p_a}{p_1}\right)^k = (10 + 273)\ \text{K}\left(\frac{1}{35}\right)^{0.286} = 104.5\ \text{K} $$

and
$$ T_2 = T_1\left(\frac{p_2}{p_1}\right)^k = (16 + 273)\ \text{K}\left(\frac{3.5}{35}\right)^{0.286} = 149.6\ \text{K} $$

Thus
$$ \frac{{}_1W_2}{c_v} = (m_1T_1 - m_2T_2) - (m_1 - m_2)\gamma T_e $$

$$ = \left(\frac{p_1V}{R} - \frac{p_2V}{R}\right) - \gamma T_e\left(\frac{p_1V}{RT_1} - \frac{p_2V}{RT_2}\right) $$

where V is the volume of the bottle.

Thus
$$ V = \frac{{}_1W_2R}{c_v}\left[\frac{1}{(p_1 - p_2) - \gamma T_e\left(\dfrac{p_1}{T_1} - \dfrac{p_2}{T_2}\right)}\right] $$

Thus
$$ V = \frac{120\ \text{kJ} \times 0.287\ \dfrac{\text{kJ}}{\text{kg K}}}{0.718\ \dfrac{\text{kJ}}{\text{kg K}}} \times $$

$$ \frac{1}{(35 - 3.5)\ \text{bar}\dfrac{[10^5\ \text{kN}]}{[\text{bar m}^2]} - 1.4 \times 104.5\ \text{K}\ \dfrac{35}{289} - \dfrac{3.5}{149.6}\ \dfrac{\text{bar}}{\text{K}}\dfrac{[10^2\ \text{kN}]}{[\text{bar m}^2]}} $$

$$ V = \frac{47.97\ \text{kJ}}{(31.5 - 14.3) \times 100\ \dfrac{\text{kN}}{\text{m}^2}} = 0.028\ \text{m}^3 $$

---

5. A rigid vessel of volume 0.3 m³ contains a perfect gas initially at a pressure of 1 bar. In order to reduce the pressure in the vessel it is connected to an extraction pump. The volume flow rate of gas leaving the vessel is constant at 0.014 m³/min.

Assuming the temperature of the gas within the vessel to remain constant, calculate

(a) the time taken to reduce the pressure in the vessel to 0.35 bar,

(b) the magnitude and sense of the heat transfer between the vessel and its surroundings during this time.

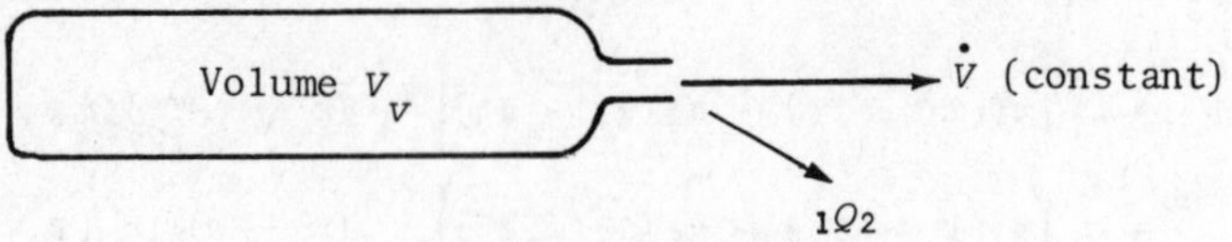

Figure 9.5

Conservation of Mass

$$\dot{m} = \frac{dm}{dt} = \frac{\dot{V}}{v} = \frac{p}{RT} \times \dot{V}$$

or $$dm = \frac{\dot{V}}{RT} \times p\, dt \qquad \text{(where } \dot{V}, R \text{ and } T \text{ are all constant)}$$

At any instant the mass in the vessel is given by

$$m = \frac{pV_v}{RT} \qquad \text{(where } V_v \text{ is the volume of the vessel)}$$

Thus $p = \dfrac{mRT}{V_v}$ and substituting above

$$dm = \frac{\dot{V}}{RT} \times \frac{mRT}{V_v}\, dt$$

$$\int_{m_2}^{m_1} \frac{dm}{m} = \frac{\dot{V}}{V_v} \int_0^t dt \quad \text{and integrating we get}$$

$$\ln \frac{m_1}{m_2} = \frac{\dot{V}t}{V_v}$$

$$t = \frac{V_v}{\dot{V}} \ln \frac{m_1}{m_2} = \frac{V_v}{\dot{V}} \ln \frac{\left(\dfrac{p_1 V_v}{RT}\right)}{\left(\dfrac{p_2 V_v}{RT}\right)} = \frac{V_v}{\dot{V}} \ln \frac{p_1}{p_2}$$

Thus $$t = \frac{0.3 \text{ m}^3}{0.014 \dfrac{\text{m}^3}{\text{min}}} \times \ln \frac{1}{0.35} = 22.5 \text{ min}$$

Conservation of Energy

$$_1Q_2 + \sum_i (\delta m \times h) + m_1 e_1 = {_1W_2} + \sum_e (\delta m \times h) + m_2 e_2$$

Now $\sum_i (\delta m \times h) = {_1W_2} = 0.$

Thus $_1Q_2 = m_2 e_2 - m_1 e_1 + \sum_e (\delta m \times h)$

Now h_e = constant; $\sum_e(\delta m \times h) = m_1 - m_2$

Also $e_1 = e_2$

Thus $_1Q_2 = c_v(T - T_0)(m_2 - m_1) + (e_e + RT_e)(m_1 - m_2)$

$= c_v(T - T_0)(m_2 - m_1) + \; c_v(T - T_0) + RT_e \; (m_1 - m_2)$

Now $e_2 = e_1 = e_e = c_v(T - T_0)$; $\quad T_e = T$

$$_1Q_2 = (m_2 - m_1)T(c_v - c_p) = (m_1 - m_2)RT$$

$$_1Q_2 = \left(\frac{p_1V_v}{RT} - \frac{p_2V_v}{RT}\right)RT = V_v(p_1 - p_2)$$

$$_1Q_2 = (1 - 0.35)\text{ bar} \times 0.3\text{ m}^3 \frac{[10^2\text{ kJ}]}{[\text{bar m}^3]} = 19.5\text{ kJ}$$

6. A cylinder containing Freon-12 in the liquid and vapour phases is arranged with a tap at the bottom by means of which it is connected to a refrigerant circuit.

When the tap is opened, liquid Freon-12 flows from the cylinder into the circuit. If the temperature of the Freon-12 in the cylinder remains constant at 15 °C while 10 kg of Freon-12 flows into the circuit, calculate the heat transfer between the cylinder and its surroundings.

Conservation of Energy

$$_1Q_2 + \sum_i(\delta m \times h) + m_1e_1 = {_1W_2} + \sum_e(\delta m \times h) + m_2e_2$$

In this equation

$$\sum_i(\delta m \times h) = {_1W_2} = 0$$

Thus $_1Q_2 = (m_2e_2 - m_1e_1) + \sum_e(\delta m \times h)$

Now h_e is constant at h_f for Freon-12 at 15 °C and

$$\sum_e\delta m = m_1 - m_2$$

Also $e_2 = e_{f_2} + x_2e_{fg_2}$; $e_1 = e_{f_1} + x_1e_{fg_1}$

where the values of e_{f_2} and e_{f_1} are given by e_f and the values of e_{fg_2} and e_{fg_1} are given by e_{fg}, both values being constant since T is constant and the fluid is always a liquid/vapour mixture.

Now $v_1 = v_f + x_1v_{fg}$; $v_2 = v_f + x_2v_{fg}$.

Thus $m_1 = \dfrac{V}{v_1}$; $m_2 = \dfrac{V}{v_2}$ where V is the cylinder volume

and $x_1 = \dfrac{v_1 - v_f}{v_{fg}}$; $x_2 = \dfrac{v_2 - v_f}{v_{fg}}$ and substituting for e

$$e_1 = e_f + \frac{v_1 - v_f}{v_{fg}} e_{fg}; \qquad e_2 = e_f + \frac{v_2 - v_f}{v_{fg}} e_{fg}$$

Substituting into the energy equation

$$_1Q_2 = \frac{V}{v_2}\left(e_f + \frac{v_2 - v_f}{v_{fg}} e_{fg}\right) - \frac{V}{v_1}\left(e_f + \frac{v_1 - v_f}{v_{fg}} e_{fg}\right) + h_f(m_1 - m_2)$$

$$_1Q_2 = \frac{Ve_f}{v_2} + \frac{Ve_{fg}}{v_{fg}} - \frac{Vv_f e_{fg}}{v_2 v_{fg}} - \frac{Ve_f}{v_1} - \frac{Ve_{fg}}{v_{fg}} + \frac{Vv_f e_{fg}}{v_1 v_{fg}} + h_f(m_1 - m_2)$$

$$= Ve_f\left(\frac{1}{v_2} - \frac{1}{v_1}\right) + \frac{Vv_f e_{fg}}{v_{fg}}\left(\frac{1}{v_1} - \frac{1}{v_2}\right) + h_f(m_1 - m_2)$$

$$= V\left(\frac{1}{v_1} - \frac{1}{v_2}\right)\left(-e_f + \frac{e_{fg} v_f}{v_{fg}}\right) + h_f(m_1 - m_2)$$

$$= (m_1 - m_2)\left(\frac{e_{fg} v_f}{v_{fg}} - e_f\right) + (m_1 - m_2) h_f$$

$$= (m_1 - m_2)\left(h_f - e_f + \frac{e_{fg}}{\rho_f v_g - 1}\right)$$

Now ρ_f at 15 °C (288 K) for Freon-12 $= 1468 + \frac{(288 - 250)}{(300 - 250)} \times (1304 - 1468)$

or $\rho_f = 1343.4 \frac{\text{kg}}{\text{m}^3}$ (page 15)

Also $v_g = 0.0354 \frac{\text{m}^3}{\text{kg}}$ (page 13)

$h_f = 50.1 \frac{\text{kJ}}{\text{kg}}$ (page 13)

$$e_f = h_f - pv_f = 50.1 \frac{\text{kJ}}{\text{kg}} - \left(4.914 \text{ bar} \times \frac{1}{1343.4} \frac{\text{m}^3}{\text{kg}} \frac{[10^2 \text{ kJ}]}{[\text{bar m}^3]}\right)$$

$$e_f = 49.73 \frac{\text{kJ}}{\text{kg}}$$

$$e_g = h_g - pv_g = 193.78 - (100 \times 4.914 \times 0.0354) = 176.38 \frac{\text{kJ}}{\text{kg}}$$

Thus $e_{fg} = e_g - e_f = 126.65 \frac{\text{kJ}}{\text{kg}}$

Substituting these values in the expression above we get

$$_1Q_2 = 10 \text{ kg}\left[(50.1 - 49.73) \frac{\text{kJ}}{\text{kg}} + \frac{126.65 \frac{\text{kJ}}{\text{kg}}}{(0.0354 \times 1343.4) - 1}\right]$$

$$_1Q_2 = 10(0.37 + 2.72) = 30.9 \text{ kJ}$$

Further Examples

7. Air is flowing in a main at constant pressure and temperature of 10 bar and 200 °C respectively. A valve connecting the main to an insulated vessel is slowly opened and air flows from the main into the vessel.

Determine the final temperature of the air in the vessel if

(a) the vessel is initially evacuated,

(b) the vessel is fitted with a piston restrained by a spring; the displacement of the piston is directly proportional to the applied pressure and the space above the piston is evacuated; assume that the initial length of the spring is the free length,

(c) the vessel is fitted with a piston which is loaded with a weight so that a pressure of 10 bar is needed to raise it.

In each case there is negligible heat transfer between the air in the main and the air in the vessel. (389 °C, 279 °C, 200 °C)

8. A rigid vessel of 0.1 m^3 capacity contains 0.5 kg of H_2O only at 1 bar. A valve connects the vessel to a pipe carrying steam at 15 bar and 250 °C. The valve is opened so that steam enters the vessel until the pressure rises to 15 bar. Assuming that there is no heat transfer to or from the surroundings and that the volume of the liquid is negligible compared with that of the vapour, find the mass of steam which must enter the vessel. (0.68 kg)

9. (a) Write down the energy equation in a form suitable for application to problems of the filling and emptying of vessels. Explain carefully the significance of each term in the equation.

(b) An evacuated tank of capacity 0.07 m^3 is connected by means of a valve to a pipe carrying air at the ambient temperature of 20 °C and a pressure of 70 bar. The valve is then opened allowing air to flow into the tank until the pressure reaches 50 bar, when the valve is closed. Determine the mass of air which enters the tank if the filling process is sufficiently rapid to be assumed adiabatic.

(c) The tank is left with the valve closed until the temperature of the air inside reaches the ambient value of 20 °C. What is the final pressure in the tank? (2.97 kg, 35.7 bar)

10 GAS AND VAPOUR MIXTURES

The only equations used in this chapter are the characteristic gas equation and that expressing the principle embodied in Dalton's law of partial pressures.

The gas equation can be expressed in one of two ways

(a) $pV = mRT$ when based on masses in kg

(b) $pV = nR_0T$ when based on kilogram-moles (kg-mol)

Since both left-hand sides of the above equations are the same we can equate the right-hand sides as follows.

$mRT = nR_0T$ which gives

$$\frac{m}{n} = m_w = \frac{R_0}{R}$$

where R_0 is the universal gas constant and m_w is the molecular mass

Thus in a given case, say for CO_2

$$R = \frac{R_0}{m_w} = \frac{8.3143 \text{ kJ/(kg-mol K)}}{44 \dfrac{\text{kg}}{\text{kg-mol}}} = 0.189 \frac{\text{kJ}}{\text{kg K}} \quad \text{(using page 20)}$$

The molar heat capacities C_p and C_v are related to R_0 by

$$C_p - C_v = R_0$$

where

$$C_p = m_w c_p; \text{ and } C_v = m_w c_v$$

Dalton's Law: For a mixture of gases the total pressure is

$$p_t = \sum_i p \quad \text{where i refers to any constituent gas}$$

Thus for a mixture of CO_2, CO and O_2 at temperature T

$$p_t = p_{CO_2} + p_{CO} + p_{O_2}$$

and $p_tV = nR_0T$

$$p_{CO_2}V = n_{CO_2}R_0T$$
$$p_{CO}V = n_{CO}R_0T$$
$$p_{O_2}V = n_{O_2}R_0T$$

Thus $\dfrac{p_{CO_2}}{p_t} = \dfrac{n_{CO_2}}{n_t} = x_{CO_2}$ where x is percentage by volume

$$\frac{p_{CO}}{p_t} = \frac{n_{CO}}{n_t} = x_{CO} \text{ etc.}$$

Also $\dfrac{p_{CO_2}}{p_{CO}} = \dfrac{n_{CO_2}}{n_{CO}} = \dfrac{x_{CO_2}}{x_{CO}}$ etc.

That is the partial pressures are in the same ratios as the number of kilogram-mols.

Also $\overline{c_p} = \dfrac{\sum\limits_i mc_p}{\sum\limits_i m}$; $\overline{R} = \dfrac{\sum\limits_i mR}{\sum\limits_i m}$ etc.

However gas analyses are often given in percentages by volume and it is more useful to recast these expressions to take account of this.

Thus $m = nm_w$; $x = \dfrac{n_i}{n_t}$ and therefore

$$\overline{c_p} = \frac{\sum\limits_i nm_w c_p}{\sum\limits_i nm_w}$$

or $$\overline{c_p} = \frac{\sum\limits_i xm_w c_p}{\sum\limits_i xm_w}$$

Also $\overline{c_v} = \dfrac{\sum\limits_i xm_w c_v}{\sum\limits_i xm_w}$ and $\overline{R} = \dfrac{\sum\limits_i xm_w R}{\sum\limits_i xm_w} = \dfrac{\sum\limits_i xR_0}{\sum\limits_i xm_w} = \dfrac{R_0\sum\limits_i x}{\sum\limits_i xm_w} = \dfrac{R_0}{\sum\limits_i xm_w}$

Thus in the last expression, for example for a volumetric analysis in a mixture of 20% CO_2, 30% CO and 50% O_2

$$\overline{R} = \frac{R_0}{\sum\limits_i xm_w} = \frac{8.3143 \text{ kJ/(kg-mol K)}}{[(0.2 \times 44) + (0.3 \times 28) + (0.5 \times 32)] \text{ kg/kg-mol}}$$

$$= 0.250 \frac{\text{kJ}}{\text{kg K}}$$

1. The volumetric analysis of a mixture of gases shows it to contain 80% H_2 and 20% O_2, and a vessel holds 0.7 m^3 of this mixture at 38 °C and 350 kN/m^2.

Calculate the masses of hydrogen and oxygen in the vessel and the heat required to raise the temperature to 120 °C at constant pressure.

$$p_{H_2} = x_{H_2} p_t = 0.8 \times 350 \frac{\text{kN}}{\text{m}^2} = 280 \frac{\text{kN}}{\text{m}^2}$$

$$p_{O_2} = x_{O_2} p_t = 0.2 \times 350 \frac{\text{kN}}{\text{m}^2} = 70 \frac{\text{kN}}{\text{m}^2}$$

$$\text{Thus } m_{H_2} = \left(\frac{pV}{RT}\right)_{H_2} = \left(\frac{m_w pV}{R_0 T}\right)_{H_2} = \frac{2\ \frac{\text{kg}}{\text{kg-mol}} \times 280\ \frac{\text{kN}}{\text{m}^2} \times 0.7\ \text{m}^3\ \frac{[\text{kJ}\ ]}{[\text{kNM}]}}{8.3143\ \frac{\text{kJ}}{\text{kg-mol K}} \times (38 + 273)\ \text{K}}$$

$$m_{H_2} = 0.152 \text{ kg}$$

$$\text{Also } m_{O_2} = \frac{32 \times 70 \times 0.7}{8.3143 \times 311} = 0.606 \text{ kg}$$

$$c_p\ (H_2) = 14.31 + \frac{11}{25}(14.38 - 14.31) = 14.341\ \frac{\text{kJ}}{\text{kg K}} \quad \text{(page 17)}$$

$$c_p\ (O_2) = 0.918 + \frac{11}{25}(0.923 - 0.918) = 0.920\ \frac{\text{kJ}}{\text{kg K}} \quad \text{(page 17)}$$

$$_1Q_2 = \sum_i mc_p(T_2 - T_1) = (T_2 - T_1)\sum_i mc_p$$

$$= (120 - 38)\ \text{K}\left[\left(0.152\ \text{kg} \times 14.341\ \frac{\text{kJ}}{\text{kg K}}\right) + \left(0.606\ \text{kg} \times 0.92\ \frac{\text{kJ}}{\text{kg K}}\right)\right]$$

$$_1Q_2 = 224.5 \text{ kJ}$$

2. Methane (CH_4) gas and air are mixed adiabatically in steady flow in the mass ratio of 1:20 respectively. The temperatures of the methane and air entering the mixture chamber are 30 °C and 15 °C respectively, and the pressure of the mixed stream is 100 kN/m^2. Flow velocities and changes in elevation are negligible.

Calculate

(a) the temperature of the mixture stream,

(b) the partial pressures of the gases in the mixture stream.

Let the datum temperature be T_d, the mass flow rate of CH_4 be $\dot{m}$ and the final temperature T_2.

$$\text{Then } [\dot{m}c_p(T_1 - T_d)]_{CH_4} + [20\dot{m}c_p(T_1 - T_d)]_{air}$$

$$= [\dot{m}c_p(T_2 - T_d)]_{CH_4} + [20\dot{m}c_p(T_2 - T_d)]_{air}$$

$$c_p\ (CH_4) = 2.226 + \frac{3}{25}(2.293 - 2.226) = 2.234\ \frac{\text{kJ}}{\text{kg K}} \quad \text{(page 17)}$$

$$c_p\ (\text{air}) = 1.005\ \frac{\text{kJ}}{\text{kg K}} \quad \text{(page 20)}$$

$$\text{Thus } T_2 = \frac{(c_p T_1)_{CH_4} + (20 c_p T_1)_{air}}{c_{p_{CH_4}} + 20 c_{p_{air}}}$$

$$= \frac{(2.234 \times 30) + (20 \times 1.005 \times 15)}{2.234 + (20 \times 1.005)} = \frac{368.52}{22.334}$$

$$T_2 = 16.5 \text{ °C}$$

Mass ratio CH_4:air = 1:20

Mass ratio $CH_4:O_2:N_2$ = 1:20 × 0.233:20 × 0.767 (p.20)

= 1:4.66:15.34

$$\text{Volume ratio } CH_4:O_2:N_2 = \left(\frac{m}{m_w}\right)_{CH_4} : \left(\frac{m}{m_w}\right)_{O_2} : \left(\frac{m}{m_w}\right)_{N_2}$$

$$= \frac{1}{16}:\frac{4.66}{32}:\frac{15.34}{28} = 0.0625:0.1456:0.5479 = n_{CH_4}:n_{O_2}:n_{N_2}$$

$$\text{Thus } p_{CH_4} = (xp_t)_{CH_4} = \frac{n_{CH_4}}{n_t} p_t = \frac{0.0625}{(0.0625 + 0.1456 + 0.5479)} \times 100$$

$$\underline{p_{CH_4} = 8.27 \frac{kN}{m^2}}$$

$$\text{Also } p_{O_2} = \frac{0.1456}{(0.0625 + 0.1456 + 0.5479)} \times 100 = 19.26 \frac{kN}{m^2}$$

$$\text{and } p_{N_2} = \frac{0.5479}{(0.0625 + 0.1456 + 0.5479)} \times 100 = 72.47 \frac{kN}{m^2}$$

3. Two rigid vessels A and B are connected by a short pipe and valve, the valve being initially closed. Vessel A has a volume of 0.06 m^3 and contains oxygen at 700 kN/m^2 and 40 °C. Vessel B has a volume of 0.17 m^3 and contains nitrogen at 2100 kN/m^2 and 150 °C. The volume of the pipe and valve is negligible. The valve is opened and the gases allowed to mix. During mixing a heat transfer occurs between the mixture and its surroundings. When mixing is complete the temperature of the mixture is 95 °C.

Determine

(a) the final pressure of the mixture,

(b) the magnitude and sense of the heat transfer.

$$n_{O_2} = \left(\frac{pV}{R_0 T}\right)_{O_2} = \frac{700 \frac{kN}{m^2} \times 0.06 \ m^3}{8.3143 \frac{kJ}{kg\text{-}mol\ K} \times 313\ K} \frac{[kJ\ ]}{[kNm]} = 0.01614 \text{ kg-mol}$$

$$\text{Also } n_{N_2} = \left(\frac{pV}{R_0 T}\right)_{N_2} = \frac{2100 \times 0.07}{8.3143 \times 423} = 0.1015 \text{ kg-mol}$$

$$\text{Thus } n_t = 0.01614 + 0.1015 = 0.11764 \text{ kg-mol}$$

$$\text{and } p_2 = \frac{R_0 T_2 n_t}{V_t}$$

$$= \frac{8.3143 \times 368 \times 0.11764}{(0.06 + 0.17)} \frac{kJ \quad K\ kg\text{-}mol}{kg\text{-}mol\ K} \frac{[kNm]}{[kJ\ ]} = 1565 \frac{kN}{m^2}$$

Energy Equation

$${}_1Q_2 - {}_1W_2 = E_2 - E_1 \text{ where } {}_1W_2 = 0$$

$${}_1Q_2 = E_2 - E_1 = \sum_i mc_v(T_2 - T_1) = \sum_i nm_w c_v(T_2 - T_1)$$

$$= \sum_i nC_v(T_2 - T_1)$$

$$c_p \; (O_2) \text{ at } 313 \text{ K} = 0.918 + \frac{13}{25}(0.923 - 0.918) = 0.921 \; \frac{\text{kJ}}{\text{kg K}}$$

(page 17)

$$\text{Thus } C_p \; (O_2) = (m_w c_p)_{O_2} = 32 \; \frac{\text{kg}}{\text{kg-mol}} \times 0.921 \; \frac{\text{kJ}}{\text{kg K}} = 29.472 \; \frac{\text{kJ}}{\text{kg-mol K}}$$

$$\text{and } C_v \; (O_2) = C_p - R_0 = 29.472 - 8.3143 = 21.158 \; \frac{\text{kJ}}{\text{kg-mol K}}$$

$$\text{Also } c_p \; (N_2) = 1.044 + \frac{23}{50}(1.049 - 1.044) = 1.046 \; \frac{\text{kJ}}{\text{kg K}} \text{ (page 17)}$$

$$C_p \; (N_2) = (m_w c_p)_{N_2} = 28 \times 1.046 = 29.288 \text{ kJ/(kg-mol K)}$$

$$\text{Thus } C_v \; (N_2) = C_p - R_0 = 29.288 - 8.3143 = 20.974 \; \frac{\text{kJ}}{\text{kg-mol K}}$$

$${}_1Q_2 = \left[0.01614 \text{ kg-mol} \times 21.158 \; \frac{\text{kJ}}{\text{kg-mol K}}(95 - 40) \text{ K}\right]_{O_2}$$

$$+ \left[0.1015 \text{ kg-mol} \times 20.974 \; \frac{\text{kJ}}{\text{kg-mol K}}(95 - 150) \text{ K}\right]_{N_2}$$

$${}_1Q_2 = -98.3 \text{ kJ}$$

4. A gaseous mixture contains 21% by volume of nitrogen, 50% by volume of hydrogen and 29% by volume of carbon dioxide. Calculate the characteristic gas constant, R, for the mixture and the value of the reversible adiabatic index γ.

A cylinder contains 0.085 m^3 of the mixture at 100 kN/m^2 and 10 °C. The gas undergoes a reversible non-flow process during which its volume is reduced to one-fifth of its original value. If the law of compression is $pv^{1.2}$ = constant, determine the work and heat transfers in magnitude and sense.

$$\overline{R} = \frac{R_0}{\sum_i xm_w} = \frac{8.3143 \; \frac{\text{kJ}}{\text{kg-mol K}}}{[(0.21 \times 28) + (0.5 \times 2) + (0.29 \times 44)]\frac{\text{kg}}{\text{kg-mol}}}$$

$$= \frac{8.3143}{19.64} = 0.423 \; \frac{\text{kJ}}{\text{kg K}}$$

At 10 °C (283 K) from page 17 of tables

$$c_p \; (N_2) = 1.039 + \frac{8}{25}(1.04 - 1.039) = 1.039 \; \frac{\text{kJ}}{\text{kg K}}$$

$$c_p \; (H_2) = 14.2 + \frac{8}{25}(14.32 - 14.2) = 14.235 \; \frac{\text{kJ}}{\text{kg K}}$$

$$c_p\ (O_2) = 0.819 + \frac{8}{25}(0.846 - 0.819) = 0.828\ \frac{kJ}{kg\ K}$$

Thus $\overline{c_p} = \frac{\sum_i x m_w c_p}{\sum_i x m_w}$

$$= [(0.21 \times 28 \times 1.039) + (0.5 \times 2 \times 14.235) + (0.29 \times 44 \times 0.828)]\ \frac{kJ}{kg\text{-}mol\ K} \times \frac{1}{19.64}\ \frac{kg\text{-}mol}{kg}$$

$$\overline{c_p} = \frac{30.91}{19.64} = 1.574\ \frac{kJ}{kg\ K}$$

Thus $\gamma = \frac{\overline{c_p}}{\overline{c_v}} = \frac{\overline{c_p}}{\overline{c_p} - \overline{R}} = \frac{1.574}{1.574 - 0.423} = 1.360$

Now $_1Q_2 = \frac{\gamma - n}{\gamma - 1} \times {_1W_2}$ (see 5.6)

$$p_2 = p_1\left(\frac{V_1}{V_2}\right)^n = 100\ \frac{kN}{m^2}\ (5)^{1.2} = 689.9\ \frac{kN}{m^2}$$

$$_1Q_2 = \left(\frac{\gamma - n}{\gamma - 1}\right)\left(\frac{p_1V_1 - p_2V_2}{n - 1}\right)$$

$$= \frac{1.36 - 1.2}{0.36} \times \frac{100\ \frac{kN}{m^2} \times 0.085\ m^3 - 689.9\ \frac{kN}{m^2} \times \frac{0.085}{5}\ m^3}{0.2} \times \frac{[kJ]}{[kNm]}$$

$$_1Q_2 = -7.17\ kJ$$

5. A sample of air is saturated with water vapour (i.e. the water vapour in the air is saturated vapour) at 20 °C, the total pressure being 1 bar. Calculate the partial pressures of the individual constituents of the mixture and also the absolute humidity, which is defined as the mass of water vapour per unit mass of dry air.

At 20 °C $p_{H_2O} = 0.0237$ bar (page 2)

Thus $p_{O_2} + p_{N_2} = p_t - p_{H_2O} = 1 - 0.02337 = 0.97663$ bar

Now $p_{O_2} : p_{N_2}$ as 0.21:0.79

Thus $p_{O_2} = 0.97663 \times 0.21 = 0.20509$ bar

and $p_{N_2} = 0.97663 \times 0.79 = 0.77154$ bar

$$v_{air} = \left(\frac{RT}{p}\right)_{air} = \frac{0.287\ \frac{kJ}{kg\ K} \times 293\ K}{0.97663\ bar}\ \frac{[bar\ m^3]}{[10^2\ kJ]} = 0.861\ \frac{m^3}{kg}$$

Also v_g $(H_2O) = 57.84 \frac{m^3}{kg}$ (page 2)

Thus $\frac{m_{H_2O}}{m_{air}} = \frac{v_{air}}{v_{H_2O}} = \frac{0.861}{57.84} = 0.0149 \frac{\text{kg } H_2O}{\text{kg air}}$

Further Examples

6. A gas mixture has the following volumetric analysis
CO 25%; CO_2 50%; H_2 25%
The mixture is at a temperature of 38 °C and a pressure of 200 kN/m^2.
Determine:
(a) the partial pressures of each of the constituents,
(b) the density of the mixture.
(50 kN/m^2 for CO and H_2; 100 kN/m^2 for CO_2; 2.28 kg/m^3)

7. The shell of a condenser contains a mixture of steam, water and air. The volume of the shell is 10 m^3 and, under certain conditions, the pressure in the shell is 0.03 bar when the temperature of the mixture is 22 °C. Calculate the mass of air in the shell. (0.04228 kg)

8. Methane at 20 °C flows into a mixing valve at the rate of 0.01 kg/s where it is mixed with air at 200 °C both having low velocity. The mixture is required to flow through a tube at a velocity not exceeding 100 m/s at 180 °C and 200 kN/m^2. If the mixing process is adiabatic, find the minimum air flow rate and the cross-sectional area of the tube. (0.137 kg/s, 0.001 m^2)

11 STOICHIOMETRY

In stoichiometric calculations the student is continually being required to distinguish between mass balance in his equations, which must hold good, and molecular changes.

For example in the combustion equation

$$2(CO) + 1(O_2) = 2(CO_2)$$

the molecular change is expressed as

$$2 \text{ kg-mol } CO + 1 \text{ kg-mol } O_2 \text{ give } 2 \text{ kg-mol } CO_2$$

i.e. there has been a molecular contraction from 2 + 1 = 3 kg-mol to 2 kg-mol in passing from the reactant stage to the product stage.

However, by the conservation of mass we would expect there to be a strict balance between the kilograms of reactants and the kilograms of products.

Since the numbers above represent the respective values of n_{CO}, n_{O_2} and n_{CO_2} then we may write as a mass equation

$$nm_w\,(CO) + nm_w\,(O_2) = nm_w\,(CO_2)$$

i.e. $$2 \text{ kg-mol } CO \,\frac{28 \text{ kg } CO}{\text{kg-mol } CO} + 1 \text{ kg-mol } O_2 \,\frac{32 \text{ kg } O_2}{\text{kg-mol } O_2}$$

$$= 2 \text{ kg-mol } CO \,\frac{44 \text{ kg } CO_2}{\text{kg-mol } CO_2}$$

or $56 \text{ kg } CO + 32 \text{ kg } O_2 = 88 \text{ kg } CO_2$ (a balance since 56 + 32 = 88)

Furthermore for benzene we write

$$2(C_6H_6) + 15(O_2) = 12(CO_2) + 6(H_2O)$$

where n (reactants) = 2 + 15 = 17 kg-mol

and n (products) = 12 + 6 = 18 kg-mol

i.e. there has been a molecular expansion. However the mass balance still holds good since in this case we may write

$$(2 \times 78) \text{ kg } C_6H_6 + (15 \times 32) \text{ kg } O_2 = (12 \times 44) \text{ kg } CO_2 + (6 \times 18) \text{ kg } H_2O$$

i.e. 156 + 480 = 528 + 108
or 636 = 636

Sometimes we get a balance both by mass and volume

e.g. $CO + H_2O = CO_2 + H_2$

where in this case the number of reactants and the number of products are both 2 kg-mol.

In the following examples the values of m_w used are

H_2 - 2; O_2 - 32; N_2 - 28; C - 12; S - 32

1. A gas fired boiler uses fuel of the following percentage volumetric analysis
H_2 - 48%; CH_4 - 22.5%; CO - 19%; N_2 - 6%; CO_2 - 4.5%.

The air supplied is 25% in excess of the stoichiometric air supply and, with this air/fuel ratio, combustion is complete.
Calculate the percentage analysis of the flue gases
(a) on a volumetric basis for the 'dry' flue gases,
(b) on a mass basis for the total 'wet' flue gases.

Consider 100 kg-mol fuel

The basic chemical equations involved are

$$2(H_2) + O_2 = 2(H_2O)$$

$$CH_4 + 2(O_2) = CO_2 + 2(H_2O)$$

$$2(CO) + O_2 = 2(CO_2)$$

The fuel is made up of 48 kg-mol H_2
22.5 kg-mol CH_4
19 kg-mol CO
6 kg-mol N_2
4.5 kg-mol CO_2

Of these only the first three require oxygen for combustion according to the above equations.

Thus 48 kg-mol H_2 require 24 kg-mol oxygen for combustion

22.5 kg-mol CH_4 require 45 kg-mol oxygen for combustion

19 kg-mol CO require 9.5 kg-mol O_2 for combustion

Thus the stoichiometric requirement for oxygen for the fuel is

24 + 45 + 9.5 = 78.5 kg-mol O_2 per 100 kg-mol fuel

Since the air supply is 25% in excess of stoichiometric needs, then the oxygen actually supplied will also be 25% greater than that calculated for stoichiometric needs.

Thus the actual oxygen supplied = 1.25 × 78.5 = 98.1 kg-mol
and the actual nitrogen supplied = 3.76 × 98.1 = 369.1 kg-mol
(page 20)

The products of combustion will be

368.9 + 6 = 374.9 kg-mol N_2 per 100 kg-mol fuel

48 + 45 = 93 kg-mol H_2O per 100 kg-mol fuel

4.5 + 22.5 + 19 = 46 kg-mol CO_2 per 100 kg-mol fuel

98.1 - 78.5 = 19.6 kg-mol O_2 per 100 kg-mol fuel

Thus for the 'DRY' analysis (excluding the H_2O)

$$n_t = 374.9 + 46 + 19.6 = 440.5 \text{ kg-mol}$$

$$x_{N_2} = \frac{374.9}{440.5} \times 100 = 85.1\%$$

$$x_{CO_2} = \frac{46 \times 100}{440.5} = 10.44\%$$

$$x_{O_2} = 100 - (85.1 + 10.44) = 4.45\%$$

Wet Analysis in Tabular Form

Product	n	m_w	nm_w	$\%\text{mass} = \frac{nm_w}{\Sigma nm_w} \times 100$
N_2	374.9	28	10497	$0.708 \times 100 = 70.8\%$
H_2O	93.0	18	1674	$0.1129 \times 100 = 11.29\%$
CO_2	46.0	44	2024	$0.1365 \times 100 = 13.65\%$
O_2	19.6	32	627	$0.0423 \times 100 = 4.23\%$
			14822	

2. An oil fuel of gravimetric analysis
C - 86%; H_2 - 12%; O_2 - 1%; S - 1%
is burned with air 70% in excess of the minimum for theoretically complete combustion. Determine
(a) the mass of air supplied per kilogram of fuel,
(b) the volumetric analysis of the 'wet' post-combustion gases.

Consider 1 kg of fuel

The relevant chemical equations are

$C + O_2 = CO_2$ (by mass 12 kg + 32 kg = 44 kg)

$2(H_2) + O_2 = 2(H_2O)$ (by mass 4 kg + 32 kg = 36 kg)

$S + O_2 = SO_2$ (by mass 32 kg + 32 kg = 64 kg)

Thus the stoichiometric oxygen required per kg fuel is

$$\underset{(C)}{\frac{0.86 \times 32}{12}} + \underset{(H_2)}{(8 \times 0.12)} - \underset{(O_2)}{0.01} + \underset{(S)}{0.01} = 3.253 \text{ kg}$$

Thus actual $\frac{m_{air}}{m_{fuel}} = 1.7 \times 3.253 \frac{\text{kg } O_2}{\text{kg fuel}} \times \frac{\text{kg air}}{0.233 \text{ kg } O_2}$ (page 20)

$$= 23.73 \frac{\text{kg air}}{\text{kg fuel}}$$

Products of combustion: there will be

$\frac{44}{12} \times 0.86 = 3.153$ kg CO_2 per kg fuel

$9 \times 0.12 = 1.08$ kg H_2O per kg fuel

$2 \times 0.01 = 0.02$ kg SO_2 per kg fuel

$0.7 \times 3.253 = 2.277$ kg O_2 per kg fuel

$0.767 \times 23.73 = 18.20$ kg N_2 per kg fuel

Tabulate

Product	m(kg)	$m_w\left(\dfrac{\text{kg}}{\text{kg-mol}}\right)$	$\dfrac{m}{m_w}$ (kg-mol)	$x = \dfrac{m/m_w}{\Sigma(m/m_w)}$
CO_2	9.153	44	0.0717	0.0840×100
H_2O	1.080	18	0.06	0.0703×100
SO_2	0.02	64	0.0003	0.0004×100
O_2	2.277	32	0.0712	0.0834×100
N_2	18.200	28	0.6500	0.7618×100
			0.8532	

Thus percentages by volume are respectively

CO_2 - 8.4; H_2O - 7.03; SO_2 - 0.04; O_2 - 8.34; N_2 - 76.18

3. Calculate the dry volumetric analyses of the exhaust gases resulting from combustion of ethyl alcohol (C_2H_6O) with mixture strengths of 90% and 120%.

It may be assumed that there is no free oxygen in the exhaust with the mixture rich in fuel and that combustion is complete with the mixture weak in fuel.

The relevant chemical equation is

$$\underset{46\text{ kg}}{\underset{\uparrow}{C_2H_6O}} + \underset{96\text{ kg}}{\underset{\uparrow}{3(O_2)}} = \underset{88\text{ kg}}{\underset{\uparrow}{2(CO_2)}} + \underset{54\text{ kg}}{\underset{\uparrow}{3(H_2O)}}$$

Thus the stoichiometric mass air/fuel ratio is given by

$$S\ \frac{m_a}{m_f} = \frac{3 \times 32}{46}\ \frac{\text{kg } O_2}{\text{kg fuel}} \times \frac{\text{kg air}}{0.233 \text{ kg } O_2} = 8.96\ \frac{\text{kg air}}{\text{kg fuel}}$$

Mixture strength is defined as

$$M.S. = \frac{\text{stoichiometric air supply}}{\text{actual air supply}} \times 100$$

90% Mixture strength

$$\text{Actual } \frac{m_a}{m_f} = \frac{8.96}{0.9} = 9.96\ \frac{\text{kg air}}{\text{kg fuel}} \quad \text{(weak mixture)}$$

$$C_2H_6O + \frac{(9.96 \times 0.233 \times 46)}{32}\ O_2 + \frac{(9.96 \times 0.233 \times 46)}{32} \times \frac{79}{21}\ N_2$$
$$= 2(CO_2) + 3(H_2O) + a(O_2) + b(N_2)$$

Atom balance

Oxygen

$$0.5 + 3.336 = 2 + \frac{3}{2} + a \quad \text{giving } a = 0.336$$

Nitrogen

$$12.55 = b$$

The total volume of dry products is given by

$$n_t = 2 + 0.336 + 12.55 = 14.886 \text{ kg-mol}$$

Thus $x_{CO_2} = \dfrac{n_{CO_2}}{n_t} \times 100 = \dfrac{2 \times 100}{14.886} = 13.44\%$

Also $x_{O_2} = \dfrac{0.336 \times 100}{14.886} = 2.26\%$

and $x_{N_2} = \dfrac{12.55 \times 100}{14.886} = 84.3\%$

120% Mixture strength

Actual $\dfrac{m_a}{m_f} = \dfrac{8.96}{1.2} = 7.47 \dfrac{\text{kg air}}{\text{kg fuel}}$ (rich mixture)

$$C_2H_6O + \frac{(7.47 \times 0.233 \times 46)}{32} O_2 + \frac{(7.47 \times 0.233 \times 46)}{32} \times \frac{79}{21} N_2$$

$$= a(CO_2) + b(CO) + c(H_2O) + 9.41\ N_2$$

Atom balance

Carbon

$$2 = a + b$$

Hydrogen

$$3 = c$$

Oxygen

$$2.502 + 0.5 = a + \frac{b}{2} + \frac{c}{2}$$

Thus $a = 1.004$, $b = 0.996$, $c = 3$ and for the dry products

$$n_t = 1.004 + 0.996 + 9.41 = 11.41 \text{ kg-mol}$$

Thus $x_{CO_2} = \dfrac{1.004}{11.41} \times 100 = 8.8\%$; $x_{CO} = \dfrac{0.996 \times 100}{11.41} = 8.79\%$;

$x_{N_2} = 100 - (8.8 + 8.79) = 82.41\%$

4. A fuel contains 84% carbon and 16% hydrogen by mass. After burning the fuel with air an Orsat analysis (i.e. dry volumetric analysis) of the products gave

CO_2 - 10%; CO - 1%; O_2 - 5.35%

Determine the percentage excess air supplied.

For 1 kg fuel we have 0.84 kg C and 0.16 kg H_2.

Let X kg-mol of air be supplied per kg fuel (containing $0.21X$ kg-mol O_2 and $0.79X$ kg-mol N_2)

Then in kg-mol the relevant combustion equation is

$$0.84 \frac{\text{kg C}}{\text{kg fuel}} \times \frac{\text{kg-mol C}}{12 \text{ kg C}} + 0.16 \frac{\text{kg } H_2}{\text{kg fuel}} \times \frac{\text{kg-mol } H_2}{2 \text{ kg } H_2}$$

$$+ 0.21X \frac{\text{kg-mol } O_2}{\text{kg fuel}} + 0.79X \frac{\text{kg-mol } N_2}{\text{kg fuel}}$$

$$= a\frac{\text{kg-mol } CO_2}{\text{kg fuel}} + b\frac{\text{kg-mol CO}}{\text{kg fuel}} + c\frac{\text{kg-mol } H_2O}{\text{kg fuel}} + d\frac{\text{kg-mol } O_2}{\text{kg fuel}}$$

$$+ e\frac{\text{kg-mol } N_2}{\text{kg fuel}}$$

Carbon balance: $\frac{0.84}{12} = a + b$

Oxygen balance: $0.21X = a + \frac{b}{2} + \frac{c}{2} + d$

Hydrogen balance: $\frac{0.16}{2} = c$

Nitrogen balance: $0.79X = e$

These balances give four equations for six unknowns, namely a, b, c, d, e, f, X

Further equations follow from the volumetric analysis.

Thus $\frac{a}{b} = \frac{x_{CO_2}}{x_{CO}} = 10$ Also $\frac{a}{d} = \frac{x_{CO_2}}{x_{O_2}} = \frac{10}{5.35}$

From the carbon balance

$0.07 = a + b = 10b + b = 11b$; or $b = 0.00636$, $a = 0.06364$

Thus $d = 0.06364 \times \frac{5.35}{10}$ or $d = 0.03405$, $c = 0.08$

From the oxygen balance

$$X = \frac{1}{0.21}\left(0.06364 + \frac{0.00636}{2} + 0.04 + 0.03405\right)$$

$$= 0.6708 \frac{\text{kg-mol air}}{\text{kg fuel}}$$

Now m_w (air) = 29 kg air/kg-mol air (page 20)

Thus $\frac{m_{air}}{m_{fuel}} = 0.6708 \frac{\text{kg-mol air}}{\text{kg fuel}} \times \frac{29 \text{ kg air}}{\text{kg-mol air}} = 19.45 \frac{\text{kg air}}{\text{kg fuel}}$

Now the stoichiometric mass air/fuel ratio is given by

$$S\frac{m_{air}}{m_{fuel}} = \frac{0.84 \frac{\text{kg C}}{\text{kg fuel}} \times \frac{32 \text{ kg } O_2}{12 \text{ kg C}} + 0.16 \frac{\text{kg } H_2}{\text{kg fuel}} \times 8 \frac{\text{kg } O_2}{\text{kg } H_2}}{0.233 \frac{\text{kg } O_2}{\text{kg air}}}$$

$$= 15.11 \frac{\text{kg air}}{\text{kg fuel}}$$

Thus percentage excess air is given by

$$\frac{(19.45 - 15.11)}{15.11} \times 100 = 28.7\%$$

5. A gas engine runs on a gaseous fuel of volumetric composition

CO - 26%; H_2 - 9%; CH_4 - 38%; CO_2 - 6%; O_2 - 1%; N_2 - 20%

In the engine cylinder this fuel is burned with air, the volumetric air/fuel ratio being 7/1.

Determine the volumetric composition of the exhaust gases assuming that there is no CO present in them.

Consider 1 kg-mol fuel for which the relevant chemical equation is

$$0.26(CO) + 0.09(H_2) + 0.38(CH_4) + 0.06(CO_2) + 0.01(O_2)$$
$$+ 0.20(N_2) + (0.21 \times 7)(O_2) + (0.79 \times 7)(N_2)$$
$$= a(CO_2) + b(H_2O) + c(O_2) + d(N_2)$$

Carbon balance: $0.26 + 0.38 + 0.06 = a = 0.7$

Hydrogen balance: $0.09 + 0.76 = b = 0.85$

Oxygen balance: $0.13 + 0.06 + 0.01 + 1.47 = a + \frac{b}{2} + c$

$$= 0.7 + 0.425 + c$$

or $c = 0.565$

Nitrogen balance $0.20 + 5.53 = d = 5.73$

Thus $n_t = a + b + c + d = 7.825$ kg-mol

and $x_{CO_2} = \frac{0.7}{7.825} \times 100 = 8.95\%$

$x_{H_2O} = \frac{0.85}{7.825} \times 100 = 10.86\%$

$x_{O_2} = \frac{0.545}{7.825} \times 100 = 6.96\%$

and $x_{N_2} = 100 - (8.95 + 10.86 + 6.96) = 73.23\%$

6. Determine the stoichiometric mass air/fuel ratio for a petrol approximating to hexane (C_6H_{14}) and the volumetric analysis of the (wet) post combustion gases if

(a) all the water vapour is present,

(b) the gases are cooled to 1.01325 bar and 18 °C.

The relevant chemical equation is

$$C_6H_{14} + 9.5(O_2) + \left(9.5 \times \frac{79}{21}\right)(N_2) = 6(CO_2) + 7(H_2O) + \left(9.5 \times \frac{79}{21}\right)(N_2)$$

or $C_6H_{14} + 9.5(O_2) + 35.72(N_2) = 6(CO_2) + 7(H_2O) + 35.72(N_2)$

Thus the stoichiometric mass air/fuel ratio is given by

$$s\frac{m_{air}}{m_{fuel}} = 9.5\ \frac{\text{kg-mol } O_2}{\text{kg-mol fuel}} \times \frac{\text{kg-mol fuel}}{86 \text{ kg fuel}} \times \frac{32 \text{ kg } O_2}{\text{kg-mol } O_2} \times \frac{\text{kg air}}{0.233 \text{ kg } O_2}$$

or $\quad s\ \dfrac{m_{air}}{m_{fuel}} = 15.17\ \dfrac{\text{kg air}}{\text{kg fuel}}$

For the products

$$n_t = 6 + 7 + 35.72 = 48.72 \text{ kg-mol per kg-mol fuel}$$

Thus $x_{CO_2} = \dfrac{6}{48.72} \times 100 = 12.3\%$

$$x_{H_2O} = \frac{7}{48.72} \times 100 = 14.4\%$$

$$x_{N_2} = 100 - (12.3 + 14.4) = 73.3\%$$

$$p_{H_2O} = 0.02063 \text{ bar at } 18\ ^\circ\text{C (page 2)}$$

and $p_t = 1.01325$ bar (given)

Thus $x_{H_2O} = \dfrac{n_{H_2O}}{n_t} = \dfrac{p_{H_2O}}{p_t} = \dfrac{0.02063}{1.01325} = 0.0203$ or 2%

$$n_t = n_{H_2O} + 6(CO_2) + 35.72(N_2)$$

But $n_{H_2O} = 0.02n_t = 0.02(n_{H_2O} + 41.72)$

$$n_{H_2O} = 0.85 \text{ kg-mol}$$

Thus $n_t = 42.57$ kg-mol

and $x_{CO_2} = \dfrac{6}{42.57} \times 100 = 14.1\%$

$$x_{N_2} = 100 - (14.1 + 2) = 83.9\%$$

7. A sample of flue gas had a dry, volumetric analysis of CO_2 - 9.3%; O_2 - 30.3%; N_2 - 60.4%

When the sample of the wet gas was cooled at 1.20 bar the water vapour in the gas just began to condense at 50 °C.

Determine the partial pressures of the constituents at 1.2 bar, 50 °C.

If the fuel is assumed to consist entirely of carbon and hydrogen and the water in the flue gas is produced entirely by the combustion of the hydrogen in the fuel, estimate the proportion, by mass, of the carbon and hydrogen in the fuel.

$$p_{H_2O} = p_g = 0.1233 \text{ bar at } 50\ ^\circ\text{C (p.2)}$$

Thus $0.1233 = \dfrac{n_{H_2O}}{n_t\ (\text{wet})} \times p_t = x_{H_2O} \times p_t$

$$x_{H_2O} = \frac{0.1233}{1.2} = 0.103 \text{ or } 10.3\%$$

Thus $n_{H_2O} = 0.103(n_{H_2O} + n_{CO_2} + n_{O_2} + n_{N_2}) = 0.103n_{H_2O} + 0.103n_{t\,(dry)}$

or $\quad 0.897n_{H_2O} = 0.103n_t$ (dry)

Thus $n_{H_2O} = 0.115n_t$ (dry)

and n_t (wet) $= n_t$ (dry) $+ n_{H_2O} = 1.115n_t$ (dry)

$$\text{Thus } p_{CO_2} = \frac{n_{CO_2}}{n_t(\text{wet})} \times p_t = \frac{n_{CO_2}}{1.115} \times \frac{p_t}{n_t(\text{dry})} = \frac{0.093 \times 1.2}{1.115}$$

$$= \underline{0.1001 \text{ bar}} \text{ at } 1.2 \text{ bar}, 50\ ^\circ\text{C}$$

$$\underline{p_{O_2} = \frac{n_{O_2}}{n_t(\text{wet})} \times p_t = \frac{n_{O_2}}{1.115} \times \frac{p_t}{n_t(\text{dry})} = \frac{0.303 \times 1.2}{1.115} = 0.326 \text{ bar}}$$

$$\underline{p_{N_2} = 1.2 - (0.1001 + 0.1233 + 0.326) = 0.6506 \text{ bar}}$$

If y is the percentage by mass of C in the fuel and X kg-mol of air are supplied per kg fuel

$$\frac{y}{12}(C) + \frac{(1-y)}{2}(H_2) + X(O_2) + 3.76X(N_2)$$

$$= a(CO_2) + b(H_2O) + c(O_2) + d(N_2)$$

Carbon balance: $a = \dfrac{y}{12}$

Hydrogen balance: $b = \dfrac{1-y}{2}$

Oxygen balance: $X = a + \dfrac{b}{2} + c$

Nitrogen balance: $3.76X = d$

$$\text{Now } \frac{p_{CO_2}}{p_t} = \frac{n_{CO_2}}{n_t} = \frac{a}{a+b+c+d} = \frac{0.1001}{1.2} = 0.0834$$

$$\text{and } \frac{p_{H_2O}}{p_t} = \frac{n_{H_2O}}{n_t} = \frac{b}{a+b+c+d} = 0.103$$

$$\text{Thus } \frac{a}{b} = \frac{\frac{y}{12}}{\frac{1-y}{2}} = \frac{0.0834}{0.103} = 0.8097$$

or $\quad \underline{y = 0.829;\ 1 - y = 0.171}$

Further Examples

8. Calculate the stoichiometric mass air/fuel ratio for the combustion of octane (C_8H_{18}).

Also find the mass air/fuel ratios for mixture strengths of 85% and 125%. (15.06, 17.71, 12.05)

9. A spark ignition engine uses octane (C_8H_{18}) as fuel. With

the carburettor set to give maximum power at a given speed a partial volumetric analysis of the dry exhaust gas gave

CO_2 - 8.95%; CO - 6.81%.

Calculate the mixture strength.

Calculate also the volumetric percentage of oxygen in the dry exhaust gas. Is this mixture rich or weak? (111%, about 1%,Rich)

10. Calculate the percentage molecular expansion, or contraction resulting from complete combustion of butane(C_4H_{10}) and air in stoichiometric proportions. (4.69% expansion)

12 FIRST LAW APPLIED TO REACTING SYSTEMS

Before applying the first law of thermodynamics to reacting systems a word or two on nomenclature is justified.

In the following chapter suffix R refers to reactants before combustion and suffix P refers to products after combustion. Additionally suffices $_{0},_{1},_{2}$ refer to temperatures T_0, T_1, T_2 respectively.

A combustion process generally produces a change in both chemical and thermodynamic states. Since any path may be taken between two given states for calculating property changes we find it convenient to split up the combustion process into three parts.

(a) Reactants are taken from a given initial state p_1, T_1 to a reference state p_0, T_0 with no chemical change,

(b) the reactants are then changed to products at a fixed thermodynamic state p_0, T_0 by an appropriate combustion process,

(c) the products are brought to the final state p_2, T_2 by a thermodynamic state change with no chemical change.

Then $E_{P_2} - E_{R_1}$ = final internal energy - initial internal energy

$$= (E_{P_2} - E_{P_0}) + (E_{P_0} - E_{R_0}) + (E_{R_0} - E_{R_1})$$

where

$E_{P_0} - E_{R_0} = \Delta E_0 =$ internal energy of combustion (negative numerically since $E_R > E_P$ at same value of temperature)

and $E_{P_2} - E_{P_0} = \sum_P m_i c_{v_i} (T_2 - T_0)$

and $E_{R_0} - E_{R_1} = \sum_R m_i c_{v_i} (T_0 - T_1)$

If any phase change occurs in these two thermodynamic state changes then the appropriate value of e_{fg} must be used.

Similarly for steady flow calculations

$$H_{P_2} - H_{R_1} = (H_{P_2} - H_{P_0}) + (H_{P_0} - H_{R_0}) + (H_{R_0} - H_{R_1})$$

$$= \sum_P m_i c_{p_i} (T_2 - T_0) + \Delta H_0 + \sum_R m_i c_{p_i} (T_0 - T_1)$$

where ΔH_0 is the enthalpy of combustion which is numerically negative since $H_R > H_P$ at the same temperature.

The reference temperature T_0 is generally 25 °C (298 K) and values of ΔE_0 and ΔH_0 are quoted per kg-mol of fuel most commonly.

Note that ΔE_0 and ΔH_0 are connected as follows

$$\Delta H_0 = (H_{P_0} - H_{R_0}) = (E_{P_0} - p_{P_0} V_{P_0}) - (E_{R_0} - p_{R_0} V_{R_0})$$

$$= (E_{P_0} - E_{R_0}) + (p_{P_0} V_{P_0} - p_{R_0} V_{R_0})$$

$= (\Delta E_0) + R_0 T_0 (n_P - n_R)$ for gaseous reactants and products

Thus if $n_P = n_R$, $\Delta H_0 = \Delta E_0$, as for example in the reaction

$CO + H_2O = CO_2 + H_2$ where $n_R = n_P = 2$ kg-mol

Since the temperature ranges met with in practical combustion processes are large the use of mean values of c_V and c_p is not justified. Thus included here are tables of values of E and H for the common combustion gases for a temperature range

$175 \text{ K} < T < 3000 \text{ K}$

Additionally there is a table giving values of enthalpy of formation H_f^0 in kJ/kg-mol for common combustion substances.

$$\text{Then } (E_{P_2} - E_{P_0}) = \sum_R m_i c_{v_i} (T_2 - T_0) = \sum_R n_i m_{w_i} c_{v_i} (T_2 - T_0)$$

$$= \sum_R n_i C_{v_i} (T_2 - T_0) = \sum_R n_i (E_{i_2} - E_{i_0}) \text{ etc.}$$

$$\text{and } (H_{P_2} - H_{P_0}) = \sum_P m_i c_{p_i} (T_2 - T_0) = \sum_P n_i (H_{i_2} - H_{i_0}) \text{ etc.}$$

SOME VALUES OF ENTHALPY OF FORMATION (H_f^0) at 25 °C and 1.01325 bar

SUBSTANCE	SYMBOL	PHASE	H_f^0 (kJ/kg-mol)
ACETYLENE	C_2H_2	GAS	+ 226899
AMMONIA	NH_3	GAS	- 46222
BENZENE	C_6H_6	GAS	+ 82982
n-BUTANE	C_4H_{10}	GAS	- 126232
1-BUTENE	C_4H_8	GAS	- 12.6
CARBON	C	GRAPHITE	0
	C	GAS	+ 718864
CARBON DIOXIDE	CO_2	GAS	- 393776
CARBON MONOXIDE	CO	GAS	- 110597
n-DODECANE	$C_{12}H_{26}$	GAS	- 291066
ETHANE	C_2H_6	GAS	- 84725
ETHYLENE	C_2H_4	GAS	+ 52319
n-HEPTANE	C_7H_{16}	GAS	- 187945
n-HEXANE	C_6H_{14}	GAS	- 167305
HYDROGEN	H_2	GAS	0
HYDROGEN SULPHIDE	H_2S	GAS	- 20159
METHANE	CH_4	GAS	- 74897
NITRIC OXIDE	NO	GAS	+ 90435
NITROGEN	N_2	GAS	0
n-OCTANE	C_8H_{18}	GAS	- 208586
		LIQUID	- 250119
OXYGEN	O_2	GAS	0
n-PENTANE	C_5H_{12}	GAS	- 146538
PROPANE	C_3H_8	GAS	- 103916
SULPHUR DIOXIDE	SO_2	GAS	- 297095
WATER	H_2O	GAS	- 241988
		LIQUID	- 286031

INTERNAL ENERGY OF UNDISSOCIATED GASES AT LOW PRESSURE
(kJ/kg-mole relative to 298 K)

T(K)	CO_2	CO	H_2O	H_2	O_2	N_2
175	-3186	-2553	-3077	-2414	-2561	-2555
200	-2600	-2034	-2458	-1934	-2048	-2034
225	-1981	-1515	-1835	-1448	-1532	-1515
250	-1331	-997	-1210	-957	-1011	-996
275	-651	-478	-582	-461	-487	-477
298	0	0	0	0	0	0
300	58	42	51	40	42	42
325	794	562	687	545	576	561
350	1556	1085	1328	1054	1115	1081
375	2344	1609	1973	1566	1658	1603
400	3155	2136	2623	2080	2206	2126
450	4845	3196	3939	3118	3318	3178
500	6618	4269	5277	4164	4450	4241
550	8467	5356	6640	5216	5603	5315
600	10385	6457	8028	6275	6776	6401
650	12366	7574	9443	7339	7970	7502
700	14403	8707	10886	8406	9184	8618
750	16492	9857	12358	9478	10417	9748
800	18629	11023	13859	10554	11669	10895
850	20808	12207	15390	11634	12938	12057
900	23026	13407	16952	12718	14225	13235
950	25280	14623	18544	13807	15527	14429
1000	27566	15854	20168	14902	16845	15638
1050	29881	17101	21822	16002	18177	16861
1100	32223	18362	23508	17109	19522	18099
1150	34590	19637	25224	18223	20878	19351
1200	36979	20924	26971	19346	22246	20615
1250	39390	22223	28749	20477	23624	21891
1300	41819	23533	30556	21618	25012	23179
1350	44266	24854	32393	22768	26407	24478
1400	46730	26183	34259	23930	27811	25787
1500	51703	28868	38076	26287	30638	28431
1600	56729	31580	42001	28691	33488	31106
1700	61803	34315	46029	31144	36358	33807
1800	66920	37068	50150	33646	39247	36530
1900	72075	39837	54359	36196	42152	39270
2000	77263	42619	58644	38789	45076	42027
2100	82482	45412	62995	41423	48020	44798
2200	87728	48218	67400	44090	50986	47581
2300	92997	51035	71846	46786	53976	50378
2400	98266	53866	76317	49506	56994	53189
2500	103593	56711	80795	52245	60041	56012

T(K)	CO_2	CO	H_2O	H_2	O_2	N_2
2600	108915	59570	85261	55000	63118	58850
2700	114251	62442	89692	57772	66223	61700
2800	119600	65324	94060	60565	69353	64561
2900	124964	68212	98337	63389	72498	67429
3000	130348	71098	102488	66258	75647	70297

ENTHALPY OF UNDISSOCIATED GASES AT LOW PRESSURE
(kJ/kg-mole relative to 298 K)

T(K)	CO_2	CO	H_2O	H_2	O_2	N_2
175	-4209	-3575	-4100	-3437	-3583	-3578
200	-3415	-2848	-3272	-2749	-2863	-2849
225	-2588	-2122	-2442	-2055	-2139	-2122
250	-1730	-1396	-1609	-1356	-1410	-1395
275	-842	-669	-773	-652	-678	-668
298	0	0	0	0	0	0
300	74	58	67	57	59	58
325	1018	787	912	770	801	785
350	1989	1517	1760	1486	1547	1513
375	2984	2249	2613	2206	2298	2243
400	4003	2984	3471	2928	3054	2974
450	6109	4460	5203	4381	4582	4442
500	8298	5949	6957	5843	6130	5920
550	10562	7451	8735	7312	7698	7410
600	12896	8968	10539	8786	9287	8912
650	15292	10500	12370	10265	10897	10429
700	17745	12049	14228	11749	12526	11960
750	20250	13615	16116	13236	14175	13506
800	22803	15197	18033	14728	15842	15069
850	25398	16796	19980	16223	17528	16647
900	28031	18412	21957	17723	19230	18241
950	30701	20044	23965	19228	20948	19850
1000	33402	21691	26004	20738	22682	21475
1050	36133	23353	28075	22254	24429	23114
1100	38891	25030	30176	23777	26190	24767
1150	41674	26720	32308	25307	27962	26434
1200	44479	28423	34471	26845	29746	28114
1250	47305	30138	36664	28392	31540	29807
1300	50150	31864	38887	29949	33343	31510
1350	53013	33600	41140	31515	35154	33225
1400	55892	35346	43422	33092	36873	34949
1500	61696	38861	48070	36280	40632	38424
1600	67554	42405	52827	39516	44313	41931
1700	73460	45972	57685	42801	48015	45463

T(K)	CO_2	CO	H_2O	H_2	O_2	N_2
1800	79408	49556	62639	46134	51735	49018
1900	85394	53156	67678	49515	55472	52590
2000	91414	56770	72794	52940	59227	56178
2100	97465	60395	77977	56405	63002	59780
2200	103542	64032	83214	59904	66799	63395
2300	109642	67681	88491	63432	70621	67024
2400	115763	71343	93793	66983	74471	70665
2500	121901	75019	99103	70553	78349	74321
2600	128054	78709	104401	74140	82258	77990
2700	134222	82413	109663	77743	86194	81671
2800	140402	86127	114863	81368	90155	85364
2900	146598	89846	119971	85022	94132	89063
3000	152813	93563	124953	88724	98112	92762

1. Using the table of values of enthalpy of formation, determine the enthalpies of combustion at 25 °C, in both kJ/kg-mol and kJ/kg of:
(a) methane (CH_4), (b) ethane (C_2H_6), (c) n-octane (C_8H_{18}).

(a) The relevant chemical equation is

$$CH_4 + 2(O_2) + (2 \times 3.76)(N_2) = CO_2 + 2(H_2O) + (2 \times 3.76)(N_2)$$

First law of thermodynamics

$Q = H_{P_0} - H_{R_0}$ in the absence of significant kinetic energy, potential energy and with no work transfer.

i.e. $Q = \Delta H_0$ = enthalpy of combustion and using the table for H_f^0

$$\left.\begin{aligned} Q = {} & \frac{1 \text{ kg-mol } CO_2}{\text{kg-mol } CH_4}\left(-393776 \frac{\text{kJ}}{\text{kg-mol } CO_2}\right) \\ & + \frac{2 \text{ kg-mol } H_2O}{\text{kg-mol } CH_4}\left(-241988 \frac{\text{kJ}}{\text{kg-mol } H_2O}\right) \\ & + \frac{2 \times 3.76 \text{ kg-mol } N_2}{\text{kg-mol } CH_4}(0) \end{aligned}\right\} H_{P_0}$$

$$\left.\begin{aligned} & - \frac{1 \text{ kg-mol } CH_4}{\text{kg-mol } CH_4}\left(-74897 \frac{\text{kJ}}{\text{kg-mol } CH_4}\right) \\ & - 0 - 0 \text{ (oxygen and nitrogen)} \end{aligned}\right\} H_{R_0}$$

or $$Q = -393776 - 483976 + 74897 = -802855 \frac{\text{kJ}}{\text{kg-mol } CH_4}$$

Also $$Q = -802855 \frac{\text{kJ}}{\text{kg-mol } CH_4} \times \frac{\text{kg-mol } CH_4}{16 \text{ kg } CH_4} = -50178 \frac{\text{kJ}}{\text{kg } CH_4}$$

(b) The relevant chemical equation this time is

$$C_2H_6 + 3.5(O_2) + (3.5 \times 3.76)(N_2) = 2(CO_2) + 3(H_2O) + (3.5 \times 3.76)(N_2)$$

$$\text{Thus } Q = \left.\begin{matrix} \dfrac{2\text{ kg-mol } CO_2}{\text{kg-mol } C_2H_6}\left(-393776 \dfrac{\text{kJ}}{\text{kg-mol } CO_2}\right) \\ + \dfrac{3\text{ kg-mol } H_2O}{\text{kg-mol } C_2H_6}\left(-241988 \dfrac{\text{kJ}}{\text{kg-mol } H_2O}\right) \\ + 0 \quad \text{(nitrogen)} \end{matrix}\right\} H_{P_0}$$

$$\left.\begin{matrix} - \dfrac{1\text{ kg-mol } C_2H_6}{\text{kg-mol } C_2H_6}\left(-84725 \dfrac{\text{kJ}}{\text{kg-mol } C_2H_6}\right) \\ - 0 - 0 \quad \text{(oxygen and nitrogen)} \end{matrix}\right\} H_{R_0}$$

$$\text{or} \quad Q = -781552 - 725964 - 84725 = -1428191 \frac{\text{kJ}}{\text{kg-mol } C_2H_6}$$

$$\text{Also } Q = -1428791 \frac{\text{kJ}}{\text{kg-mol } C_2H_6} \frac{\text{kg-mol } C_2H_6}{30\text{ kg } C_2H_6} = -47626 \frac{\text{kJ}}{\text{kg } C_2H_6}$$

(c) The relevant chemical equation this time is

$$C_8H_{18} + 12.5(O_2) + (12.5 \times 3.76)(N_2) = 8(CO_2) + 9(H_2O) + (12.5 \times 3.76)(N_2)$$

$$\text{and} \quad Q = \left.\begin{matrix} \dfrac{8\text{ kg-mol } CO_2}{\text{kg-mol } C_8H_{18}}\left(-393776 \dfrac{\text{kJ}}{\text{kg-mol } CO_2}\right) \\ + \dfrac{9\text{ kg-mol } H_2O}{\text{kg-mol } C_8H_{18}}\left(-241988 \dfrac{\text{kJ}}{\text{kg-mol } H_2O}\right) \\ + 0 \quad \text{(nitrogen)} \end{matrix}\right\} H_{P_0}$$

$$\left.\begin{matrix} - \dfrac{1\text{ kg-mol } C_8H_{18}}{\text{kg-mol } C_8H_{18}}\left(-208586 \dfrac{\text{kJ}}{\text{kg-mol } C_8H_{18}}\right) \\ - 0 - 0 \quad \text{(oxygen and nitrogen)} \end{matrix}\right\} H_{R_0}$$

$$\text{or} \quad Q = -3150208 - 2177892 + 208586 = -5119514 \frac{\text{kJ}}{\text{kg-mol } C_8H_{18}}$$

$$\text{Also } Q = -5119514 \frac{\text{kJ}}{\text{kg-mol } C_8H_{18}} \frac{\text{kg-mol } C_8H_{18}}{114\text{ kg } C_8H_{18}} = -44908 \frac{\text{kJ}}{\text{kg } C_8H_{18}}$$

2. Calculate the enthalpy of combustion of propane at 25 °C for the following conditions on both a kg-mol and a kg basis.

(a) Gaseous propane with liquid H_2O in the products.
(b) Gaseous propane with H_2O vapour in the products.
(c) Liquid propane with liquid H_2O in the products.
(d) Liquid propane with H_2O vapour in the products.

The enthalpy of evaporation of propane at 25 °C is 370 kJ/kg.

(a) The relevant chemical equation is

$$C_3H_8 + 5(O_2) + (5 \times 3.76)(N_2) = 3(CO_2) + 4(H_2O) + (5 \times 3.76)(N_2)$$

$$Q = H_{P_0} - H_{R_0} \quad \text{(when as in question 1, } T_1 = T_2 = T_0\text{)}$$

$$= \frac{3 \text{ kg-mol } CO_2}{\text{kg-mol } C_3H_8}\left(-393776 \frac{\text{kJ}}{\text{kg-mol CO}}\right) + \frac{4 \text{ kg-mol } H_2O}{\text{kg-mol } C_3H_8}\left(-286031 \frac{\text{kJ}}{\text{kg-mol } H_2O}\right) \Bigg\} H_{P_0}$$

(↑ liquid H_2O)

$$- \frac{1 \text{ kg-mol } C_3H_8}{\text{kg-mol } C_3H_8}\left(-103916 \frac{\text{kJ}}{\text{kg-mol } C_3H_8} -370 \frac{\text{kJ}}{\text{kg } C_3H_8} \times \frac{44 \text{ kg } C_3H_8}{\text{kg-mol } C_3H_8}\right) \Bigg\} H_{R_0}$$

(↑ −103916: gaseous propane; ↑ −370: h_{fg} for propane)

or $Q = -1181328 - 1144124 + 120196 = -2205256 \dfrac{\text{kJ}}{\text{kg-mol } C_3H_8}$

or $Q = -2205256 \dfrac{\text{kJ}}{\text{kg-mol } C_3H_8} \times \dfrac{\text{kg-mol } C_3H_8}{44 \text{ kg } C_3H_8} = -50119 \dfrac{\text{kJ}}{\text{kg } C_3H_8}$

(b) Similarly to (a)

$$Q = \frac{3(-393776) + 4(-241988) + 120196}{44} = -46115 \frac{\text{kJ}}{\text{kg } C_3H_8}$$

(c) $$Q = \frac{3(-393776) - 4(-286021) + 103916}{44} = -50489 \frac{\text{kJ}}{\text{kg } C_3H_8}$$

(d) $$Q = \frac{3(-393776) - 4(-241988) + 103916}{44} = -46486 \frac{\text{kJ}}{\text{kg } C_3H_8}$$

3. Calculate the enthalpy of gaseous propane at 450 K. (At this temperature all the H_2O formed during combustion will be in the vapour phase.) The average specific heat at constant pressure for propane between 298 K and 450 K is 1.675 kJ/kg K.

The enthalpy change 1 - 2 can be evaluated using ANY path between state 1 and state 2 since H is a property. Thus we choose the arrowed path which corresponds to the second scheme in figure 12.3.

The relevant chemical equation is that given in the previous example.

First law of thermodynamics:

$$H_2 - H_1 = \Delta H_{450} = (H_2 - H_0)_P + (H_{0_P} - H_{0_R}) + (H_0 - H_1)_R$$

(↑ ΔH_0)

or $$\Delta H_{450} = (H_2 - H_0)_P - 46486 \frac{\text{kJ}}{\text{kg fuel}} + (H_0 - H_1)_R$$

(↑ from 12.2d)

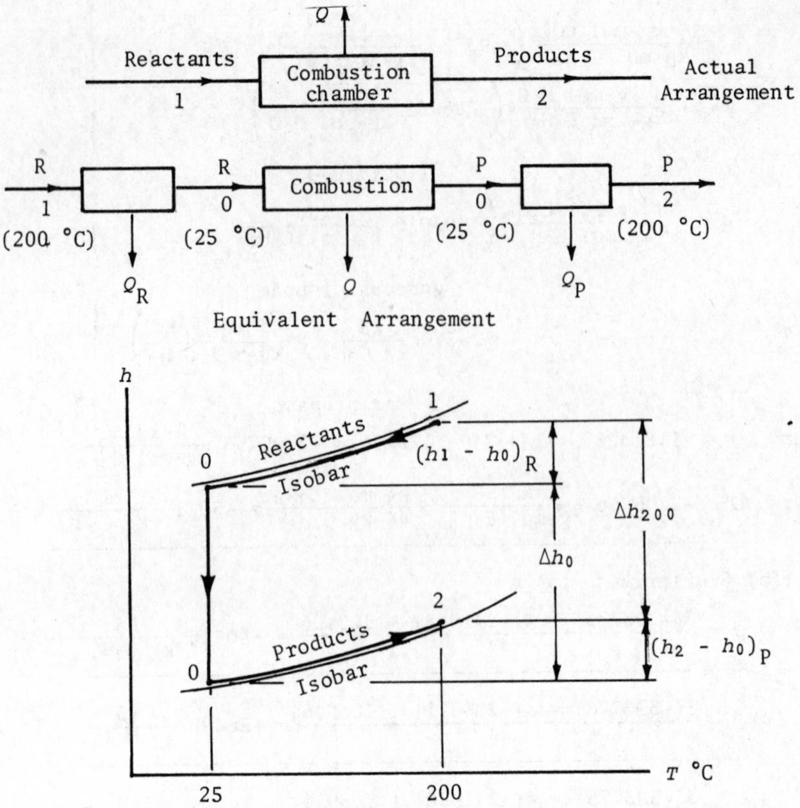

Figure 12.3

$$\text{Now} \quad (H_2 - H_0)_P = 3\ \frac{\text{kg-mol } CO_2}{\text{kg-mol } C_3H_8}\left(6109\ \frac{\text{kJ}}{\text{kg-mol } CO_2}\right)$$

$$+\ 4\ \frac{\text{kg-mol } H_2O}{\text{kg-mol } C_3H_8}\left(5203\ \frac{\text{kJ}}{\text{kg-mol } H_2O}\right)$$

$$+\ (5 \times 3.76)\ \frac{\text{kg-mol } N_2}{\text{kg-mol } C_3H_8}\left(4442\ \frac{\text{kJ}}{\text{kg-mol } N_2}\right)$$

$$(H_2 - H_0)_P = 18327 + 20812 + 83510 = 122649\ \frac{\text{kJ}}{\text{kg-mol } C_3H_8}$$

$$\text{Also} \quad (H_0 - H_1)_R = \underset{\substack{\uparrow \\ \text{fuel}}}{c_p}(T_0 - T_1) + n_0 \Delta H_{O_2} + n_{N_2} \Delta H_{N_2}$$

$$= 1.675\ \frac{\text{kJ}}{\text{kg } C_3H_8\ \text{K}} \times \frac{44 \text{ kg } C_3H_8}{\text{kg-mol } C_3H_8}\ (-152 \text{ K})$$

$$+\ 5\ \frac{\text{kg-mol } O_2}{\text{kg-mol } C_3H_8}\left(-4582\ \frac{\text{kJ}}{\text{kg-mol } O_2}\right)$$

$$+\ (5 \times 3.76)\ \frac{\text{kg-mol } N_2}{\text{kg-mol } C_3H_8}\left(4442\ \frac{\text{kJ}}{\text{kg-mol } N_2}\right)$$

$$(H_0 - H_1)_R = -11202 - 22910 - 83510 = -117622 \frac{\text{kJ}}{\text{kg-mol } C_3H_8}$$

$$\text{Thus } \Delta H_{450} = 122649 \frac{\text{kJ}}{\text{kg-mol } C_3H_8} - 46486 \frac{\text{kJ}}{\text{kg } C_3H_8}\left(\frac{44 \text{ kg } C_3H_8}{\text{kg-mol } C_3H_8}\right)$$

$$- 117622 \frac{\text{kJ}}{\text{kg-mol } C_3H_8}$$

$$= -2040357 \frac{\text{kJ}}{\text{kg-mol } C_3H_8}\left(\frac{\text{kg-mol } C_3H_8}{44 \text{ kg } C_3H_8}\right)$$

$$\underline{\Delta H_{450} = -46372 \frac{\text{kJ}}{\text{kg } C_3H_8}}$$

4. A petrol engine delivers 200 hp. The fuel used is C_8H_{18} in liquid form and it enters the engine at 25 °C. The air supply is 15% in excess of stoichiometric requirements and enters at 325 K. The products of combustion leave at 750 K and the heat transfer rate from the engine is 205 kW. Determine the fuel consumption if complete combustion is achieved.

The relevant chemical equation is

$$C_8H_{18} + 1.15(12.5)(O_2) + (3.76 \times 1.15 \times 12.5)(N_2)$$
$$= 8(CO_2) + 9(H_2O) + (3.76 \times 12.5 \times 1.15)(N_2)$$

First law

$$H_P - H_R = H_{P_{750}} - H_{air_{325}} - H_{fuel_{298}}$$

$$H_P - H_R = (H_{750} - H_{298})_P + (H_P - H_{air} - H_{fuel})_{298}$$
$$+ (H_{298} - H_{325})_{air}$$

where

$$(H_P - H_{air} - H_{fuel})_{298} = \Delta H_{298}$$

$$= 8 \frac{\text{kg-mol } CO_2}{\text{kg-mol } C_8H_{18}}\left(-393776 \frac{\text{kJ}}{\text{kg-mol } CO_2}\right)$$

$$+ 9 \frac{\text{kg-mol } H_2O}{\text{kg-mol } C_8H_{18}}\left(-241988 \frac{\text{kJ}}{\text{kg-mol } H_2O}\right)$$

$$- \quad -250119 \frac{\text{kJ}}{\text{kg-mol } C_8H_{18}}$$

$$= -3150208 - 2177892 + 250119$$

$$= -5077981 \frac{\text{kJ}}{\text{kg-mol } C_8H_{18}}$$

$$\text{Also } (H_{298} - H_{325})_{air} = (1.15 \times 12.5) \frac{\text{kg-mol } O_2}{\text{kg-mol } C_8H_{18}}(-801) \frac{\text{kJ}}{\text{kg-mol } O_2}$$

$$+ (3.76 \times 1.15 \times 12.5) \frac{\text{kg-mol } N_2}{\text{kg-mol } C_8H_{18}} \times$$

$$(-785) \frac{\text{kJ}}{\text{kg-mol } N_2}.$$

$$= -11514 - 42429$$

$$= -53943 \frac{kJ}{kg\text{-mol } C_8H_{18}}$$

Also $$(H_{750} - H_{298})_P = 8 \frac{kg\text{-mol } CO_2}{kg\text{-mol } C_8H_{18}} \left(20250 \frac{kJ}{kg\text{-mol } CO_2}\right)$$

$$+ 9 \frac{kg\text{-mol } H_2O}{kg\text{-mol } C_8H_{18}} \left(16116 \frac{kJ}{kg\text{-mol } H_2O}\right)$$

$$+ (0.15 \times 12.5) \frac{kg\text{-mol } O_2}{kg\text{-mol } C_8H_{18}} \times$$

$$14175 \frac{kJ}{kg\text{-mol } O_2}$$

$$+ (3.76 \times 1.15 \times 12.5) \frac{kg\text{-mol } N_2}{kg\text{-mol } C_8H_{18}} \times$$

$$13506 \frac{kJ}{kg\text{-mol } N_2}$$

$$= 162000 + 145044 + 26578 + 729999$$

$$= 1063621 \frac{kJ}{kg\text{-mol } C_8H_{18}}$$

Thus $$-205 \text{ kW} - 200 \text{ hp} \left[\frac{0.746 \text{ kW}}{\text{hp}}\right] = \dot{m}_f(1063621 - 5077981 - 53943)$$

$$\frac{kJ}{kg\text{-mol } C_8H_{18}} \left(\frac{kg\text{-mol } C_8H_{18}}{114 \text{ kg } C_8H_{18}}\right)$$

$$(-205 - 149.2) \text{ kW} = -35687 \frac{kJ}{kg\ C_8H_{18}} \left[\frac{kWs}{kJ}\right] \times \dot{m}_f$$

or $$\dot{m}_f = 0.00993 \frac{kg\ C_8H_{18}}{s}$$

5. Liquid octane (C_8H_{18}) is burnt completely in steady flow with air in excess of stoichiometric requirements. The reactants enter at 25 °C and the products leave at 727 °C. Neglect heat transfer to or from the environment, changes in kinetic and potential energy, assume no work transfer and calculate the mass air to fuel ratio.

The combustion equation is as follows when X kg-mol air are supplied per kg-mol fuel.

$$C_8H_{18} + (0.21X)(O_2) + (0.79X)(N_2) = a(CO_2) + b(H_2O) + c(O_2) + d(N_2)$$

Carbon balance: $8 = a$

Hydrogen balance: $9 = b$

Oxygen balance: $0.21X = a + \frac{b}{2} + c = c + 12.5$

Nitrogen balance: $d = 0.79X$

First law

$$H_{R_1} = H_{P_2} \quad \text{(all other terms being zero)}$$

$$\text{Thus } H_{R_1} - H_{P_2} = 0 = \underset{\substack{\uparrow \\ \text{zero} \\ (T_0 = T_1)}}{(H_{R_1} - H_{R_0})} + \underset{\substack{\uparrow \\ \Delta H_0}}{(H_{R_0} - H_{P_0})} + \underset{\substack{\uparrow \\ T_2 = 1000\ \text{K}}}{(H_{P_0} - H_{P_2})}$$

$$\text{Thus } 0 = \underset{\substack{\uparrow \\ \text{see 12.4}}}{5077981} \frac{\text{kJ}}{\text{kg-mol } C_8H_{18}} - 8 \frac{\text{kg-mol } CO_2}{\text{kg-mol } C_8H_{18}} \left(33402 \frac{\text{kJ}}{\text{kg-mol } CO_2}\right)$$

$$- 9 \frac{\text{kg-mol } H_2O}{\text{kg-mol } C_8H_{18}} \left(26004 \frac{\text{kJ}}{\text{kg-mol } H_2O}\right)$$

$$- (0.21X - 12.5) \frac{\text{kg-mol } O_2}{\text{kg-mol } C_8H_{18}} \left(22682 \frac{\text{kJ}}{\text{kg-mol } O_2}\right)$$

$$- (0.79X) \frac{\text{kg-mol } N_2}{\text{kg-mol } C_8H_{18}} \left(21475 \frac{\text{kJ}}{\text{kg-mol } N_2}\right)$$

$$\text{or} \quad 0 = 5077981 - 26726 - 234036 - 4763.2X + 283525 - 16965.3X$$

$$\text{or} \quad X = \frac{480254}{21728.5} = 223.7 \frac{\text{kg-mol air}}{\text{kg-mol } C_8H_{18}}$$

$$\text{and} \quad \frac{m_{air}}{m_{fuel}} = 223.7 \frac{\text{kg-mol air}}{\text{kg-mol } C_8H_{18}} \times \frac{29 \text{ kg air}}{\text{kg-mol air}} \times \frac{\text{kg-mol } C_8H_{18}}{114 \text{ kg } C_8H_{18}}$$

$$= 56.9 \frac{\text{kg air}}{\text{kg } C_8H_{18}}$$

Further Examples

6. Determine the internal energy of combustion at 25 °C for each of the compounds given in question 12.1.
(-802855 kJ/kg-mol; -1430030 kJ/kg-mol; -5128200 kJ/kg-mol)

7. A small gas turbine uses liquid octane (C_8H_{18}) for fuel, and 400% theoretical air. The air and fuel enter at 25 °C and the products of combustion leave at 850 K. The output of the turbine and the fuel consumption are measured and it is found that the specific fuel consumption is 0.169×10^{-3} g/J. Determine the heat transfer from the turbine per kg-mol of fuel assuming complete combustion. (-233500 kJ/kg-mol)

8. Methane vapour (CH_4) is burnt steadily at 1 bar with twice the stoichiometric requirement of air. Both reactants enter the system at 25 °C and the products leave at 127 °C. Calculate the heat transfer per kg of fuel. (-46159 kJ)

13 SECOND LAW OF THERMODYNAMICS - INTRODUCTORY CONCEPTS

The chief aim in introducing the second law of thermodynamics is to derive the property entropy and the basic difficulty lies as much in the rather lengthy preamble as in any conceptual obscurity in the property itself.

One has to define various terms such as forward and reversed heat engines, thermodynamic temperature, efficiency and coefficient of performance before the idea of entropy can be mooted.

One has to distinguish between the word reversed, which means operating in the opposite sense, and reversibility, which is quite a different word with a very distinctive thermodynamic meaning which was partly discussed in the introduction to this volume under the heading - the nature of work transfer.

Chapter 13 is an extensive one dealing with all the concepts in the preamble leading up to entropy.

Chapter 14 deals with entropy itself, its calculation and use.

Chapter 15 deals with vapour power cycles which can only be analysed once entropy has been established.

Chapter 16 deals with gas power cycles and chapter 17 broaches the concept of available energy and energy degradation which is a logical outcome of the preceding three or four chapters.

Once entropy is established the fundamental work in engineering thermodynamics is finished - the rest is pure application. Entropy follows from the second law of thermodynamics in much the same way as internal energy follows from the first.

1. A heat engine working at the rate of 750 kW has an efficiency of 20%. Evaluate the heat transfer rates to and from the working fluid.

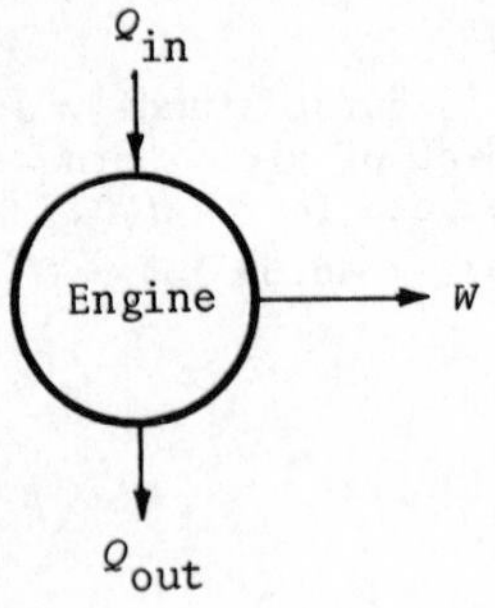

Figure 13.1

$$\eta = \frac{W}{Q_{in}}$$

where η is the efficiency, W is the work output, and Q_{in} is the heat supplied to the heat engine.

Thus $\underline{Q_{in} = \frac{W}{\eta} = \frac{750 \text{ kW}}{0.2} = 3750 \text{ kW}}$

Now $Q_{in} = Q_{out} + W$ (first law of thermodynamics)

Thus $\underline{Q_{out} = Q_{in} - W = 3750 - 750 = 3000 \text{ kW}}$

2. The coefficient of performance of a heat pump is 5 when the power supplied to drive it is 400 kW. Evaluate the heat transfer rates to and from the working fluid.

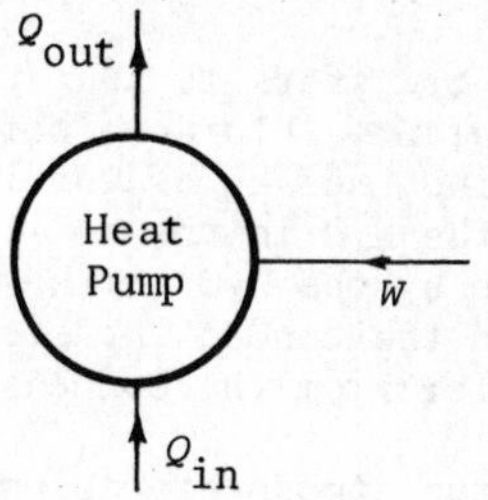

Figure 13.2

$$COP_{hp} = \frac{Q_{out}}{W}$$

or $\underline{Q_{out} = COP_{hp} \times W = 5 \times 400 = 2000 \text{ kW}}$

Thus $\underline{Q_{in} = Q_{out} - W = 2000 - 400 = 1600 \text{ kW}}$ (first law)

3. In a reversed heat engine, the work done on the engine is 75 kJ and the heat transfer to the engine from the low temperature region is 220 kJ. Evaluate the heat transfer to the high temperature region and the coefficient of performance as a refrigerator and as a heat pump.

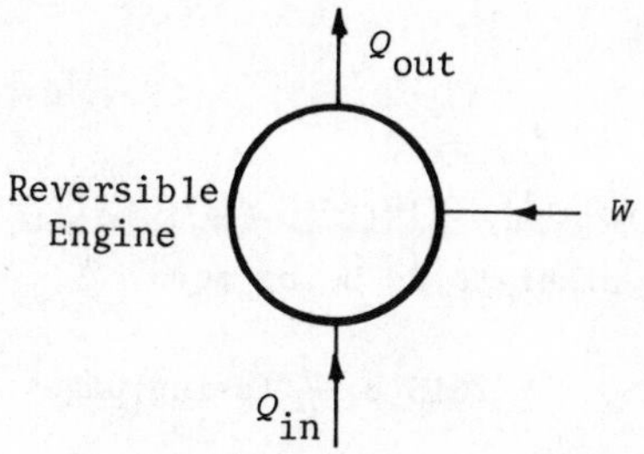

Figure 13.3

$$\underline{Q_{out} = Q_{in} + W = 220 + 75 = 295 \text{ kJ}}$$

$$\underline{COP_{ref} = \frac{Q_{in}}{W} = \frac{220}{75} = 2.93}$$

$$\underline{COP_{hp} = \frac{295}{75} = 3.93}$$

4. A steam power plant, incorporating a reciprocating steam engine gave the following results during a test under steady conditions:

Boiler:	Steam outlet conditions - 7 bar, 200 °C
	Feed water - temperature 55 °C, mass flow 1.6 kg per min
Engine:	Shaft power - 6.75 kW
	Steam inlet conditions - as boiler output
Condenser:	Cooling water - flow rate 46 kg/min, temperature rise 19 K

There are unmeasured heat transfers to the atmosphere from the exposed hot surfaces of the plant. Fluid velocities may be assumed to be negligible. Determine, per kg of working fluid (H_2O)

(a) the heat transfer to the H_2O in the boiler,

(b) the external work done by the H_2O in the engine,

(c) the heat transfer from the condensing steam in the condenser, assuming the heat transfer from the condenser casing to the atmosphere to be zero,

(d) the heat transfer to the atmosphere assuming the feed pump work to be zero,

(e) the efficiency of the plant.

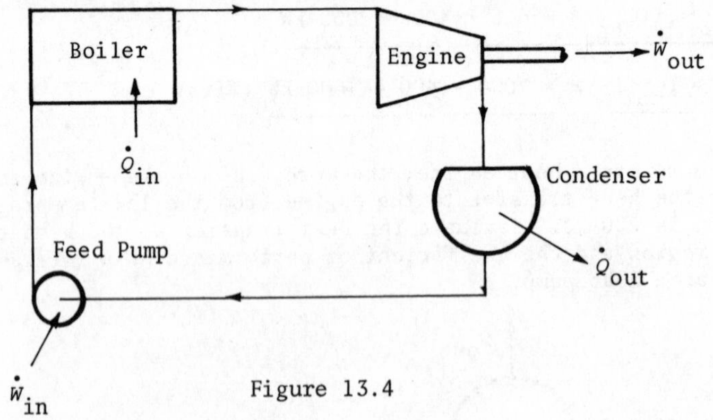

Figure 13.4

Energy equation applied to the boiler

$\dot{Q}_{in} = \dot{m}(h_1 - h_4)$ all other terms being zero

$$\frac{\dot{Q}}{\dot{m}} = h_1 - h_4 = 2846 - 230.2 = 2615.8 \ \frac{\text{kJ}}{\text{kg}} \quad \text{(using pages 7 and 2)}$$

$$\frac{\dot{W}}{\dot{m}} = \frac{6.75 \text{ kW}}{1.6 \ \frac{\text{kg}}{\text{min}}} \left[\frac{\text{kJ}}{\text{kW s}}\right]\left[\frac{60 \text{ s}}{\text{min}}\right] = 253 \ \frac{\text{kJ}}{\text{kg}}$$

$$\frac{\dot{Q}_{out}}{\dot{m}} = \frac{46 \ \frac{\text{kg}}{\text{min}} \times 4.18 \ \frac{\text{kJ}}{\text{kg K}} \times 19 \text{ K}}{1.6 \ \frac{\text{kg}}{\text{min}}} = 2283 \ \frac{\text{kJ}}{\text{kg}}$$

Energy equation for the whole plant

$$\dot{Q}_{in} + \dot{W}_{in} = \dot{Q}_{out} + \dot{W}_{out} + \dot{Q}_{transfer}$$

or $\quad \dot{Q}_{transfer} = \dot{Q}_{in} - \dot{Q}_{out} - \dot{W}_{out} \quad (\text{since } \dot{W}_{in} = 0)$

$$\frac{\dot{Q}_{transfer}}{\dot{m}} = 2615.8 - 2283 - 253 = 79.8 \ \frac{\text{kJ}}{\text{kg}}$$

$$\text{Efficiency } \eta = \frac{\dot{W}_{out}}{\dot{Q}} = \frac{253}{2615.8} \times 100 = 9.67\%$$

5. A heat engine is used to drive a heat pump. The heat transfers from the heat engine and from the heat pump are used to heat the water circulating through the radiators of a building. The efficiency of the heat engine is 27% and the coefficient of performance of the heat pump is 4. Evaluate the ratio of the heat transfer to the circulating water to the heat transfer to the heat engine.

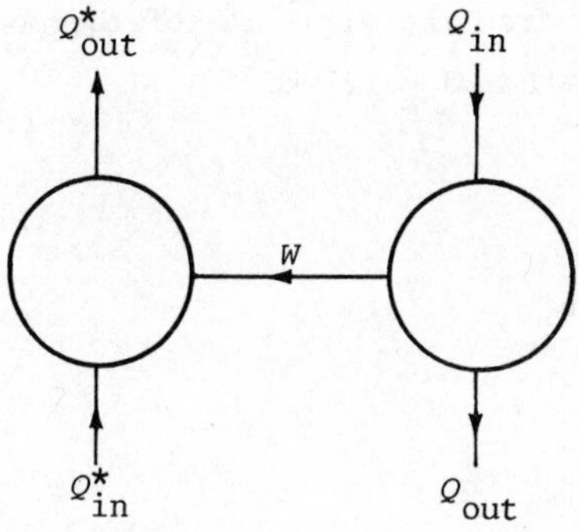

Figure 13.5

Referring to figure 13.5

$$W = 0.27Q_{in}$$

$$Q^*_{out} = 4W = 4 \times 0.27Q_{in} = 1.08Q_{in}$$

$$Q_{in} = Q_{out} + W$$

or $\quad Q_{out} = Q_{in} - W = 0.73Q_{in}$

Thus $\quad Q^*_{out} + Q_{out} = 1.08Q_{in} + 0.73Q_{in}$

or $\quad \dfrac{Q^*_{out} + Q_{out}}{Q_{in}} = 1.08 + 0.73 = 1.81$

6. (a) A reversible heat engine operating between hot and cold reservoirs delivers a work output of 57 kJ. The heat transfer from the engine is 70 kJ. Evaluate the efficiency of the engine.

(b) The engine in (a) is reversed and operates as a heat pump between the same reservoirs. Evaluate

(i) the coefficient of performance of the heat pump,

(ii) the power input to the pump when the heat transfer to the hot reservoir is 8 kW.

(c) If the reversed engine in (b) were considered to be a refrigerator, what would be its coefficient of performance?

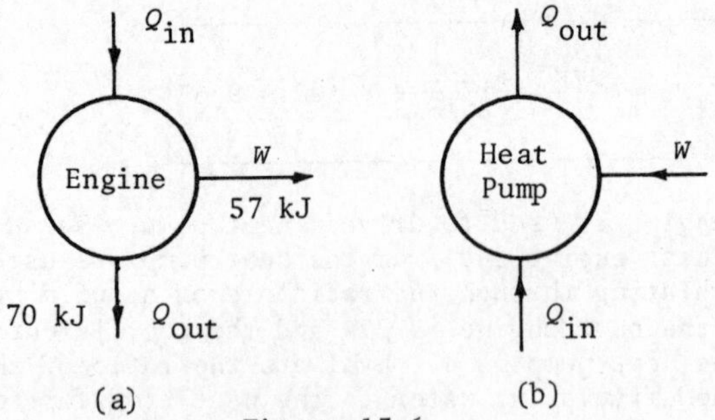

Figure 13.6

Referring to figure 13.6a from the first law of thermodynamics

$$Q_{in} = Q_{out} + W = 70 \text{ kJ} + 57 \text{ kJ} = 127 \text{ kJ}$$

Thus $\eta = \dfrac{W}{Q_{in}} = \dfrac{57}{127} = 44.9\%$

Referring now to figure 13.6b

$$\text{COP}_{hp} = \frac{Q_{out}}{W} = \frac{127}{57} = 2.23$$

$$W = \frac{Q_{out}}{W} = \frac{8 \text{ kW}}{2.23} = 3.59 \text{ kW}$$

(c) $\text{COP}_{ref} = \text{COP}_{hp} - 1 = 1.23$

7. An inventor claims to have designed a device which will produce shaft work continuously at a steady rate when it is supplied with a steady stream of steam. The device consists of a well-insulated box, through the side of which projects a shaft; an essential requirement, it is stated, is that the insulation be such that it reduces the heat transfer from the device to the surroundings to negligible proportions. Steam flows steadily into the box at one point and flows steadily out at another. The only fact divulged by the inventor is that the steam merely condenses in a coiled tube inside the box. The claim is that when saturated steam at 1.4 bar is supplied steadily at the rate of 3.5 kg/min it will leave at 1 bar with a dryness of 0.98 while the shaft power developed will be 3.5 kW.

Examine the feasibility of these claims with reference to the first and second laws of thermodynamics.

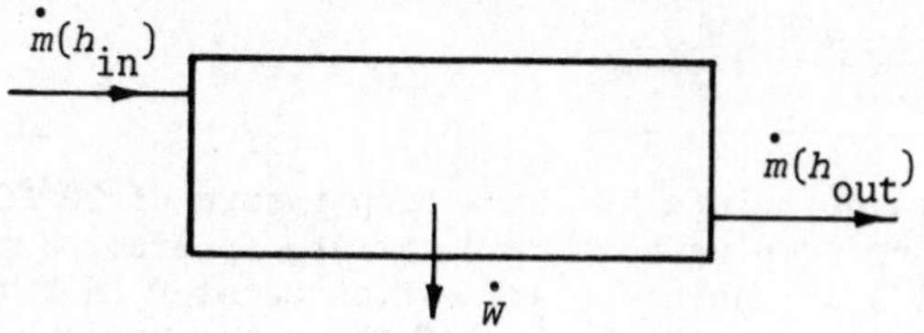

Figure 13.7

Heat from condensing steam = $\dot{m}(h_{in} - h_{out})$

$= 3.5 \dfrac{\text{kg}}{\text{min}}(2690 - 2629.84) \dfrac{\text{kJ}}{\text{kg}} \dfrac{[\text{min}\ ]}{[60\ \text{s}]}$

$= 3.5\ \text{kW} = \dot{W}$ (as given above)

It is possible for all heat supplied to be converted to work according to the first law but quite impossible according to the second law. The claim should therefore be rejected.

8. (a) A reversible heat engine operates between reservoirs at temperatures of 150 °C and 10 °C. Evaluate the efficiency of the engine.

(b) The work output from the engine is 2.7 kJ. Evaluate the heat transfer from the 150 °C reservoir and the heat transfer to the 10 °C reservoir.

(c) the engine in (a) is reversed and operates as a heat pump between the same reservoirs. Evaluate the coefficient of performance of the heat pump and the power input required when the heat transfer rate from the 10 °C reservoir is 4.5 kW.

(a) $\eta_{rev} = 1 - \dfrac{T_2}{T_1} = 1 - \dfrac{283}{423} = 0.331$ or 33.1%

(b) $Q_{in} = \dfrac{W}{\eta} = \dfrac{2.7\ \text{kJ}}{0.331} = 8.15\ \text{kJ}$

$Q_{out} = Q_{in} - W = 8.15 - 2.7 = 5.45\ \text{kJ}$

(c) $\text{COP}_{hp} = \dfrac{T_1}{T_1 - T_2} = \dfrac{423}{423 - 283} = 3.02 = \dfrac{Q_{out}}{W}$

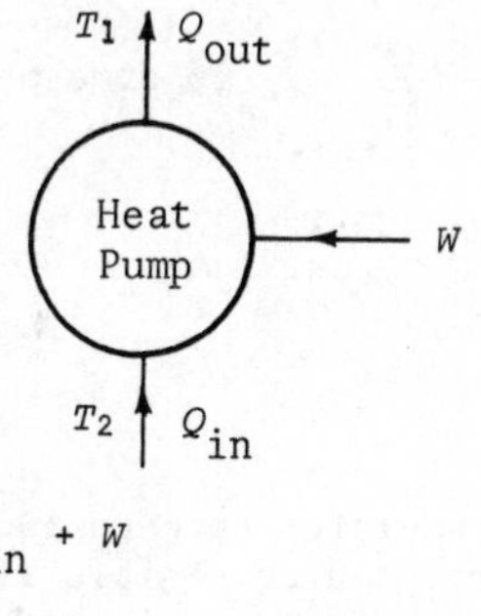

Figure 13.8c

$Q_{out} = Q_{in} + W$

$3.02W = Q_{in} + W$

$2.02W = Q_{in}$

$$W = \frac{Q_{in}}{2.02} = \frac{4.5 \text{ kW}}{2.02} = 2.23 \text{ kW}$$

9. A house is to be maintained at a temperature of 20 °C by means of a heat pump pumping heat from the atmosphere. Heat losses through the walls of the house are estimated at 0.65 kW/K temperature difference between the inside of the house and the atmosphere.

(a) If the atmospheric temperature is -10 °C what is the minimum power required to drive the pump?

(b) It is proposed to use the same heat pump to cool the house in summer. For the same room temperature, the same heat loss rate, and the same power input to the pump, what is the maximum permissible atmospheric temperature?

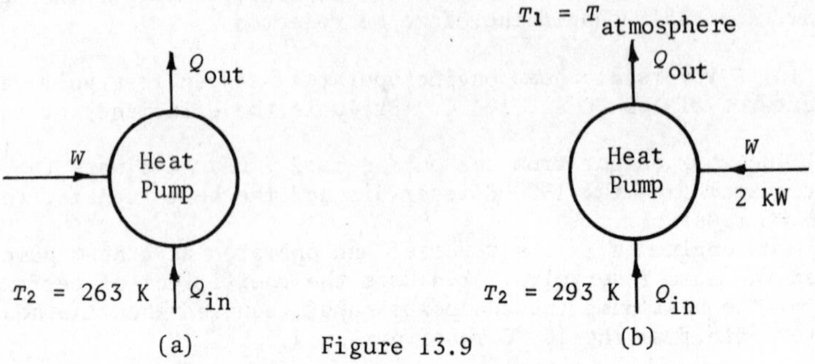

Figure 13.9

(a) $$Q_{out} = 0.65\left[20 - (-10)\right] \frac{\text{kW}}{\text{K}} \text{ K} = 19.5 \text{ kW}$$

$$\text{Maximum COP} = \frac{T_1}{T_1 - T_2} = \frac{293}{30} = 9.77$$

$$\text{Minimum power required} = \frac{Q_{out}}{\text{COP}} = \frac{19.5 \text{ kW}}{9.77} = 2 \text{ kW}$$

(b) For a reversible heat pump (or refrigerator)

$$\frac{W}{T_1 - T_2} = \frac{Q_{in}}{T_2} = \frac{Q_{out}}{T_1}$$

Thus $$\frac{2 \text{ kW}}{T_a - 293 \text{ K}} = \frac{0.65(T_a - 293 \text{ K})}{293 \text{ K}}\frac{\text{kW}}{\text{K}}$$ (T_a is atmospheric temperature)

$$(T_a - 293 \text{ K})^2 = \frac{293 \times 2 \text{ K}^2}{0.65} = 900 \text{ K}^2$$

$$T_a - 293 \text{ K} = \pm 30 \text{ K}$$

$$T_a = 323 \text{ K} = 50 \text{ °C}$$

10. A reversible heat engine operates between two reservoirs at 600 °C and 40 °C. The engine drives a reversible refrigerator which operates between the same 40 °C reservoir and a reservoir at -18 °C. The heat transfer to the heat engine is 2100 kJ and there is a net work output from the combined plant of 370 kJ.

(a) Evaluate the heat transfer to the refrigerant and the net heat transfer to the 40 °C reservoir.

(b) Repeat (a) if the efficiency of the heat engine and the coefficient of performance of the refrigerator are each 40% of the respective maximum possible values.

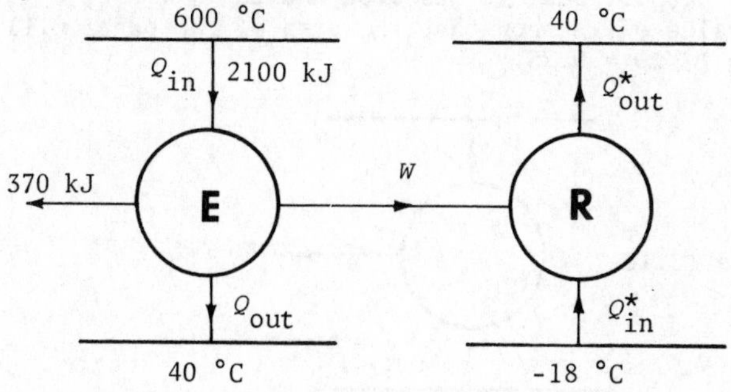

Figure 13.10

(a) $\eta = 1 - \frac{40 + 273}{600 + 273} = 0.642$

$370 \text{ kJ} + W = 0.642 \times 2100 = 1347 \text{ kJ}$

$W = 977 \text{ kJ}$

$Q_{out} = 2100 - 1347 = 753 \text{ kJ}$

$\frac{Q^*_{in}}{273 - 18} = \frac{W}{40 - (-18)} = \frac{W}{58}$

$Q^*_{in} = \frac{977 \times 255}{58} \text{ kJ} = 4295 \text{ kJ}$

$Q^*_{out} = Q^*_{in} + W = 4295 + 977 = 5272 \text{ kJ}$

$Q^*_{out} + Q_{out} = 5272 + 753 = 6025 \text{ kJ}$

(b) $\eta_{Carnot} = 0.642$

Thus $\eta_{actual} = 0.4 \times 0.642 = 0.257$

$370 \text{ kJ} + W = 0.257 \times 2100 \text{ kJ} = 539 \text{ kJ}$

$W = 169 \text{ kJ}$

$COP_{Carnot} = \frac{273 - 18}{58} = 4.4$

$COP_{actual} = 0.4 \times 4.4 = \frac{Q^*_{in}}{W}$

$Q^*_{in} = 0.4 \times 4.4 \times 169 = 297 \text{ kJ}$

$Q_{out} = 2100 - 539 = 1561 \text{ kJ}$

$Q^*_{out} = 297 + 169 = 466 \text{ kJ}$

$$Q^*_{out} + Q_{out} = 466 + 1561 = 2027 \text{ kJ}$$

11. A reversible heat engine in a satellite operates between a hot reservoir at T_H and a radiating panel at T_1. Radiation from the panel is proportional to its area and to T_1^4. For a given work output and value of T_H show that the area of the panel will be a minimum when $T_1/T_H = 0.75$.

Figure 13.11

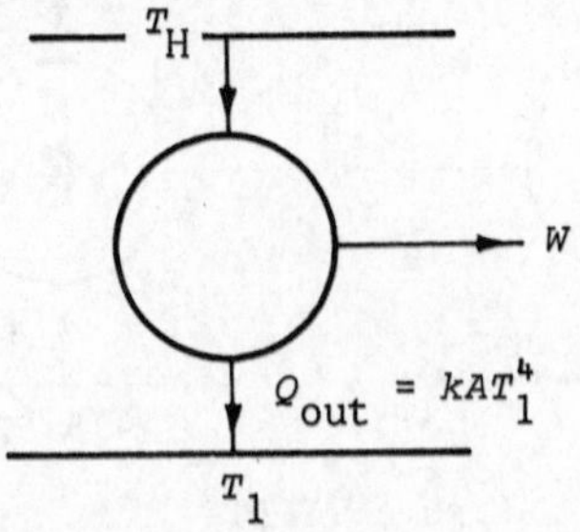

$$\frac{KAT_1^4}{T_1} = \frac{W}{T_H - T_1}$$

or $A = \dfrac{W}{KT_1^3(T_H - T_1)}$ and is a minimum when $T_1^3(T_H - T_1)$ is a maximum

$$\frac{d\left(T_1^3 T_H - T_1^4\right)}{d(T_1)} = 0$$

or $3T_1^2 T_H - 4T_1^3 = 0$ giving

$$\frac{T_1}{T_H} = \frac{3}{4}$$

also $\dfrac{d^2\left(T_1^3 T_H - T_1^4\right)}{d(T_1)^2} = 6T_1 T_H - 12T_1^2$ and substituting $\dfrac{T_1}{T_H} = \dfrac{3}{4}$

$$6T_1 T_H - 12T_1^2 = 6T_H(0.75T_H) - 12(0.75T_H)^2 = -2.25T_H^2 \text{ (maximum)}$$

Further Examples

12. By applying the second law of thermodynamics show that the following processes are irreversible.
(a) Flow of electric current through a resistance.
(b) Flow of a river over a waterfall.
(c) Driving a nail with a hammer.

13. An inventor claims to have designed a heat engine which has an efficiency of 38% when using the exhaust gas from an engine at a temperature of 145 °C as the high temperature reservoir. Using the second law of thermodynamics what judgement would you give on this claim? (Maximum possible efficiency is 31.1%)

14. A heat engine operating between two reservoirs at 1000 K and 300 K is used to drive a heat pump which extracts heat from

the reservoir at 300 K at a rate twice that at which the engine rejects heat to it.

If the efficiency of the engine is 40% of the maximum possible and the coefficient of performance of the heat pump is 50% of the maximum possible what is the temperature of the reservoir to which the heat pump rejects heat?

What is the rate of heat rejection from the heat pump if the rate of supply of heat to the engine is 50 kJ/s? (326.6 K, 85.9 kJ)

14 ENTROPY

Entropy (a property of the fluid) follows from the second law in much the same way as internal energy follows from the first.

It is defined by

$$dS = \frac{\delta Q_{rev}}{T}$$

The subscript 'rev' is essential since the derivation of the property from fundamental reasoning using the second law makes full use of this concept of a reversible process. As further qualification of this statement we can write that

$\delta W_{rev} = p\,dV$ for reversible work transfer

and $\delta Q_{rev} = T\,dS$ for reversible heat transfer

By contrast δW and δQ are the infinitesimal work and heat transfers associated with a real process in which the fluid is turbulent. In the latter the value of any given property is not the same at all points in the fluid at any one time, which is essential to a reversible process and the mathematical arguments associated with it.

i.e. $\delta W \neq p\,dV$ and $\delta Q \neq T\,dS$

However, because entropy is a property, it is possible to find the change in its value in a real process provided the end states of the process are known, since the path between two known states is immaterial in calculating property changes. It is only in the calculation of work and heat transfers that the process path must be identified or other information made available.

The second law states that all real processes display an increase in entropy of the system and surroundings involved, that the net entropy change for these two taken together is zero in the hypothetical, reversible case and that the net entropy change can never be negative.

Entropy is a difficult concept to envisage because unlike other properties (e.g. pressure, volume etc.) it cannot be measured in a laboratory - there is no entropy meter.

However, without entropy there can be no real progress towards the calculation of property changes and heat and work transfers in real processes and it is this point that needs most emphasis.

Consider the adiabatic expansion of fluid in a turbine. The commonly available information would probably be

(a) the nature of the fluid,

(b) the initial state,

(c) the final pressure,

(d) some value based on experience for the efficiency of the process. The last compares the actual process with that obtaining under ideal, reversible conditions.

Generally a turbine is a high-speed device and the processes therein are assumed adiabatic. However, because of the high speed of flow the latter is necessarily turbulent and highly irreversible. Thus we might be given that

(a) the fluid is steam,
(b) the initial state is p_1 and T_1,
(c) the final pressure is p_2,
(d) the process efficiency is η.

The efficiency will be defined as

$$\eta = \frac{{}_1w_2}{{}_1w_{2\,\mathrm{rev}}}$$

since the work output of the reversible process will be the greatest obtainable. From the steady-flow energy equation neglecting changes in potential and kinetic energy and taking the heat transfer to be zero

$${}_1w_2 = h_1 - h_2$$

and $${}_1w_{2\,\mathrm{rev}} = h_1 - h_{2\,\mathrm{rev}}$$

where $h_{2\,\mathrm{rev}}$ refers to the specific enthalpy after a reversible expansion.

The whole point about this argument is that without a knowledge of entropy the latter value of specific enthalpy cannot be obtained.

The qualification of the word 'adiabatic' by the word 'reversible' is both essential to this argument and to any calculation which is intended to lead ultimately to the assessment of the performance of real plant.

Thus we need a picture of real and perfect processes for the purposes of comparison and the temperature-specific entropy field is the obvious one to begin with.

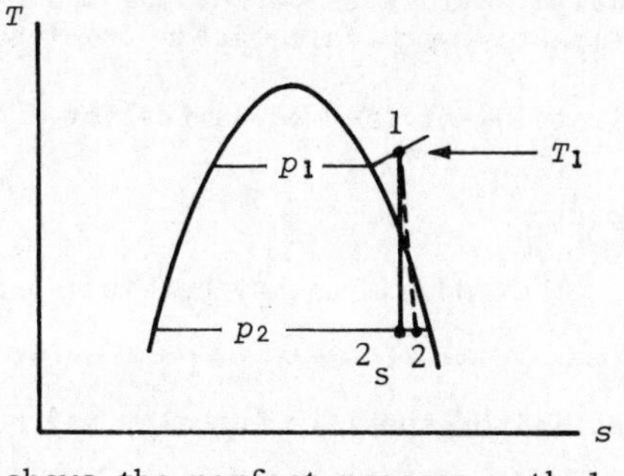

Figure 14a

The figure shows the perfect process path 1-2_s where subscript s implies reversible adiabatic ($\delta q_{\mathrm{rev}} = 0$) i.e. isentropic (since $ds = \delta q_{\mathrm{rev}}/T = 0$ because $T \neq 0$).

For this path therefore

$$s_1 = s_{2_s}$$

where the value of s_{2_s} together with the value of p_2 gives two independent properties to fix the state 2_s. By applying the first law of thermodynamics to this path

$$_1w_{2_s} = h_1 - h_{2_s}$$

The value of h_{2_s} is calculated from h_{f_2}, h_{g_2} and the value of x_{2_s} at point 2_s.

Note that because entropy is a property

$$\frac{s_{2_s} - s_{f_2}}{s_{g_2} - s_{f_2}} = x_{2_s} = \frac{h_{2_s} - h_{f_2}}{h_{g_2} - h_{f_2}}$$

Having determined h_{2_s} we can now apply the value of η and find

$$h_1 - h_2 = \eta(h_1 - h_{2_s})$$

for the irreversible real process 1-2 and the real work transfer. This is shown dotted on the temperature-specific entropy field since there are no known states between 1 and 2. Values of η are accumulated by experience in practice because they cannot be deduced by mathematical argument.

For example we know that a radial-flow compressor has a lower value of η between given pressure limits than its axial-flow counterpart. This is because the latter has blading designed aerodynamically (albeit more expensively) and the former is of simpler construction. They each have their particular applications.

It is the above use of entropy that makes it such an important property in the subject of thermodynamics. It is the last and most important barrier between the most elementary statements in the subject and real process calculations.

Once a student is fully aware of this last fact he will be prepared to wrestle with the problems set by virtue of its definition.

As mentioned at the beginning of chapter 4 we now need to demonstrate the way in which entropy is calculated and used and the first few examples deal directly with calculation from tables of properties.

Note that the first law of thermodynamics for a reversible process is given by

$$\delta q_{\text{rev}} = \mathrm{d}e + p\,\mathrm{d}v$$

The second law of thermodynamics may be expressed as

$$\delta q_{\text{rev}} = T\,\mathrm{d}s$$

Also the differential of specific enthalpy may be expressed as

$$\mathrm{d}h = \mathrm{d}e + p\,\mathrm{d}v + v\,\mathrm{d}p$$

From these three we get

$$\mathrm{d}s = \frac{\mathrm{d}e - p\,\mathrm{d}v}{T} = \frac{\mathrm{d}h - v\,\mathrm{d}p}{T} \text{ for all fluids}$$

1. Show that the listed values of h_{fg} and s_{fg} are consistent for

(a) H_2O at 40 bar,
(b) Ammonia at 0 °C,
(c) Freon-12 at -15 °C,
(d) Mercury at 22 bar.

Generally

$$ds = \frac{dh - v\,dp}{T}$$

and $$(ds)_p = \frac{dh}{T}_p$$

or $$\int_f^g ds = \int_f^g \frac{dh}{T} = \frac{1}{T_{sat}} \int_f^g dh$$

where T_{sat} is the constant saturation temperature.

Thus $$s_{fg} = \frac{h_{fg}}{T_{sat}}$$

(a) H_2O at 40 bar (T_{sat} = 250.3 °C = 523.3 K)

$$s_{fg} = \frac{1714 \frac{kJ}{kg}}{523.3\ K} = 3.275 \frac{kJ}{K\ kg}$$

(compare with the listed value of 3.273 kJ/(K kg)).
Note that the units quoted give the denominator with K first and kg second because entropy is defined firstly by

$$dS = \frac{\delta Q_{rev}}{T} \quad \text{dimensions } \frac{kJ}{K}$$

and $$ds = \frac{\delta Q_{rev}}{Tm} \quad \text{dimensions } \frac{kJ}{K\ kg}$$

Of course these dimensions are the same as for mass specific heat capacity but this minor distinction is, in my view, valuable.

(b) $$s_{fg} = \frac{h_{fg}}{T_{sat}} = \frac{h_g - h_f}{T_{sat}} = \frac{(1444.4 - 181.2) \frac{kJ}{kg}}{(0 + 273)\ K} = 4.627 \frac{kJ}{K\ kg}$$

where the values are taken from page 12 of tables and the listed value of s_{fg} is given by 5.340 - 0.715 = 4.625 kJ/(K kg).

(c) $$s_{fg} = \frac{h_{fg}}{T_{sat}} = \frac{h_g - h_f}{T_{sat}} = \frac{(180.97 - 22.33) \frac{kJ}{kg}}{(-15 + 273)\ K} = 0.6149 \frac{kJ}{K\ kg}$$

the listed value = 0.7051 - 0.0906 = 0.6145 kJ/(K kg), see page 13.

(d) $$s_{fg} = \frac{h_{fg}}{T_{sat}} = \frac{288.05 \frac{kJ}{kg}}{(595.1 + 273)\ K} = 0.3318 \frac{kJ}{K\ kg}$$

the listed value = 0.3318 kJ/(K kg), see page 14.

2. The information given at the foot of page 11 of tables gives the isentropic expansion of steam as being characterised by the following equations.

Wet expansion $pv^{1.135}$ = constant (approximately)

Superheated expansion $pv^{1.3}$ = constant (approximately)

Test the validity of this information by considering the isentropic expansion of steam from 15 bar, 250 °C to 0.4 bar.

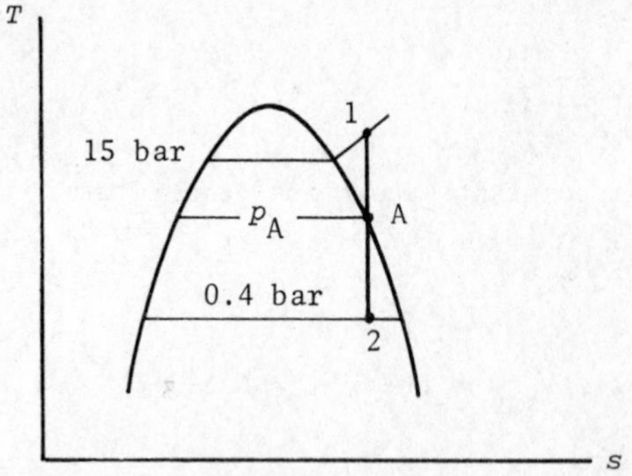

Figure 14.2

In the figure the expansion is superheated from 1 to A (on the saturated vapour line) and wet from A to 2.

To find p_A by trial and error

(a) Try p_A = 4 bar

$$v_A = v_1\left(\frac{p_1}{p_A}\right)^{1/n} = 0.152\ \frac{m^3}{kg}\left(\frac{15}{4}\right)^{1/1.3} = 0.420\ \frac{m^3}{kg} \quad \text{(page 7)}$$

But v_{gA} at 4 bar = $0.4623\ \frac{m^3}{kg}$

(b) Try p_A = 5 bar

$$v_A = 0.152\left(\frac{15}{5}\right)^{1/1.3} = 0.3537\ \frac{m^3}{kg} \quad \left(\text{listed } v_{gA} = 0.3748\ \frac{m^3}{kg}\right)$$

(c) Try p_A = 6 bar

$$v_A = 0.152\left(\frac{15}{6}\right)^{1/1.3} = 0.3075\ \frac{m^3}{kg} \quad \left(\text{listed } v_{gA} = 0.3156\ \frac{m^3}{kg}\right)$$

(d) Try p_A = 7 bar

$$v_A = 0.152\left(\frac{15}{7}\right)^{1/1.3} = 0.2730\ \frac{m^3}{kg} \quad \left(\text{listed value} = 0.2728\ \frac{m^3}{kg}\right)$$

Thus $p_A \simeq 7$ bar since the vapour is just saturated here.

Note that at this point $s_{gA} = 6.709\ \frac{kJ}{K\ kg}$

Note also that $s_1 = 6.711\ \frac{kJ}{K\ kg}$ from page 7

Thus points A and 1 lie on a line of constant entropy.

$$\text{Now} \quad v_2 = v_A\left(\frac{p_A}{p_2}\right)^{1/n} = 0.273\ \frac{\text{m}^3}{\text{kg}}\left(\frac{7}{0.4}\right)^{1/1.135} = 3.398\ \frac{\text{m}^3}{\text{kg}}$$

$$\text{and} \quad x_2 = \frac{v_2}{v_{g_2}} \quad (\text{ignoring } v_{f_2})$$

$$\text{or} \quad x_2 = \frac{3.398}{3.992} = 0.852$$

$$\text{Thus } s_2 = s_{f_2} + x_2 s_{fg_2} = 1.026 + 0.852(6.643) = 6.681\ \frac{\text{kJ}}{\text{K kg}} \quad (\text{page } 4)$$

Thus point 2 lies approximately on the same isentrope as 1 and A.

3. CO_2 (gas) expands isentropically from 6 bar, 300°C to 1 bar. Calculate the final temperature given that the average value of c_p is 1.00 kJ/(kg K).

$$s_2 - s_1 = \int_1^2\left(\frac{dh - v\,dp}{T}\right) = \int_1^2 \frac{dh}{T} - \int_1^2 \frac{v\,dp}{T} \quad \text{where } T \text{ is variable}$$

$$= \int_1^2 \frac{c_p\,dT}{T} - \int_1^2 \frac{R\,dp}{p}$$

and for a perfect gas with constant values of c_p and R

$$s_2 - s_1 = c_p \ln\frac{T_2}{T_1} - R\ln\frac{p_2}{p_1}$$

$$\text{or} \quad 0 = c_p \ln\frac{T_2}{T_1} - \frac{R}{m_w}\ln\frac{p_2}{p_1}$$

$$\text{or} \quad \ln\frac{T_2}{T_1} = \frac{R_0}{m_w c_p}\ln\frac{p_2}{p_1} = \frac{8.3143\ \frac{\text{kJ}}{\text{kg-mol K}}}{44\ \frac{\text{kg}}{\text{kg-mol}} \times 1.0\ \frac{\text{kJ}}{\text{kg K}}}\ln\frac{1}{6} = -0.3386$$

$$\text{thus} \quad \frac{T_2}{T_1} = \text{antilog}\ (-0.3386) = 0.7128$$

$$\text{and} \quad T_2 = 0.7128 \times (300 + 273)\ \text{K} = 479.7\ \text{K}\ (206.7\ ^\circ\text{C})$$

4. A mass of one kilogram of air undergoes a reversible, adiabatic expansion in a cylinder from an initial temperature of 300 °C. The ratio of the final volume of the air to the initial volume is 4. Determine the final temperature of the air and the ratio of the initial pressure to the final pressure.

For the reversible adiabatic expansion of a perfect gas

$$p_1 v_1^{\gamma} = p_2 v_2^{\gamma}$$

For the equation of state of a perfect gas we may write

$$\frac{p_1 v_1}{T_1} = \frac{p_2 v_2}{T_2} = R$$

From these two equations

$$\frac{T_2}{T_1} = \left(\frac{p_2}{p_1}\right)^k = \left(\frac{v_1}{v_2}\right)^{\gamma-1}$$

Thus $T_2 = T_1\left(\frac{v_2}{v_1}\right)^{\gamma-1} = 573 \text{ K} \times \left(\frac{1}{4}\right)^{0.4} = 329.1 \text{ K } (56\ ^\circ\text{C})$

and $\frac{p_1}{p_2} = \left(\frac{v_2}{v_1}\right)^{\gamma} = 4^{1.4} = 6.964$

5. Steam expands in a turbine from a pressure of 20 bar and a temperature of 300 °C to a pressure of 0.05 bar. If the expansion is isentropic determine the dryness fraction of the steam at exit from the turbine and the power output for a steam mass flow of 5 kg/s.

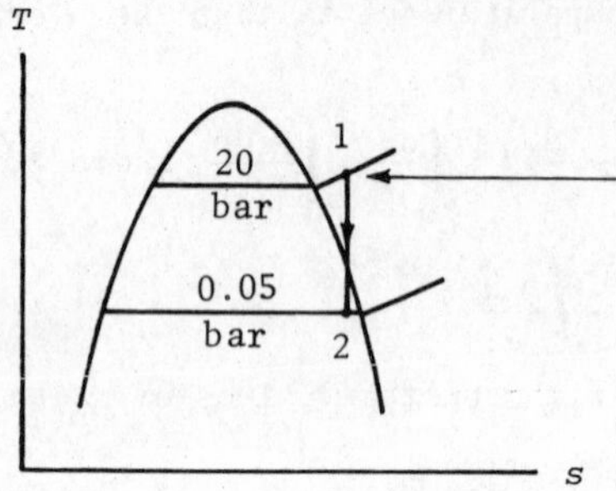

Figure 14.5

From tables page 7

$$s_1 = s_2 = 6.768 \frac{\text{kJ}}{\text{K kg}}; \quad h_1 = 3025 \frac{\text{kJ}}{\text{kg}}$$

Interpolating from page 3 of tables

$$x_2 = \frac{s_2 - s_{f_2}}{s_{fg_2}} = \frac{6.768 - 0.476}{7.918} = 0.795$$

Also $h_2 = h_{f_2} + x_2 h_{fg_2} = 138 + 0.795(2423) = 2064.3 \frac{\text{kJ}}{\text{kg}}$

and from the steady-flow energy equation

$${}_1w_2 = h_1 - h_2 \quad \text{(all other terms being negligible)}$$

Thus power output is given by

$${}_1\dot{W}_2 = \dot{m}_1 w_2 = \dot{m}(h_1 - h_2) = 5 \frac{\text{kg}}{\text{s}} (3025 - 2064.3) \frac{\text{kJ}}{\text{kg}} \left[\frac{\text{MW}}{10^3 \text{ kW}}\right]$$

$${}_1\dot{W}_2 = 4.803 \text{ MW}$$

6. Air compressed adiabatically in steady flow by a rotary compressor. The initial and final temperatures are 20 °C and 200 °C respectively and the pressure ratio is 4.2. Calculate the temperature after compression if the air is compressed isentropically through the same pressure ratio and from the same initial temperature.

Hence determine the ratio of work done in isentropic compression to that done in actual compression (known as the isentropic efficiency or process efficiency of the compressor).

Determine also the specific entropy change during the process and show the process on a temperature-specific entropy diagram.

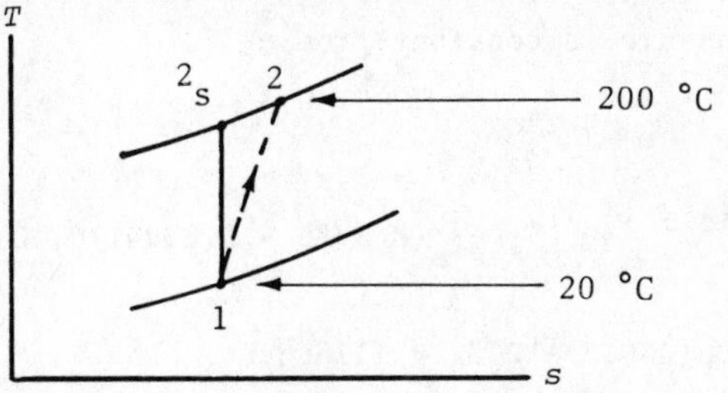

Figure 14.6

$$\frac{T_{2_s}}{T_1} = \left(\frac{p_2}{p_1}\right)^k = 4.2^{0.286} = 1.507$$

$$T_{2_s} = 1.507 \times (273 + 20)\ \text{K} = 441.6\ \text{K}\ (168.6\ °\text{C})$$

$$\frac{w_s}{w_{actual}} = \frac{h_{2_s} - h_1}{h_2 - h_1} \quad \text{from the energy equation}$$

$$= \frac{c_p(T_{2_s} - T_1)}{c_p(T_2 - T_1)} = \frac{441.6 - 293}{473 - 293} = 0.826$$

$$s_2 - s_1 = c_p \ln\frac{T_2}{T_1} - R\ln\frac{p_2}{p_1}$$

$$= 1.005\ \frac{\text{kJ}}{\text{kg K}} \ln\frac{473}{293} - 0.287\ \frac{\text{kJ}}{\text{kg K}} \ln 4.2$$

$$s_2 - s_1 = (0.4813 - 0.4119) = 0.0694\ \frac{\text{kJ}}{\text{K kg}}$$

7. Saturated mercury vapour enters a compressor at a pressure of 1.0 bar and is compressed isentropically to a pressure of 5.0 bar. Determine the work done in kJ/kg of mercury compressed.

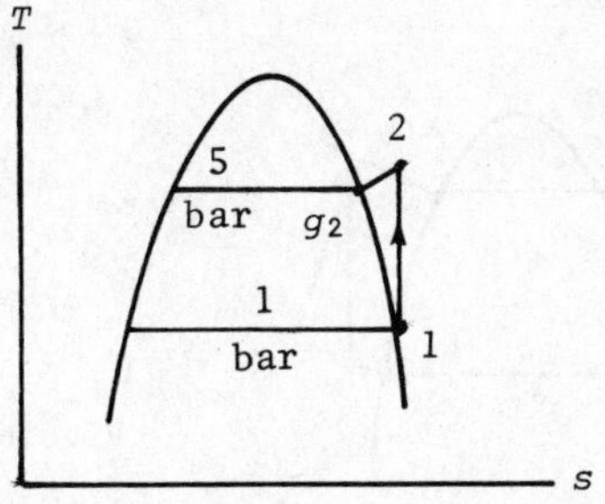

Figure 14.7

From tables page 14

$$h_1 = h_{g_1} = 341 \frac{\text{kJ}}{\text{kg}};\ s_1 = s_{g_1} = 0.5785 \frac{\text{kJ}}{\text{K kg}} = s_2$$

Thus point 2 is superheated ($s_{g_2} < s_2$)

Now the pressure is constant from g_2 to 2.

Thus $s_2 - s_{g_2} = c_p \ln \frac{T_2}{T_{g_2}}$

or $\frac{T_2}{T_{g_2}} = e^{(s_2 - s_{g_2})/c_p} = e^{(0.5785 - 0.5294)/0.1036} = 1.606$

$$T_2 = 1.606(460.7 + 273) = 1178.3 \text{ K}$$

Also $h_2 - h_{g_2} = c_p(T_2 - T_{g_2}) = 0.1036 \frac{\text{kJ}}{\text{kg K}} (1178.3 - 733.7) \text{ K}$

$$= 46.06 \frac{\text{kJ}}{\text{kg}}$$

$$h_2 = 46.06 + 352.78 = 398.8 \frac{\text{kJ}}{\text{kg}}$$

and from the steady flow energy equation

$${}_1w_2 = \frac{{}_1W_2}{m} = h_2 - h_1 \quad \text{(all other terms zero)}$$

$$= 398.8 - 34.1 = 57.8 \frac{\text{kJ}}{\text{kg}}$$

---

8. Steam at 200 bar and 600 °C is expanded adiabatically in the first stage nozzles of a turbine to a pressure of 30 bar. If the ratio

$$\frac{\text{actual increase of kinetic energy}}{\text{kinetic energy increase after isentropic expansion through the same pressure ratio and from the same initial conditions}}$$

known as the isentropic efficiency of the nozzle is equal to 0.87, determine the state of the steam and its velocity at exit from the nozzles. Assume the steam approaching the nozzles to have negligible velocity and show the process on a temperature-specific entropy diagram.

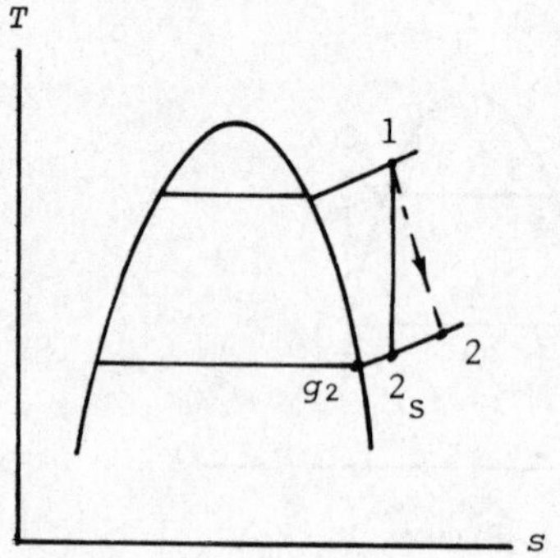

Figure 14.8

From tables page 8

$$h_1 = 3537 \frac{\text{kJ}}{\text{kg}}; \; s_1 = 6.505 \frac{\text{kJ}}{\text{K kg}} = s_{2_s}$$

Thus point 2 is superheated since $s_{g_2} = 6.186 \frac{\text{kJ}}{\text{K kg}}$

From tables page 7 at 30 bar

$$h_{2_s} = 2858 + \frac{(6.505 - 6.289)}{(6.541 - 6.289)}(2995 - 2858) = 2975.4 \frac{\text{kJ}}{\text{kg}}$$

Steady flow energy equation

$$_1\dot{Q}_2 - {_1\dot{W}_2} + \dot{m}\left[\left(h_1 + \frac{u_1^2}{2} + gz_1\right) - \left(h_2 + \frac{u_2^2}{2} + gz_2\right)\right] = 0$$

or $\frac{u_2^2}{2} = h_1 - h_2$ (all other terms cancelling or zero)

$$\frac{u_{2_s}^2}{2} = h_1 - h_{2_s}$$

$$\eta_{\text{nozzle}} = \frac{u_2^2 - u_1^2}{u_{2_s}^2 - u_1^2} = \frac{h_1 - h_2}{h_1 - h_{2_s}}$$

Thus $h_1 - h_2 = \eta(h_1 - h_{2_s}) = 0.87(3537 - 2975.4) \frac{\text{kJ}}{\text{kg}} = 488.6 \frac{\text{kJ}}{\text{kg}}$

and $h_2 = 3537 - 488.6 = 3084.4 \frac{\text{kJ}}{\text{kg}}$

Thus $T_2 = 300\ ^\circ\text{C} + \frac{3048.4 - 2995}{3117 - 2995}(50\ \text{K}) = 321.9\ ^\circ\text{C}$

and $u_2 = \sqrt{2 \times 488.6 \frac{\text{kJ}}{\text{kg}} \frac{[10^3\ \text{Nm}]}{[\ \text{kJ}\ ]} \frac{[\text{kg m}]}{[\text{N s}^2]}} = 988.5 \frac{\text{m}}{\text{s}}$

9. A rigid vessel is in the form of a cylinder, closed at both ends and containing two leak-proof pistons. Initially the pistons are fixed in position by catches, the region between them is evacuated, one of the end regions contains substance A and the other contains substance B. The catches are then released, heat and work transfers between the two substances A and B (hitherto prevented by the evacuated space and the catches respectively) become possible. Finally equilibrium is attained.

The two relevant states for each of the substances are given in the table below, the order in which is without significance.

Neglecting all heat transfer save that between substance A and substance B, and assuming that the vessel and pistons undergo negligible changes in their internal energies and entropies

(a) find which lines in the table relate to the final states,

(b) calculate the ratio of the mass of substance A to that of substance B.

Line	Substance	Specific entropy (kJ/K kg)	Specific internal energy (kJ/kg)
1	A	1.7624	1079.2
2	A	1.5281	1150.0
3	B	0.1669	87.0
4	B	0.2361	100.0

(London University)

Before　　After

Figure 14.9

First law of thermodynamics

Since the external heat and work transfers are both zero

final internal energy = initial internal energy

$$E_{A_1} + E_{B_1} = E_{A_2} + E_{B_2}$$

or $\quad m_A(e_{A_1} - e_{A_2}) = m_B(e_{B_2} - e_{B_1})$

or $\quad \dfrac{m_A}{m_B} = \dfrac{e_{B_2} - e_{B_1}}{e_{A_1} - e_{A_2}}$

Suppose *pro tem*.

$$e_{B_2} = 100 \ \frac{\text{kJ}}{\text{kg}} \text{ (line 4); and}$$

$$e_{A_2} = 1079.2 \ \frac{\text{kJ}}{\text{kg}} \text{ (line 1)}$$

This will give

$$e_{B_1} = 87.0 \ \frac{\text{kJ}}{\text{kg}}; \ e_{A_1} = 1150.0 \ \frac{\text{kJ}}{\text{kg}}$$

or $\quad \dfrac{m_A}{m_B} = \dfrac{100 - 87}{1150 - 1079.2} = 0.184 \text{ (b)}$

Note the same result follows from the alternative choice of *e* values.

Second law of thermodynamics

With the same selection of initial and final states as above

$$\Delta S_A = m_A(s_{A_2} - s_{A_1}) = m_A(1.7624 - 1.5281) = +0.2343 \ m_A$$

$$\Delta S_B = m_B(s_{B_2} - s_{B_1}) = \frac{m_A}{0.184}(0.2361 - 0.1609) = +0.4087 \ m_A$$

Thus the net entropy change for the whole system is positive, which is acceptable according to the second law of thermodynamics.

Note that the alternative selection of states, although acceptable by the first law would yield a net entropy change for the

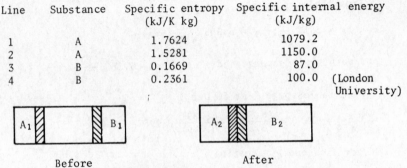

system which is negative, which would be impossible according to the second law.

10. A rigid cylinder enclosing a volume of 0.1 m³ is divided into two compartments by a freely sliding non-conducting piston of negligible thickness. Initially one half of the cylinder is filled with steam at 7 bar, 0.9 dry and the other half of the cylinder is filled with steam at 7 bar, 500 °C. No energy transfers as heat to or from the steam which was initially wet while the steam which was initially superheated is cooled slowly until its pressure is 3.5 bar.

Find the final dryness of the steam in each compartment.

Figure 14.10

Let A_1, A_2 refer to the initial and final states of the initally WET steam

B_1, B_2 refer to the initial and final states of the initially SUPERHEATED steam

$$m_A = \frac{V_{A_1}}{v_{A_1}} = \frac{V_{A_1}}{x_1 v_{g_{A_1}}} = \frac{0.05\ \text{m}^3}{0.9 \times 0.2728\ \frac{\text{m}^3}{\text{kg}}} = 0.2036\ \text{kg (page 4)}$$

$$m_B = \frac{V_{B_1}}{v_{B_1}} = \frac{0.05\ \text{m}^3}{0.5069\ \frac{\text{m}^3}{\text{kg}}} = 0.0986\ \text{kg (page 7)}$$

The left-hand side undergoes an adiabatic process without friction i.e. a reversible adiabatic or isentropic process.

Thus $s_{A_1} = s_{A_2}$ (since m_A is fixed)

or $s_{f_{A_1}} + x_{A_1} s_{fg_{A_1}} = s_{f_{A_2}} + x_{A_2} s_{fg_{A_2}}$

or $1.992 + 0.9(4.717) = 1.727 + x_{A_2}(5.214)$ (from page 4)

thus $x_{A_2} = \frac{1.992 + 0.9(4.717) - 1.727}{5.214} = 0.865$

Now $v_{A_2} = x_{A_2} v_{g_{A_2}} = 0.865 \times 0.5241 = 0.453\ \frac{\text{m}^3}{\text{kg}}$ (page 4)

and $V_{A_2} = m_A v_{A_2} = 0.204 \times 0.453 = 0.0925\ \text{m}^3$

thus $V_{B_2} = 0.1 - 0.0925 = 0.0075\ \text{m}^3$

Also $p_{B_2} = p_{A_2} = 3.5$ bar

Thus $x_{B_2} = \frac{v_{B_2}}{v_{g_{B_2}}} = \frac{V_{B_2}}{m_B v_{g_{B_2}}} = \frac{0.0075\ \text{m}^3}{0.0986\ \text{kg} \times 0.5241\ \frac{\text{m}^3}{\text{kg}}} = 0.145$

11. Show that when a perfect gas undergoes a process, the change in specific entropy is

$$s_2 - s_1 = c_p \ln \frac{T_2}{T_1} - R \ln \frac{p_2}{p_1}$$

where p, T and s are pressure, temperature and specific entropy respectively and the subscripts 1 and 2 relate to the initial and final states.

Air is flowing steadily through a well-lagged duct. Pressure and temperature measurements of the air are taken at two stations A and B as given below.

Deduce the direction of flow of the air in the duct. Air may be assumed to be a perfect gas with R = 0.287 kJ/(kg K), c_p = 1.005 kJ/(kg K). (London University 1968)

	Station A	Station B
Pressure	1.3 bar	1.0 bar
Temperature	50 °C	13 °C

For the derivation of the expression called for see 14.3.

The first law of thermodynamics cannot help us in this problem since it is impossible to distinguish between accelerated, expansive flow from A to B and retarded, compressive flow from B to A. However, by the second law of thermodynamics since the duct is well lagged, then heat transfer to or from the surroundings is zero and thus the entropy change in the surroundings is also zero.

Now the entropy change in the system (the duct) must be positive since the net entropy change cannot be negative and this is a real process.

Thus if the value of $s_B - s_A$ is positive the flow is from A to B.

$$s_B - s_A = c_p \ln \frac{T_B}{T_A} - R \ln \frac{p_B}{p_A}$$

$$= 1.005 \frac{\text{kJ}}{\text{kg K}} \ln \frac{273 + 13}{273 + 50} - 0.287 \frac{\text{kJ}}{\text{kg K}} \ln \frac{1}{1.3}$$

$$= -0.1223 + 0.0753 = -0.047 \frac{\text{kJ}}{\text{K kg}}$$

which is impossible.

Thus A is the final state and the flow must be from B to A.

12. For a fluid for which (pv/T) is a constant quantity and equal to R, show that the change in specific entropy between two states A and B is given by

$$s_B - s_A = \int_{T_A}^{T_B} \left(\frac{c_p}{T}\right) \mathrm{d}T - R \ln \left(\frac{p_B}{p_A}\right)$$

A fluid for which R is constant and equal to 0.287 kJ/(kg K), flows steadily through an adiabatic machine, entering and leaving via two adiabatic pipes. In one of these pipes the pressure and temperature are 500 kN/m^2 and 450 K and in the other pipe the pressure and temperature are 100 kN/m^2 and 300 K respectively. Determine which pressure and temperature refer to the inlet pipe.

For the given temperature range, c_p is given by

$$c_p = a \ln |T| + b$$

where $|T|$ is the numerical value of the absolute temperature, and

$$a = 0.026 \frac{\text{kJ}}{\text{kg K}}; \; b = 0.86 \frac{\text{kJ}}{\text{kg K}}$$

(London University Part I 1972 No. 7)

The expression required is identical in derivation to that given in 14.3 except that here c_p is a variable and remains under the integral sign.

Assume that A is the inlet state ($p_A = 500 \frac{\text{kN}}{\text{m}^2}$, $T_A = 450$ °C). Once again, as in the previous example, the entropy change in the surroundings is zero since there is no external heat transfer.

Thus $$s_B - s_A = \int_{T_A}^{T_B} \left(\frac{c_p}{T}\right) dT - R \ln \left(\frac{p_B}{p_A}\right)$$

and with T in K

$$s_B - s_A = \int_{T_A}^{T_B} \left(\frac{a \ln T + b}{T}\right) dT - R \ln \left(\frac{p_B}{p_A}\right)$$

$$= \int_{T_A}^{T_B} \left(\frac{a \ln T}{T}\right) dT + b \ln \left(\frac{T_B}{T_A}\right) - R \ln \left(\frac{p_B}{p_A}\right)$$

For the integral let $T = e^x$, from which $dT = e^x \, dx$ and $\ln T = x$.

Thus $$\int_{T_A}^{T_B} \left(\frac{a \ln T}{T}\right) dT = \int \frac{axe^x \, dx}{e^x} = \int ax \, dx = \frac{ax^2}{2} = \frac{a}{2}\Big[(\ln T)^2\Big]_{T_A}^{T_B}$$

and $$s_B - s_A = \frac{a}{2}[(\ln T)^2]_{450}^{300} + b \ln \frac{300}{450} - R \ln \frac{100}{500}$$

$$= \left[\frac{0.026}{2}[(\ln 300)^2 - (\ln 450)^2] + 0.86 \ln \frac{300}{450} - 0.287 \ln \frac{100}{500}\right] \frac{\text{kJ}}{\text{K kg}}$$

$$= -0.0623 - 0.3487 + 0.4619 = +0.0509 \frac{\text{kJ}}{\text{K kg}}$$

which is possible, and thus the chosen states are correct: A is the inlet state and B is the outlet state. The reverse choice would give a negative entropy change which is unacceptable.

Further Examples

13. A salesman reports that he has a steam turbine available that delivers 2 800 kW. The steam enters the turbine at 7 bar,

250 °C and leaves at 0.14 bar when the required steam flow rate is 13 500 kg/h.

(a) How would you evaluate his claim?

(b) Suppose he changed his claim and said the flow rate was 15 250 kg/h?

14. Two separate cylinders are insulated from their surroundings but energy in the form of heat can transfer readily between them. 0.5 kg of steam is contained in one by a piston, which exerts a constant pressure of 4 bar. In the second 1 kg of air is compressed slowly by a second piston while the temperature of the air and steam rises from 150 °C to 250 °C. All processes are reversible and the thermal capacity of the cylinders and pistons may be neglected. What thermodynamic property of the system comprising steam and air remains constant? Find the ratio of p_2 to p_1. (4.6)

15. A rigid vessel of volume 1.5 m^3 is divided into two parts by a diaphragm. On one side of the diaphragm there is initially 0.01 m^3 of a saturated liquid at a temperature of 10 °C, the space on the other side being a vacuum. The diaphragm bursts and as the fluids expands to fill the whole volume an energy transfer in the form of heat transfer occurs between the fluid and its surroundings. Eventually the energy transfer stops and when conditions throughout the vessel are uniform the pressure is 2 bar. Using the data given find the magnitude and direction of the energy transfer and the increase of entropy of the fluid in the process.

EXTRACT FROM TABLES OF SATURATION PROPERTIES OF FLUID

Temperature (° C)	Pressure (bar)	Specific Volume (m^3/kg)		Specific Enthalpy (kJ/kg)	
		Liquid	Vapour	Liquid	Vapour
10	2	0.002	0.404	18.1	197.6

(+368 kJ, 11.75 kJ/kg)

16. Air at 0.8 bar and 5 °C enters the intake (i.e. diffuser) of a jet engine with a velocity of 300 m/s. The air decelerates reversibly in the intake to a negligible velocity before entering the compressor. Calculate the pressure of the air at inlet to the compressor

(a) if the process can be assumed adiabatic,

(b) if heat is transferred at such a rate that the temperature remains at 5 °C throughout the process. (1.349 bar, 1.408 bar)

17. Two vessels A and B each of volume 3 m^3 may be connected together by a tube of negligible volume. Vessel A contains air at 7 bar, 95 °C while B contains air at 3.5 bar, 205 °C. Find the change of entropy when A is connected to B by working from first principles and assuming the mixing to be complete and adiabatic. (0.975 kJ/K kg)

15 VAPOUR POWER CYCLES

In chapters 15 and 16 we attempt to apply the fundamental work of previous chapters to vapour and gas power cycles respectively. Three fundamental criteria need defining here.

(1) Cycle efficiency η

$$\eta = \frac{\text{net work transfer}}{\text{total positive heat transfer to the cycle}} = \frac{w_{net}}{q+}$$

This is to some scale the ratio of output over input and thus a measure of energy consumption per unit power output.

(2) Work ratio r_w

$$r_w = \frac{\text{net work transfer}}{\text{total positive work transfer from cycle}} = \frac{w_{net}}{w+}$$

If the value of r_w is close to zero then low component efficiencies tend to reduce the net work output to zero, and conversely if r_w is close to unity, low component efficiencies have less effect on the overall plant or cycle efficiency.

(3) Specific fluid consumption (SFC)

$$\text{SFC} = \frac{\text{mass flow rate of fluid}}{\text{unit power output}} = \frac{\dot{m}}{\dot{W}_{net}}$$

or $$\text{SFC} = \frac{1}{w_{net}} \frac{\text{kg}}{\text{kJ}} \left[\frac{\text{kJ}}{\text{kW s}}\right]\left[\frac{3600\ \text{s}}{\text{h}}\right] = \frac{3600}{w_{net}} \frac{\text{kg}}{\text{kW h}}$$

This is a size criterion for plant since plant size clearly depends upon the amount of fluid passing through.

Thus a high cycle efficiency together with a high work ratio and a low specific fluid consumption give a plant of optimum design.

1. A steam plant operates on the Rankine cycle with a boiler pressure of 100 bar and a condenser pressure of 0.035 bar. The steam leaving the boiler is saturated and the turbine expansion and feed pump compression processes are isentropic.

Calculate the efficiency and work ratio of the plant.

It is convenient now to state that for all the following examples the values of specific enthalpies will be in kJ/kg and those of specific entropy will be in kJ/(K kg) and until such time as a dimensional balance becomes necessary the numbers alone will be quoted to save space and for the sake of brevity.

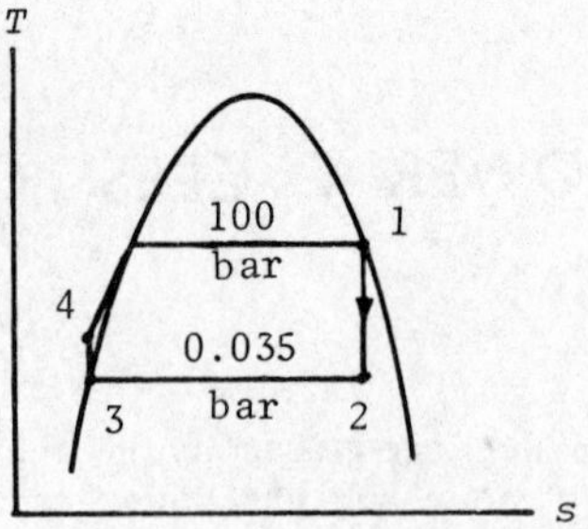

Figure 15.1

From pages 5 and 3 respectively

$$h_1 = 2725; \; s_1 = 5.616 = s_2 = s_{f_2} + x_2 s_{fg_2} = 0.391 + 8.13x_2$$

Thus $x_2 = 0.643$

$$\text{and} \quad h_2 = h_f + \frac{s_2 - s_{f_2}}{s_{fg_2}} = 112 + \frac{5.615 - 0.391}{8.13} = 1678.6$$

Also $h_3 = h_{f_2} = 112$

As explained in the introduction the work done in a steady-flow isentropic process is given by

$$_1w_2 = \int_1^2 v \, dp$$

In the case where the specific volume is held to be constant as in the feed pump work of a steam power plant we may write

$$_1w_2 = v(p_2 - p_1)$$

Applying the steady-flow equation to the feed pump in this case

$$h_4 = h_3 + {_3w_4} = h_3 + v_3(p_4 - p_3)$$

where w is work in (i.e. negative) as written here, and from page 3

$$h_4 = 112 \frac{\text{kJ}}{\text{kg}} + 0.001035 \frac{\text{m}^3}{\text{kg}}(100 - 0.035) \text{ bar } \frac{[10^2 \text{ kJ}]}{[\text{bar m}^3]}$$

$$= 122.0 \frac{\text{kJ}}{\text{kg}}$$

$$\eta = \frac{(h_1 - h_2) - (h_4 - h_3)}{h_1 - h_4} = \frac{2725 - 1678.6 - 10.0}{2725 - 122.0} = 0.398$$

$$r_w = \frac{(h_1 - h_2) - (h_4 - h_3)}{h_1 - h_2} = \frac{1036.4}{1046.4} = 0.99$$

2.(a) Determine the efficiency and work ratio of a Carnot cycle with the same boiler and condenser pressures as the Rankine cycle of question 1. Assume the working fluid enters the boiler as saturated liquid and leaves as saturated vopour.

(b) Recalculate the Rankine and Carnot cycle efficiencies for the same steam conditions if, in both cycles, the actual work done during adiabatic expansion is 0.8 × the isentropic work and during adiabatic compression is 1.3 × the isentropic work. Again assume that in the Carnot cycle the working fluid enters the boiler as saturated liquid and leaves as saturated vapour.

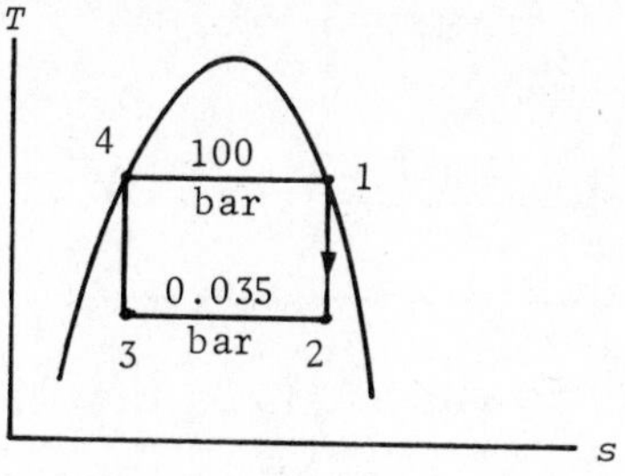

Figure 15.2

(a) $h_1 = 2725$; $h_2 = 1678.6$; $h_4 = 1408$;

$s_4 = 3.36 = s_3 = 0.391 + x_3(8.13)$

Thus $x_3 = 0.365$

and $h_3 = 112 + 0.365(2438) = 1002.3$

Thus $$\eta = \frac{(2725 - 1678.6) - (1408 - 1002.3)}{2725 - 1408} = \underline{0.486}$$

$$r_w = \frac{(2725 - 1678.6) - (1408 - 1002.3)}{2725 - 1678.6} = \underline{0.612}$$

(b) $$\eta_R = \frac{0.8(2725 - 1678.6) - 1.3(10.0)}{2725 - (112 + 1.3 \times 10.0)} = \underline{0.317}$$

$$\eta_C = \frac{0.8(2725 - 1678.6) - 1.3(1408 - 1002.3)}{2725 - 1408} = \underline{0.235}$$

These calculations readily show the adverse effect of component inefficiencies on the Carnot cycle overall thermal efficiency due to the low work ratio of this cycle and the much less serious effect on the Rankine cycle which has a much higher work ratio.

3. A steam plant operates on the Rankine cycle with the same boiler and condenser pressures as in question 1. The turbine expansion and feed pump compression processes are isentropic. Determine the cycle efficiency if

(a) the steam is superheated to 500 °C before entering the turbine

(b) the steam leaves the boiler as saturated vapour but is now throttled to 50 bar before entering the turbine.

Draw up a table to assist comparison of these basic results with those of question 1, showing for each of the three cycles, in addition to the efficiency, the dryness at turbine outlet and the specific fluid consumption in kg/kW h.

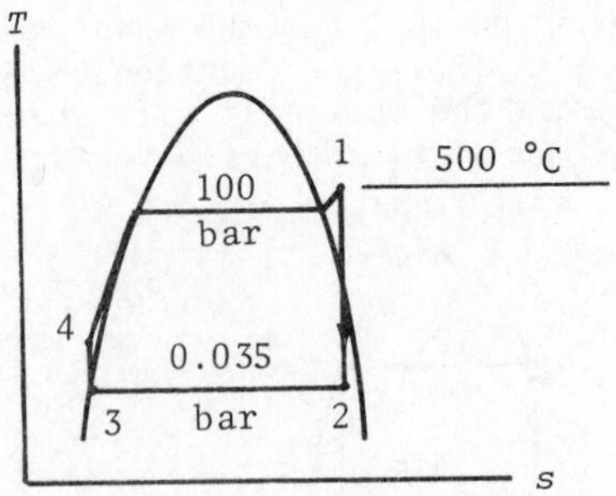

Figure 15.3i

(a) $h_1 = 3373$; $s_1 = 6.596 = s_2 = 0.391 + x_2(8.13)$ (pages 8,3)

Thus $x_2 = 0.763$

and $h_2 = 112 + \dfrac{6.596 - 0.391}{8.13}(2438) = 1972.7$

Thus $\eta = \dfrac{(3373 - 1972.7) - 10.0}{3373 - 122.0} = 0.428$

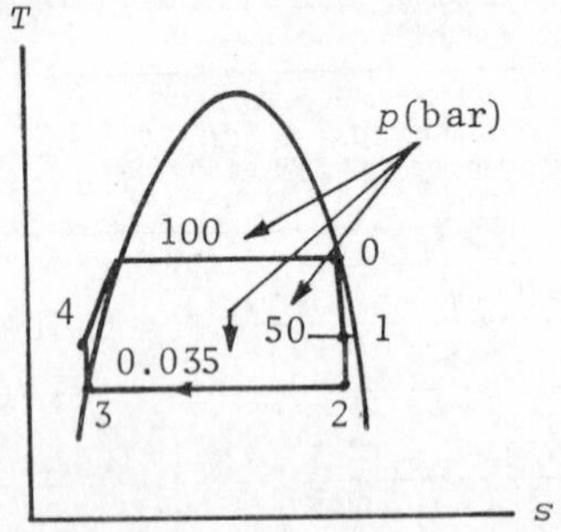

Figure 15.3ii

(b) $h_0 = 2725 = h_1 = h_f + x_1 h_{fg}$ (at $p = 50$ bar)

since in a steady-flow throttling process the final specific enthalpy is equal to the initial specific enthalpy with the usual assumptions.

$x_1 = \dfrac{2725 - 1155}{1639} = 0.958$ (page 5)

Thus $s_1 = 2.921 + 0.958(3.052) = s_2 = s_f + x_2 s_{fg}$ (at $p = 0.035$ bar)

$5.8445 = 0.391 + x_2(8.13)$

or $x_2 = 0.671$

and $h_1 = 112 + 0.671(2438) = 1747.4$

$$\eta = \frac{(h_1 - h_2) - (h_4 - h_3)}{h_0 - h_4} = \frac{(2725 - 1747.4) - 10.0}{2725 - 122.0} = 0.372$$

SUMMARY	η	x_2	SFC
Question 1	0.398	0.643	$\frac{3600}{1036.4} = 3.474\ \frac{\text{kg}}{\text{kW h}}$
Question 3a	0.428	0.763	$\frac{3600}{2725 - 1972.7 - 10} = 2.589$ kg/kW h
Question 3b	0.372	0.671	$\frac{3600}{2725 - 1847.4 - 10} = 3.721$ kg/kW h

Of these three cycles cycle 3a appears to be the most attractive because of its higher efficiency and lowest value of SFC and additionally because although the dryness at turbine exit is impractically low it is better than the others.

4. Compare the following proposals for a vapour power plant.

(a) Working fluid mercury vapour for which the boiler pressure is 22 bar, the condenser pressure is 0.0006 bar and the vapour is just saturated at exit from the boiler.

(b) Working fluid steam for which the boiler pressure is 50 bar, the condenser pressure is 1.4 bar and the vapour is superheated to 595 °C at boiler exit.

In each case determine the Rankine efficiency, the work ratio, the specific fluid consumption (kg/kW h) and the specific volume flow rate (m^3/kW h). Assume isentropic expansion and compression.

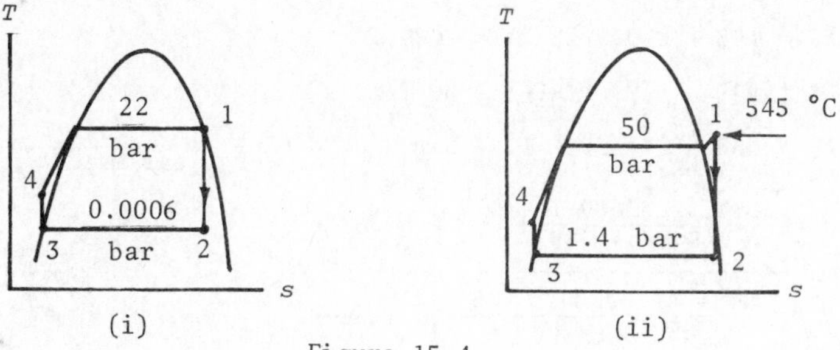

Figure 15.4

(a) Referring to page 14 of tables for mercury

$$h_1 = 367.59;\ s_1 = 0.4864 = s_2 = 0.0466 + x_2(0.7774)$$

or $x_2 = 0.5657$

and $h_2 = 15.13 + 0.5657(297.20) = 183.27$

also $h_3 = 15.13$

and $h_4 = h_3 + v_3(p_4 - p_3) = h_3 + \dfrac{(p_4 - p_3)}{\rho_3}$

Now the saturation temperature at 0.0006 bar for mercury is

$$T_{\text{sat}} = 109.2 + 273 = 382.2\ \text{K}$$

and referring to page 15 of tables for liquid mercury and interpolating at 382.2 K, we get

$$\rho_3 = 13332.7\ \frac{\text{m}^3}{\text{kg}}$$

Thus $h_4 = 15.13 + \frac{(22 - 0.0006)}{13332.7} \frac{\text{bar m}^3}{\text{kg}} \frac{[10^2 \text{ kJ}]}{[\text{bar m}^3]} = 15.13 + 0.17$

$= 15.30$

$$\eta = \frac{367.59 - 183.27 - 0.17}{367.59 - 15.3} = 0.523$$

$$r_w = \frac{367.59 - 183.27 - 0.17}{367.59 - 183.27} = 0.999$$

$$\text{SFC} = \frac{3600}{367.59 - 183.27 - 0.17} = 19.55 \frac{\text{kg}}{\text{kW h}}$$

$$v_2 = x_2 v_{g_2} = 0.5657 \times 259.6 \frac{\text{m}^3}{\text{kg}} = 146.9 \frac{\text{m}^3}{\text{kg}}$$

$$\frac{\dot{V}_2}{\dot{W}} = \frac{\dot{m}v_2}{\dot{W}} = \text{SFC} \times v_2 = 19.55 \frac{\text{kg}}{\text{kW h}} \times 146.9 \frac{\text{m}^3}{\text{kg}} = 2871 \frac{\text{m}^3}{\text{kW h}}$$

(b) Referring to tables page 7 for superheated steam

$h_1 = 3433 + 0.95(3666 - 3433) = 3654.4$

$s_1 = 6.975 + 0.95(7.258 - 6.975) = 7.2439 = s_2$

$$x_2 = \frac{7.2439 - 1.411}{5.835} = 0.999$$

$h_2 = 458 + 0.999(2232) = 2689.1$

$h_3 = 458$ (from tables page 4)

$$h_4 = 458 \frac{\text{kJ}}{\text{kg}} + (50 - 1.4) \text{ bar} \times 0.00105 \frac{\text{m}^3}{\text{kg}} \frac{[10^2 \text{ kJ}]}{[\text{bar m}^3]} = 463.4$$

$$\eta = \frac{3654.4 - 2689.1 - 5.4}{3654.4 - 463.4} = 0.301$$

$$r_w = \frac{3654.4 - 2689.1 - 5.4}{3654.4 - 2689.1} = 0.994$$

$$\text{SFC} = \frac{3600}{3654.4 - 2689.1 - 5.4} = 3.75 \frac{\text{kg}}{\text{kW h}}$$

$$\frac{\dot{V}_2}{\dot{W}} = \frac{\dot{m}v_2}{\dot{W}} = \frac{\dot{m}x_2 v_{g_2}}{\dot{W}} = 3.75 \times 0.999 \times 1.236 = 4.63 \frac{\text{m}^3}{\text{kW h}}$$

5. A steam plant operates on the Rankine cycle with a boiler pressure of 100 bar and a condenser pressure of 0.035 bar. The steam leaves the boiler at 500 °C and is expanded isentropically until it becomes saturated. It is then returned to the boiler and resuperheated to 500 °C at constant pressure. Finally it is expanded isentropically to condenser pressure. Feed pump compression is isentropic.

Calculate the efficiency, dryness at turbine outlet and specific fluid consumption. Compare these results with those given in question 15.3.

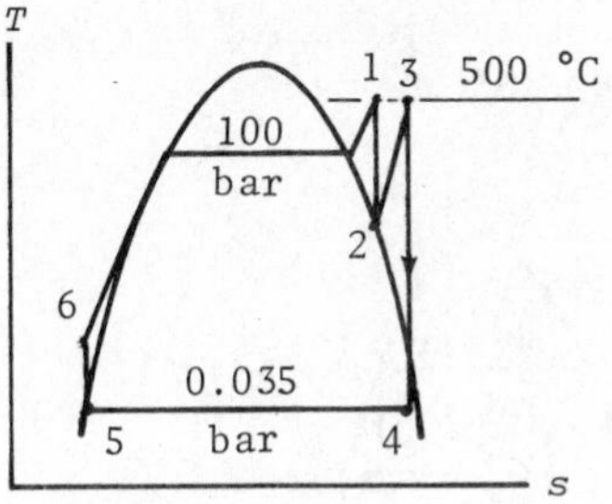

Figure 15.5

One of the most convenient ways of determining the values of specific enthalpy and entropy in vapour plant is by graphical means if the calculation is to be performed in a reasonable time.

Such a graphical method is readily available for steam by use of the enthalpy-entropy chart for steam (or Mollier diagram as it is sometimes known).

All values in the remaining questions are taken from the h/s chart for steam with the exception of liquid states which are best read from tables as before.

$h_1 = 3373$

$h_2 = 2778$

$h_3 = 3478$

$h_4 = 2322$; $x_4 = 0.907$ (read directly from the h/s chart)

$h_5 = 112$ (tables page 3)

$$h_6 = 112 + 0.10035(100 - 0.035)\frac{\text{bar m}^3}{\text{kg}}\frac{[10^2 \text{ kJ}]}{[\text{bar m}^3]} = 112 + 10$$
$$= 122.0$$

$$\text{Total work done} = {}_1W_2 + {}_3W_4 = (h_1 - h_2) + (h_3 - h_4)$$
$$= 3373 - 2778 + 3478 - 2322 = 1751 \text{ in expansion}$$

Thus $\eta = \dfrac{1751 - 10}{(3373 - 122) + (3478 - 2778)} = 0.44$

$$\text{SFC} = \frac{3600}{(3373 - 2778) + (3478 - 2322) - 10} = 2.07 \ \frac{\text{kg}}{\text{kW h}}$$

6. In a nuclear power plant saturated steam at 30 bar enters a high-pressure turbine and expands isentropically to a pressure at which its dryness fraction is 0.841. At this pressure the steam is passed through a moisture separator which removes all the liquid.

Saturated vapour leaves the separator and is expanded isentropically to 0.04 bar in a low-pressure turbine, while the saturated liquid leaving the separator is returned via a feed pump to the boiler. The condensate leaving the condenser at 0.04 bar is also returned to the boiler via a second feed pump.

Calculate the cycle efficiency and turbine outlet dryness taking into account the feed pump term. Recalculate the same quantities for a cycle with the same boiler and condenser pressures but without moisture separation.

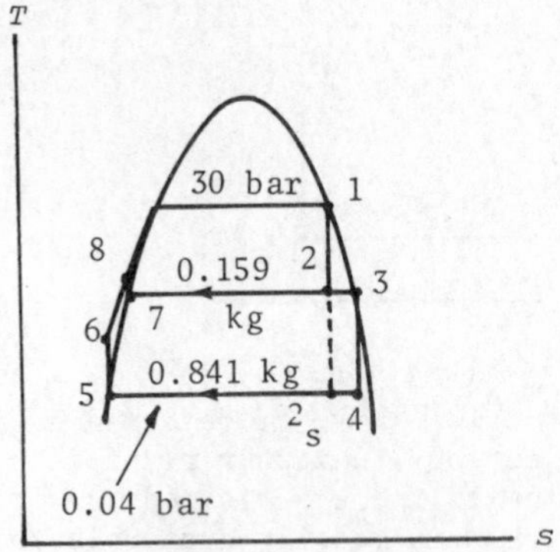

Figure 15.6

From the h/s chart

$h_1 = 2803$

$h_2 = 2370$

$h_3 = 2717$

$h_4 = 2125$

$x_4 = \dfrac{h_4 - h_5}{h_{fg}} = \dfrac{2125 - 121}{2435} = 0.824$ (tables page 3)

$h_5 = 121$ (page 3)

$h_7 = 535$ (page 4 since $p_7 = 2.5$ bar from the chart)

$$h_6 = h_5 + {}_5w_6 = h_5 + v_5(p_6 - p_5)$$

$$= 121 + 0.00104(30 - 0.04)\ \frac{\text{bar m}^3}{\text{kg}}\frac{[10^2\ \text{kJ}]}{[\text{bar m}^3]}$$

$$= 121 + 3.0 = 124$$

Also $h_8 = h_7 + {}_7w_8 = h_7 + v_7(p_8 - p_7)$

$$= 535 + 0.0010675(30 - 2.5)\ \frac{\text{bar m}^3}{\text{kg}}\frac{[10^2\ \text{kJ}]}{[\text{bar m}^3]}$$

$$= 535 + 2.9 = 537.9$$

Thus $\eta = \dfrac{2803 - 2370 + 0.841(2717 - 2125) - 0.841(3) - 0.159(2.9)}{0.841(2803 - 124) + 0.159(2803 - 537.9)}$

$= 0.355$

$s_1 = 6.186 = s_{2_s} = 0.422 + x_{2_s}(8.051)$ (pages 4 and 3)

$x_{2_s} = \dfrac{6.186 - 0.422}{8.051} = 0.716$ (for the cycle without separation)

$h_{2_s} = 121 + 0.716(2433) = 1863$

$$\eta = \frac{2803 - 1863 - 3.0}{2803 - 124} = 0.350$$ (for the cycle without separation)

7. Geothermal energy from a natural geyser can be obtained as a continuous supply of steam 0.87 dry at 2 bar and at a flow rate of 2700 kg/h. This is utilised in a mixed-pressure cycle to augment the superheated exhaust from a high-pressure turbine of isentropic efficiency 0.83 which is supplied with 5500 kg/h of steam at 40 bar and 500 °C. The mixing process is adiabatic and the mixture is expanded to a condenser pressure of 0.10 bar in a low-pressure turbine having an isentropic efficiency of 0.78.

Determine the power output and the thermal efficiency of the plant.

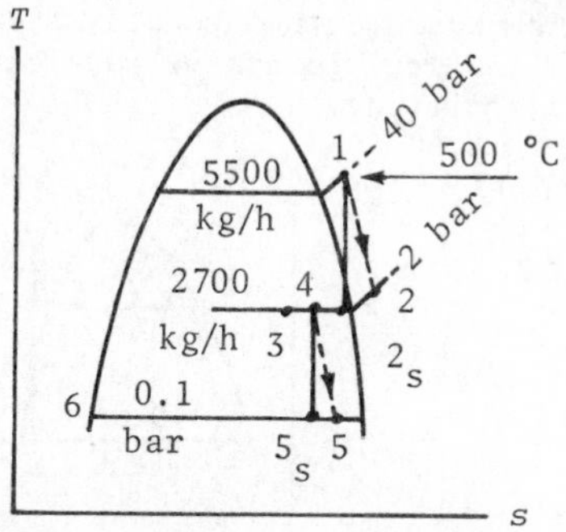

Figure 15.7

$h_1 = 3445$

$h_{2_s} = 2692$

$h_1 - h_2 = 0.83(h_1 - h_{2_s}) = 0.83(3445 - 2692) = 622.5$

$h_2 = 3445 - 622.5 = 2822.5$

$h_3 = 2420.7$

$h_6 = 192$ (page 3)

On mixing we may write

$$2700 \frac{\text{kg}}{\text{h}} (h_3) + 5500 \frac{\text{kg}}{\text{h}} (h_2) = (2700 + 5500) \frac{\text{kg}}{\text{h}} (h_4)$$

or $$h_4 = \frac{(2700 \times 2420.7) + (5500 \times 2822.5)}{8200} = 2690.2$$

$h_{5_s} = 2244$ (from the h/s chart isentropically below h_4)

Thus $h_4 - h_5 = 0.78(h_4 - h_{5_s}) = 0.78(2690.2 - 2244) = 348$

and $$\dot{W} = 5500 \frac{\text{kg}}{\text{h}} (h_1 - h_2) + 8200 \frac{\text{kg}}{\text{h}} (h_4 - h_5)$$

$$= [(5500 \times 622.5) + (8200 \times 348)] \frac{\text{kg}}{\text{h}} \frac{\text{kJ}}{\text{kg}} \left[\frac{\text{h}}{3600\ \text{s}}\right]\left[\frac{\text{kW s}}{\text{kJ}}\right]$$

$$= 1744\ \text{kW}$$

$$\dot{Q} = 5500 \frac{\text{kg}}{\text{h}} (h_1 - h_6) = 5500 (3445 - 192) \frac{\text{kg}}{\text{h}} \frac{\text{kJ}}{\text{kg}} \left[\frac{\text{h}}{3600 \text{ s}}\right]\left[\frac{\text{kW s}}{\text{kJ}}\right]$$

$$= 4970 \text{ kW}$$

Thus $\eta = \frac{1744}{4970} = 0.351$

8. The mercury cycle of a binary vapour plant works between pressures of 10 bar and 0.08 bar and the mercury enters the turbine as saturated vapour. The feed water, preheated to saturation temperature in an economiser is evaporated in the mercury condenser, and the temperature difference between the mercury and steam must be about 16 K. After evaporation the steam is externally superheated to 450 °C and expanded to a condenser pressure corresponding to about 33 °C. Calculate the mercury to steam mass flow ratio and the cycle efficiency.

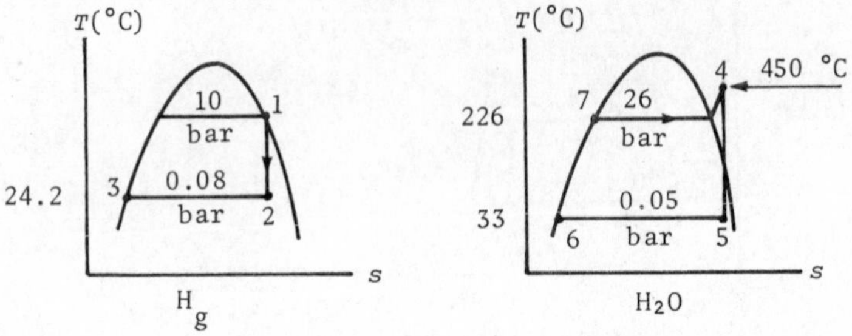

Figure 15.8

From tables page 14 for mercury

$h_1 = 359.11$

$s_1 = 0.5089 = s_2 = 0.087 + x_2(0.5721)$

or $\quad x_2 = \frac{0.5089 - 0.087}{0.5721} = 0.7375$

$h_2 = 33.21 + 0.7375(294.7) = 250.55$

$h_3 = 33.21$

$h_7 = 972$

$h_8 = 2803$

$$\frac{\dot{m}\text{ (Hg)}}{\dot{m}\text{ (H}_2\text{O)}} = \frac{h_8 - h_7}{h_2 - h_3} = \frac{2803 - 972}{250.55 - 33.21} = 8.42 \frac{\text{kg Hg}}{\text{kg H}_2\text{O}}$$

$h_4 = 3348.6$; $h_5 = 2183$; $h_6 = 138$ (h/s chart and page 3)

$$\text{Thus } \eta = \frac{\dot{m}(\text{Hg})(h_1 - h_2) + \dot{m}(\text{H}_2\text{O})(h_4 - h_5)}{\dot{m}(\text{Hg})(h_1 - h_3) + \dot{m}(\text{H}_2\text{O})(h_7 - h_6) + \dot{m}(\text{H}_2\text{O})(h_4 - h_8)}$$

$$= \frac{8.42(359.11 - 250.55) + (3348.6 - 2183)}{8.42(359.11 - 33.21) + (972 - 138) + (3348.6 - 2803)}$$

$$= 0.504$$

9. Power and heating are to be provided by steadily operating steam plant as follows: steam enters the high-pressure stage of a two-stage turbine with a pressure of 1 MN/m^2 and a temperature of 200 °C. At exit from this stage the pressure is 0.3 MN/m^2. At this point some of the steam is 'bled off' and passed through a heat-exchanger which it leaves as saturated liquid at a pressure of 0.3 MN/m^2. The remaining steam passes into the low-pressure stage of the turbine. The pressure at exit from this stage is 40 kN/m^2. The turbine is required to produce a total power of 1 MW and the heat-exchanger to provide a heating rate of 500 kW. Calculate the required mass flow rate of steam into the high-pressure stage of the turbine.

Assume

(a) steady conditions throughout the plant,

(b) velocity and gravity terms in the steady-flow energy equation are negligible at the inlets and exits of the heat-exchanger and of both stages of the turbine, and

(c) both turbine stages are adiabatic with isentropic efficiencies of 0.8.

Extracts from the thermodynamic properties of water substance:

(i) liquid-vapour equilibrium (i.e. saturation) properties:

p	T_{sat}	h_f	h_{fg}	s_f	s_{fg}
(MN/m^2)	(K)	(kJ/kg)	(kJ/kg)	(kJ/K kg)	(kJ/K kg)
0.04	349.1	318	2318	1.026	6.643
0.3	406.7	561	2164	1.672	5.321

(ii) temperature above saturation temperature (i.e. superheated)

p	T	h	s
(MN/m^2)	(K)	(kJ/kg)	(kJ/K kg)
1	473.15	2829	6.695

(London University 1971 No. 7)

This problem is to be solved without the aid of the h/s chart.

$$x_{2_s} = \frac{s_{2_s} - s_{f_2}}{s_{fg_2}} = \frac{6.695 - 1.672}{5.321} = 0.944$$

$$h_{2_s} = 561 + 0.944(2164) = 2603.8$$

$$h_1 - h_{2_s} = 2829 - 2603.8 = 225.2$$

$$h_1 - h_2 = 0.8 \times 225.2 = 180.2$$

$$h_2 = 2648.8$$

$$x_2 = \frac{2648.8 - 561}{2164} = 0.965$$

$$s_2 = 1.672 + 0.965(5.321) = 6.806 = s_{3_s}$$

$$x_{3_s} = \frac{6.806 - 1.026}{6.643} = 0.87$$

$$h_{3_s} = 318 + 0.87(2318) = 2334.7$$

$h_2 - h_{3_s} = 314.1$

$h_2 - h_3 = 0.8(314.1) = 251.2$

$h_5 = 561$

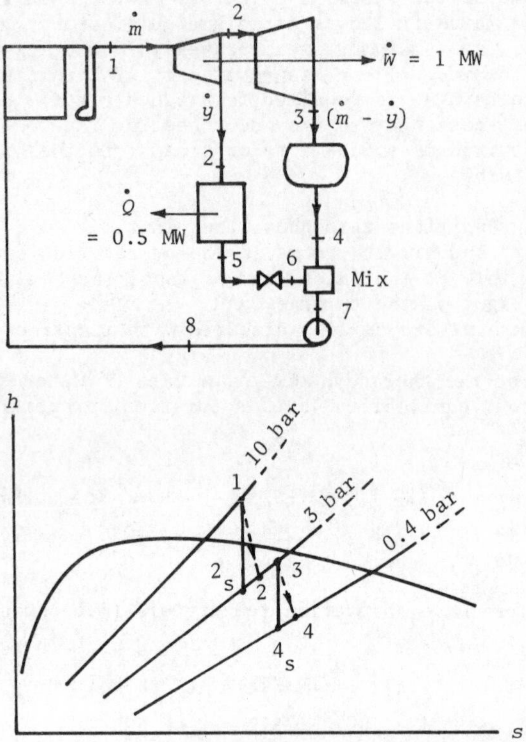

Figure 15.9

Power equation

$$\dot{m}(180.2) + (\dot{m} - \dot{y})(251.2) = 10^3 \text{ kW}$$

where $\dot{m}$ and $\dot{y}$ are the mass flows into the high-pressure turbine and heat-exchanger respectively.

Heating equation

$$\dot{y}(2648.8 - 561) = 0.5 \times 10^3 \text{ kW}$$

From these two equations we get

$$\underline{\dot{y} = 0.239 \frac{\text{kg}}{\text{s}}}$$

and $$\underline{\dot{m} = \frac{10^3 + (0.239 \times 251.2)}{251.2 + 180.2} = 2.457 \frac{\text{kg}}{\text{s}}}$$

Further Examples

10. In a steam plant working on the Rankine cycle steam is delivered to the expander at a pressure of 7 bar, 0.8 dry. The condenser pressure is 1 bar and the condensate leaves the condenser at 65 °C. Calculate the efficiency of the plant.

What would be the efficiency of the plant if the condensate leaving the condenser was saturated liquid at 1 bar?

Assume isentropic expansion in the expander and neglect feed pump work in each case. Discuss the significance of these results.
(0.13, 0.139)

11. Calculate the efficiency of a Rankine cycle with superheat, operating with an upper temperature of 600 °C and with a condenser pressure of 0.04 bar, for boiler pressures of 25, 50 and 100 bar.

Determine also the wetness at turbine exhaust in each case.

Assume isentropic expansion and compression and discuss the results.
(0.391, 0.417, 0.441)

12. A steam power plant operates on the Rankine cycle with superheat and reheat, the supply steam expanding isentropically in a high-pressure turbine from 50 bar, 450 °C to 2 bar. The steam is returned to the boiler and reheated to a temperature of 350 °C (at a constant pressure of 2 bar) before isentropic expansion in a low-pressure turbine to a condenser pressure of 0.055 bar. Determine the condition of the steam at exhaust from each turbine and the cycle efficiency. Include feed pump work.
(0.945, 0.962, 0.382)

13. For the same steam conditions as in question 12, determine the cycle efficiency if the isentropic efficiency of each turbine expansion is 0.8, the isentropic efficiency of the feed pump compression is 0.7 and the condensate is undercooled to 26 °C. Show the cycle on a T-s diagram.
(0.314)

16 GAS POWER CYCLES

In chapter 16 an attempt is made to compare the outputs and the efficiencies of various idealised gas power cycles by specifying as many common features as are consistent with the natures of the cycles considered.

The only quantity that needs defining here is mean effective pressure which is that constant pressure which, acting over the whole swept volume, will produce the same output as the actual cycle.

1. In an air-standard Otto cycle the pressure and temperature of the air at the start of compression are 1 bar and 330 K respectively. The compression ratio is 8 and the energy added at constant volume is 1250 kJ/kg.

Determine the maximum pressure and temperature of the cycle, the cycle efficiency and the mean effective pressure.

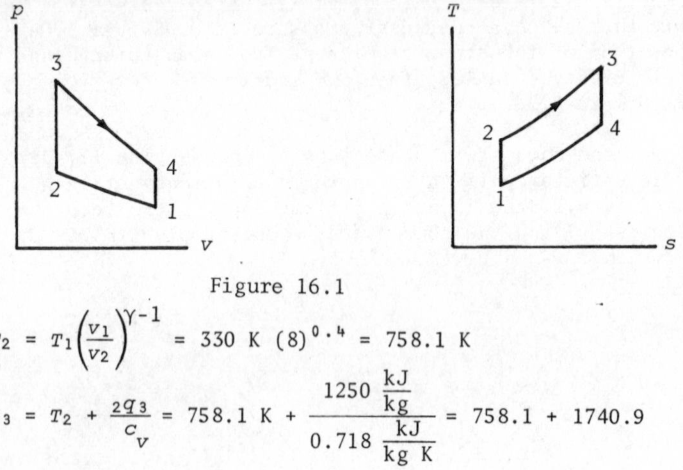

Figure 16.1

$$T_2 = T_1\left(\frac{v_1}{v_2}\right)^{\gamma-1} = 330\ \text{K}\ (8)^{0.4} = 758.1\ \text{K}$$

$$T_3 = T_2 + \frac{{}_2q_3}{c_v} = 758.1\ \text{K} + \frac{1250\ \frac{\text{kJ}}{\text{kg}}}{0.718\ \frac{\text{kJ}}{\text{kg K}}} = 758.1 + 1740.9$$

$T_3 = 2499$ K

$$p_2 = p_1\left(\frac{v_1}{v_2}\right)^{\gamma} = 1\ \text{bar}\ (8)^{1.4} = 18.38\ \text{bar}$$

$$p_3 = p_2\frac{T_3}{T_2} = 18.38\ \text{bar}\ \frac{2499}{758.1} = 60.6\ \text{bar}$$

$$\eta = \frac{w_{\text{net}}}{q_+} = \frac{q_+ + q_-}{q_+}$$

where q_+ and q_- are the positive and negative heat transfers

$$q_- = {}_4q_1 = e_1 - e_4 = c_v(T_1 - T_4)$$

$$T_4 = T_3\left(\frac{v_3}{v_4}\right)^{\gamma-1} = T_3\left(\frac{1}{r}\right)^{\gamma-1} = 2499\ \text{K}\left(\frac{1}{8}\right)^{0.4} = 1087.8\ \text{K}$$

$$q_- = 0.718\ \frac{\text{kJ}}{\text{kg K}}\ (330 - 1087.8)\ \text{K} = -544.1\ \frac{\text{kJ}}{\text{kg}}$$

$$\eta = \frac{1250 - 544.1}{1250} = 0.565$$

Mean effective pressure of the cycle = MEP = $\dfrac{w_{net}}{v_1 - v_2}$

$$\text{MEP} = \frac{w_{net}}{v_1\left(1 - \frac{1}{r}\right)} = \frac{w_{net} \times p_1}{RT_1\left(1 - \frac{1}{r}\right)} = \frac{(q_+ + q_-)p_1}{RT_1\left(1 - \frac{1}{r}\right)}$$

$$= \frac{(1250 - 544.1)\ \frac{\text{kJ}}{\text{kg}} \times 1\ \text{bar}}{0.287\ \frac{\text{kJ}}{\text{kg K}} \times 330\ \text{K}\left(1 - \frac{1}{8}\right)} = 8.52\ \text{bar}$$

---

2. In an air-standard Diesel cycle the pressure and temperature of the air at the start of compression are 1 bar and 330 K respectively. The compression ratio is 16 and the energy added at constant pressure is 1250 kJ/kg.

Determine the maximum pressure and temperature of the cycle, the cycle efficiency and the mean effective pressure.

Figure 16.2

$$p_2 = p_3 = p_1\left(\frac{v_1}{v_2}\right)^{\gamma} = 1\ \text{bar}\ (16)^{1.4} = 48.5\ \text{bar}$$

$$T_2 = T_1\left(\frac{v_1}{v_2}\right)^{\gamma-1} = 330\ \text{K}\ (16)^{0.4} = 1000.4\ \text{K}$$

$$T_3 = T_2 + \frac{{}_2q_3}{c_p} = 1000.4\ \text{K} + \frac{1250}{1.005}\ \frac{\text{kJ}}{\text{kg}}\ \frac{\text{kg K}}{\text{kJ}} = 2244.2\ \text{K}$$

$$v_3 = \frac{T_3}{T_2}(v_2) \quad (p_2 = p_3)$$

$$v_3 = \frac{T_3}{T_2}\frac{v_1}{16} = \frac{2244.2}{1000.4}\frac{v_1}{16} = 0.14v_1$$

$$v_4 = v_1$$

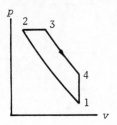

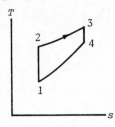

$$T_4 = T_3\left(\frac{v_3}{v_4}\right)^{\gamma-1} = 2244.2\ \text{K}\left(\frac{0.14v_1}{v_1}\right)^{0.4} = 1022.7\ \text{K}$$

$$q_- = c_v(T_1 - T_4) = 0.718\ \frac{\text{kJ}}{\text{kg K}}\ (330 - 1022.7)\ \text{K} = -497.4\ \frac{\text{kJ}}{\text{kg}}$$

$$\eta = \frac{q_+ + q_-}{q_+} = \frac{1250 + (-497.4)}{1250} = 0.602$$

$$\text{MEP} = \frac{w_{\text{net}}}{v_1 - v_2} = \frac{(q_+ + q_-)p_1}{RT_1\left(1 - \frac{1}{r}\right)} \text{ as in question 16.1}$$

$$= \frac{(1250 - 497.4)\ \frac{\text{kJ}}{\text{kg}}}{0.287\ \frac{\text{kJ}}{\text{kg K}} \times 330\ \text{K}\left(1 - \frac{1}{16}\right)}$$

MEP = 8.47 bar

---

3. In an air-standard Carnot cycle the pressure and temperature of the air at the start of compression are 1 bar and 330 K respectively. The energy added in the cycle is 1250 kJ/kg and the maximum temperature is 2500 K.

Determine the cycle efficiency and the mean effective pressure.

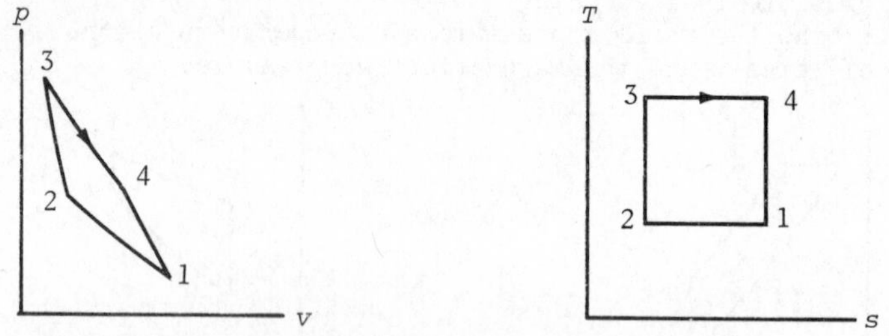

Figure 16.3

$$q_+ = \int_3^4 T\,ds = T_3R\ \ln\frac{p_3}{p_4}\ (\text{since } T_3 = T_4)$$

$$q_- = \int_1^2 T\,ds = T_1R\ \ln\frac{p_1}{p_2}\ (\text{since } T_1 = T_2)$$

$$\eta = \frac{q_+ + q_-}{q_+} = \frac{T_3 - T_2}{T_3}\quad (\text{since } s_4 - s_3 = s_1 - s_2)$$

$$= \frac{2500 - 330}{2500} = 0.868$$ (the highest value obtainable with these quoted temperatures)

$$\text{MEP} = \frac{w_{\text{net}}}{v_1 - v_3} = \frac{q_{\text{net}}}{v_1 - v_3} = \frac{\text{area of } T/s \text{ diagram}}{v_1 - v_3}$$

or $$\text{MEP} = \frac{(T_3 - T_2)(s_4 - s_3)}{v_1 - v_3}$$

where $s_4 - s_3 = R \ln (p_3/p_4)$ since $T_3 = T_4$

Now $v_3 = v_2\left(\frac{T_2}{T_3}\right)^{k-1}$

since 2-3 is an isentrope and $k = \gamma/\gamma-1$

Also $v_2 = v_1\frac{p_1}{p_2}$

since 1-2 is an isotherm

$$\text{Thus MEP} = \frac{(T_3 - T_2)\, R \ln \frac{p_3}{p_4}}{v_1 - v_1\frac{p_1}{p_2}\left(\frac{T_2}{T_3}\right)^{k-1}} = \frac{(T_3 - T_2)\, R \ln \frac{p_3}{p_4}}{v_1\left[1 - \left(\frac{p_1}{p_2}\right)\left(\frac{T_2}{T_3}\right)^{k-1}\right]}$$

$$= \frac{(T_3 - T_2)\, R \ln \frac{p_3}{p_4}}{\frac{RT_1}{p_1}\left[1 - \left(\frac{p_1}{p_2}\right)\left(\frac{T_2}{T_3}\right)^{k-1}\right]} = \frac{p_1(T_3 - T_2) \ln \frac{p_3}{p_4}}{T_1\left[1 - \left(\frac{p_1}{p_2}\right)\left(\frac{T_2}{T_3}\right)^{k-1}\right]}$$

$$\text{Now} \quad \ln \frac{p_3}{p_4} = \ln \frac{p_2}{p_1} = \frac{q_+}{RT_3} = \frac{1250 \frac{\text{kJ}}{\text{kg}}}{0.287 \frac{\text{kJ}}{\text{kg K}} \times 2500 \text{ K}} = 1.742$$

$$\text{Thus } \frac{p_3}{p_4} = \frac{p_2}{p_1} = 5.71$$

$$\text{and MEP} = \frac{1 \text{ bar } (2500 - 330) \text{ K } (1.742)}{330 \text{ K}\left[1 - \left(\frac{1}{5.71}\right)\left(\frac{330}{2500}\right)^{2.5}\right]}$$

since $k - 1 = 1/(\gamma - 1) = 2.5$

or MEP = 11.47 bar

Note that while all these values look eminently satisfactory, closer inspection will reveal that in order for them to pertain, it is necessary that the value of maximum pressure in the cycle, i.e. p_3, must be of the order of 6800 bar!

This is because the diagram on the pressure-volume field is extremely narrow with a very small net work transfer and thus any inefficiencies introduced into the cycle to render it more practical will quickly reduce the work output to zero.

The Carnot cycle is thus a purely hypothetical and quite impractical cycle having the highest possible efficiency within the given temperature limits.

4. In an air-standard dual-combustion cycle the pressure and temperature at the start of compression are 1 bar and 330 K respectively. The energy added in the cycle is 1250 kJ/kg, two-thirds of this being added at constant volume and the rest at constant pressure.

If the compression ratio is 16 determine the maximum pressure and temperature in the cycle, the cycle efficiency and the mean effective pressure.

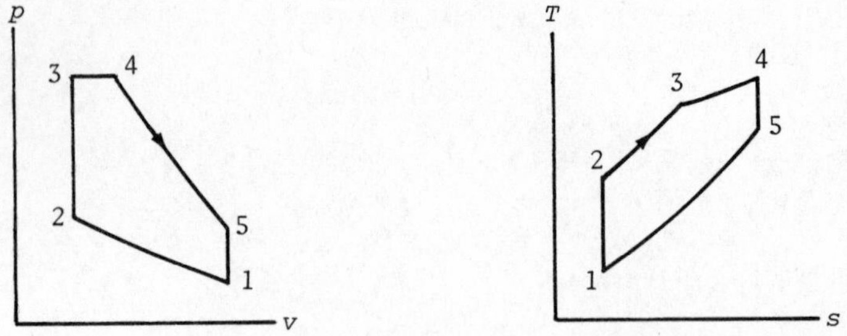

Figure 16.4

$$T_2 = T_1\left(\frac{v_1}{v_2}\right)^{\gamma-1} = 330\ \text{K}\ (16)^{0.4} = 1000.4\ \text{K}$$

$$p_2 = p_1\left(\frac{v_1}{v_2}\right)^{\gamma} = 1\ \text{bar}\ (16)^{1.4} = 48.5\ \text{bar}$$

$$T_3 = T_2 + \frac{{}_2q_3}{c_v} = 1000.4\ \text{K} + \frac{\frac{2}{3}(1250)\ \frac{\text{kJ}}{\text{kg}}}{0.718\ \frac{\text{kJ}}{\text{kg K}}} = 1000.4 + 1160.6$$

$$T_3 = 2161.0\ \text{K}$$

Thus $p_3 = p_2\frac{T_3}{T_2} = 48.5\ \text{bar}\ \frac{2161.0}{1000.4} = 104.7\ \text{bar}$

$$T_4 = T_3 + \frac{{}_3q_4}{c_p} = 2161.0\ \text{K} + \frac{1}{3}\,\frac{(1250)}{1.005}\,\frac{\text{kJ}}{\text{kg}}\,\frac{\text{kg K}}{\text{kJ}} = 2161.0 + 414.6$$

$$T_4 = 2575.6\ \text{K}$$

$$T_5 = T_4\left(\frac{v_4}{v_5}\right)^{\gamma-1} = T_4\left(\frac{v_3\frac{T_4}{T_3}}{v_5}\right)^{\gamma-1} = T_4 \times \left[\left(\frac{v_3}{v_5}\right)\left(\frac{T_4}{T_3}\right)\right]^{\gamma-1}$$

$$T_5 = 2575.6\ \text{K} \times \left(\frac{1}{16} \times \frac{2575.6}{2161}\right)^{0.4} = 911.4\ \text{K}$$

Thus $q_- = c_v(T_1 - T_5) = 0.718\ \frac{\text{kJ}}{\text{kg K}}\ (330 - 911.4)\ \text{K} = -417.5\ \frac{\text{kJ}}{\text{kg}}$

and $\eta = \frac{w_{\text{net}}}{q_+} = \frac{(q_+ + q_-)}{q_+} = \frac{1250 + (-417.5)}{1250} = 0.666$

Also $\text{MEP} = \frac{p_1(q_+ + q_-)}{RT_1\left(1 - \frac{1}{r}\right)}$ exactly as derived in question 16.1

$$= \frac{1\ \text{bar}\ (1250 - 417.5)\ \frac{\text{kJ}}{\text{kg}}}{0.287\ \frac{\text{kJ}}{\text{kg K}} \times 330\ \text{K}\left(1 - \frac{1}{16}\right)}$$

$$\text{MEP} = 9.38\ \text{bar}$$

Thus this cycle has a superior efficiency to either the Otto or Diesel cycle and also a higher MEP at the expense of a higher maximum pressure (which implies a weight penalty).

5. At the start of energy addition in a simple Lenoir cycle the pressure and temperature of the air are 1 bar and 330 K respectively. The energy added is 1250 kJ/kg at constant volume after which isentropic expansion is followed by isobaric energy rejection to the initial state.

Determine the maximum cycle temperature and pressure, the cycle efficiency and the mean effective pressure.

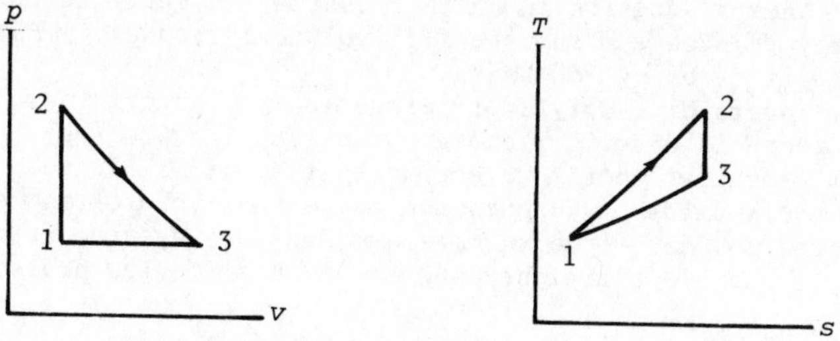

Figure 16.5

This is the basic cycle on which the 'flying bomb' of the Second World War was based (although this operated in pulse-jet form).

$$T_2 = T_1 + \frac{q_+}{c_v} = 330\text{ K} + \frac{1250\ \frac{\text{kJ}}{\text{kg}}}{0.718\ \frac{\text{kJ}}{\text{kg K}}} = 2070.9\text{ K}$$

$$p_2 = p_1\frac{T_2}{T_1} = 1\text{ bar}\ \frac{2070.9}{330} = 6.28\text{ bar}$$

$$T_3 = T_2\left(\frac{p_3}{p_2}\right)^{1/k} = T_2\left(\frac{p_1}{p_2}\right)^{1/k} = 2070.9\text{ K}\left(\frac{1}{6.28}\right)^{0.286} = 1224.7\text{ K}$$

$$q_- = c_p(T_1 - T_3) = 1.005\ \frac{\text{kJ}}{\text{kg K}}\ (330 - 1224.7)\text{ K} = -899.2\ \frac{\text{kJ}}{\text{kg}}$$

and $$\eta = \frac{1250 + (-899.2)}{1250} = 0.281$$

$$\text{MEP} = \frac{\text{net work done}}{\text{base length}} = \frac{q_+ + q_-}{v_3 - v_1}$$

Now $$v_3 = v_1\frac{T_3}{T_1} \qquad (\text{since } p_3 = p_1)$$

$$= v_1 \times \frac{1224.7}{330} = 3.711v_1$$

Thus $$\text{MEP} = \frac{q_+ + q_-}{v_1\left(\frac{v_3}{v_1} - 1\right)} = \frac{(q_+ + q_-)p_1}{RT_1\left(\frac{v_2}{v_1} - 1\right)}$$

$$= \frac{(1250 - 899.1)\ \frac{\text{kJ}}{\text{kg}} \times 1\ \text{bar}}{0.287\ \frac{\text{kJ}}{\text{kg K}} \times 330\ \text{K}\ (3.711 - 1)}$$

MEP = 1.367 bar

6. A cycle using air as the working fluid consists of the following processes in order.

(a) Reversible, polytropic compression from 1 bar, 330 K through a compression ratio of 16,

(b) energy addition in which pressure and specific volume are linearly related and the specific volume increases by 50%, the energy addition being 860 kJ/kg,

(c) reversible, polytropic expansion to the original volume in which there is a further energy addition of 390 kJ/kg,

(d) isochoric energy rejection to the initial state.

If the indices of compression and expansion are respectively 1.3 and 1.23, determine the maximum pressure and temperature in the cycle, the cycle efficiency and the mean effective pressure.

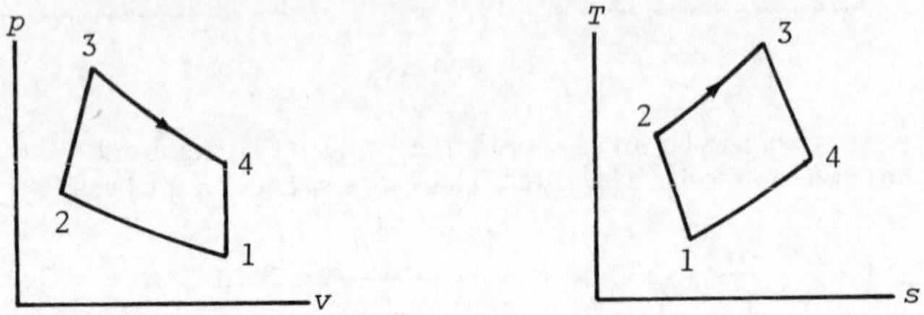

Figure 16.6

$$T_2 = T_1\left(\frac{p_2}{p_1}\right)^{k^*}$$

where $k^* = (n_c - 1)/n_c$ and n_c is the compression index

$$= 330\ \text{K}\ (16)^{0.3} = 758.1\ \text{K}$$

$${}_2q_3 = e_3 - e_2 + {}_2w_3 = c_v(T_3 - T_2) + \frac{1}{2}(p_3 + p_2)(v_3 - v_2)$$

$$= c_v(T_3 - T_2) + 0.25\frac{p_3 v_1}{16} + 0.25RT_2 \quad (\text{since } v_3 = 1.5v_2)$$

$$= c_v(T_3 - T_2) + \frac{0.25 p_3 RT_1}{16 p_1} + 0.25RT_2$$

$$860\ \frac{\text{kJ}}{\text{kg}} = \left(0.718\ \frac{\text{kJ}}{\text{kg K}} \times T_3\ \text{K}\right) - \left(0.718\ \frac{\text{kJ}}{\text{kg K}} \times 758.1\ \text{K}\right)$$

$$+ \frac{0.25\ p_3\ \text{bar} \times 0.287\ \frac{\text{kJ}}{\text{kg K}} \times 330\ \text{K}}{16 \times 1\ \text{bar}}$$

$$+ \left(0.25 \times 0.287\ \frac{\text{kJ}}{\text{kg K}} \times 758.1\ \text{K}\right)$$

or $$p_3 = \frac{1349.9 - 0.718T_3}{1.48}$$

$$_3q_4 = \frac{\gamma - n_e}{\gamma - 1}\frac{R}{n_e - 1}(T_3 - T_4)$$

see 5.6 for the derivation of the above where n_e is for expansion

$$T_4 = T_3\left(\frac{v_3}{v_4}\right)^{n_e - 1} = T_3\left(\frac{1.5v_1}{16v_1}\right)^{0.23}$$

since $v_3 = 1.5v_2 = 1.5v_1/16$ and $v_4 = v_1$

and substituting into the above expressions for heat transfer

$$390\ \frac{\text{kJ}}{\text{kg}} = \left(\frac{1.4 - 1.23}{1.4 - 1}\right)\frac{0.287\ \frac{\text{kJ}}{\text{kg K}}}{0.23}(1 - 0.58)T_3\ \text{K}$$

or $T_3 = 1750.9$ K (and $T_4 = 0.58 \times 1750.9 = 1015.5$ K)

and $p_3 = \dfrac{1349.9 - 0.718(1750.9)}{1.48} = 62.7$ bar

$_4q_1 = c_v(T_1 - T_4)$ ($_4w_1 = 0$ at constant volume)

$$= 0.718\ \frac{\text{kJ}}{\text{kg K}}(330 - 1015.5)\ \text{K} = -492.2\ \frac{\text{kJ}}{\text{kg}}$$

$$_1q_2 = \frac{\gamma - n_c}{\gamma - 1}\ {}_1w_2 = \frac{\gamma - n_c}{\gamma - 1}\left[\frac{R(T_1 - T_2)}{n_c - 1}\right]$$

$$= \left(\frac{1.4 - 1.3}{1.4 - 1}\right)\frac{0.287\ \frac{\text{kJ}}{\text{kg K}}(330 - 758.1)\ \text{K}}{0.3}$$

$$= -102.4\ \frac{\text{kJ}}{\text{kg}}$$

Thus total negative heat transfer

$$q_- = -492.2 - 102.4 = -594.6\ \frac{\text{kJ}}{\text{kg}}$$

and $\eta = \dfrac{q_+ + q_-}{q_+} = \dfrac{1250 - 594.6}{1250} = 0.524$

$$\text{MEP} = \frac{w_{net}}{v_1 - v_2} = \frac{(q_+ + q_-)p_1}{RT_1\left(1 - \frac{1}{r}\right)} \quad \text{as in question 16.1}$$

$$= \frac{(1250 - 549.6)\ \frac{\text{kJ}}{\text{kg}} \times 1\ \text{bar}}{0.287\ \frac{\text{kJ}}{\text{kg K}} \times 330\ \text{K} \times \frac{15}{16}}$$

MEP = 7.38 bar

Further Examples

7. An air cycle consists of isochoric energy addition of 1250

kJ/kg from inner dead centre followed by isentropic expansion to outer dead centre (1 bar, 330 K) followed by isothermal compression to inner dead centre. If the compression ratio is 8 find the maximum temperature and pressure, the efficiency and the mean effective pressure. (2070.9 K, 50.2 bar, 0.842, 12.7 bar)
(N.B. This cycle achieves the Carnot efficiency but is quite impractical because of the isothermal compression.)

8. An air cycle consists of the following operations in order.
(a) Isentropic compression from 1 bar, 330 K to inner dead centre
(b) isochoric energy addition of 1250 kJ/kg
(c) isentropic expansion to outer dead centre
(d) isobaric compression to inner dead centre.
If the pressure ratio in operation (a) is 4 find the maximum cycle pressure and temperature, the cycle efficiency and the mean effective pressure. (18.19 bar, 2231.5 K, 0.483, 2.47 bar)

9. A Stirling air cycle consists of the following operations in order.
(a) Isothermal compression from 1 bar, 330 K through a compression ratio of 8
(b) isochoric energy addition of 1250 kJ/kg
(c) isothermal expansion to maximum volume
(d) isochoric energy rejection to the initial state.
Find the maximum cycle pressure and temperature, the cycle efficiency and the mean effective pressure.
(2070.9 K, 50.2 bar, 0.418, 12.54 bar)

17 AVAILABLE ENERGY

Engineers have a prime concern with the production of mechanical work. Since all processes are irreversible in practice, the capacity to perform work is continually being degraded by virtue of the unwanted heat transfers which occur because of viscous friction and large temperature differences between the working fluid and its environment.

The first law of thermodynamics merely shows us how heat and work are mutually interchangeable because energy is always conserved.

However, the transformation is shown by the second law of thermodynamics to be subject to certain restrictions, e.g. work can always be continuously and completely transformed into heat (a lower grade of energy), but heat can only partly be transformed into work since some energy must be rejected as heat albeit at a lower level of temperature.

Thus we speak of high-grade energy such as work or kinetic energy and low-grade energy such as heat in all its forms. Further, even a mixing process between two fluids results in a loss of what we term available energy (i.e. a loss in capacity to produce work) since this capacity is less after mixing than before due to the irreversible nature of the mixing process with its inevitable increase in entropy.

Available energy is the capacity of a fluid to produce maximum work in a given state (being that work done when the fluid is taken reversibly from its given state to a specified ground state). It is a convenient quantitative measure by means of which the irreversibilities of a process or cycle can be ascertained and is of paramount importance in these days of fuel shortage and costs.

Several high-level studies have already been carried out in the USA on the energy requirements of that country and the bulk of the analysis is based on the use of availability or available energy which is a quantitative measure of the optimum use (or otherwise) of fuel.

Only simple examples are given since this is a first-year volume but the book would be incomplete without some mention of this topic which clearly demonstrates the vital significance of the second law of thermodynamics in real processes.

Standard texts can be consulted which derive the expressions for available energy as follows.

Non-flow available energy (a)

$$a = (e - T_0 s) - (e_0 - T_0 s_0) + p_0(v - v_0)$$

where e, s, T and v have their usual meanings with regard to the fluid and T_0, e_0, s_0, p_0 and v_0 refer to the arbitrarily chosen reference, ground (or 'dead') state at which level it is reckoned the capacity for work production is zero. (The most common reference state is 1.013 bar, 298 K, $u_0 = 0$.)

Steady-flow available energy (b)

$$b = (h - T_0 s) - (h_0 - T_0 s_0) \quad \text{(assuming low K.E.)}$$

the term allowing for work done against the environment is not included here since this effect is already embraced in the enthalpy terms.

Irreversibility (i)

$$i = w(\text{rev}) - w(\text{actual})$$

(in expansion and vice versa in compression)

It can be shown that

$$i = T_0 \left(\Delta s_{\text{system}} + \Delta s_{\text{surroundings}} \right)$$

assuming the ultimate environment is at a constant temperature T_0.

Two other definitions are of relevance here (one already encountered in this volume).

Isentropic efficiency (η)

$$\eta = \frac{w}{w_{\text{rev}}} \quad \text{(in expansion)}$$

$$\eta = \frac{w_{\text{rev}}}{w} \quad \text{(in compression)}$$

$$\eta = \frac{h_1 - h_2}{h_1 - h_{2_s}} \quad \text{(for a nozzle) etc.}$$

Effectiveness (ε)

$$\varepsilon = \frac{\text{gain of } b \text{ of surroundings}}{\text{loss of } b \text{ of system}}$$

for w or q transferring from the system to the surroundings in the case of steady flow (e.g.)

$$\text{and} \quad \varepsilon = \frac{\text{gain of } b \text{ of system}}{\text{loss of } b \text{ of surroundings}}$$

for w or q transferring to the sytem from the surroundings in the case of steady flow.

1. A stream of water at 90 °C flowing at the rate of 20 kg/s mixes adiabatically with a second stream of water at 50 °C flowing at the rate of 30 kg/s. Calculate the rate of loss of available energy.

Let the stream flowing at the rate of 20 kg/s be denoted by suffix A, the 30 kg/s stream by suffix B and the mixture by suffix C.

$$\dot{m}_A b_A + \dot{m}_B b_B = \text{initial availability rate}$$

$$\left(\dot{m}_A + \dot{m}_B \right) b_C = \text{final availability rate}$$

(Note that there is a temptation to equate these which must be very firmly resisted since these are statements deriving from the second law of thermodynamics unlike the following which derives from the first law and deals with energy conservation not availability change.)

$$\dot{m}_A h_A + \dot{m}_B h_B = \left(\dot{m}_A + \dot{m}_B\right) h_C$$

From page 2 of tables reading off values of h_f at 90 °C and 50 °C

$$h_C = \frac{(20 \times 376.9)\ \frac{\text{kg}}{\text{s}}\frac{\text{kJ}}{\text{kg}} + (30 \times 209.3)\ \frac{\text{kg}}{\text{s}}\frac{\text{kJ}}{\text{kg}}}{50\ \frac{\text{kg}}{\text{s}}} = 276.3\ \frac{\text{kJ}}{\text{kg}}$$

and $$s_C = 0.893 + \left(\frac{276.3 - 272}{293.0 - 272}\right)(0.955 - 0.893) = 0.906\ \frac{\text{kJ}}{\text{K kg}}$$

Thus $$\dot{m}_A b_A + \dot{m}_B b_B = 20\ \frac{\text{kg}}{\text{s}}[376.9 - 298(1.192)]\ \frac{\text{kJ}}{\text{kg}}$$

$$+ 30\ \frac{\text{kg}}{\text{s}}[209.3 - 298(0.704)]\ \frac{\text{kJ}}{\text{kg}} \quad (T_0 = 298\ \text{K})$$

$$= 419\ \text{kW}$$

$$\dot{m}_A + \dot{m}_B\ b_C = 50[276.3 - 298(0.906)] = 315.6\ \text{kW}$$

and rate of loss of availability = 419 - 315.6 = 103.4 kW

2. Steam at 15 bar, 400 °C is expanded adiabatically in a nozzle to 1 bar, with an isentropic efficiency of 90%.

Calculate the loss in available energy expressed as a percentage of the original available energy.

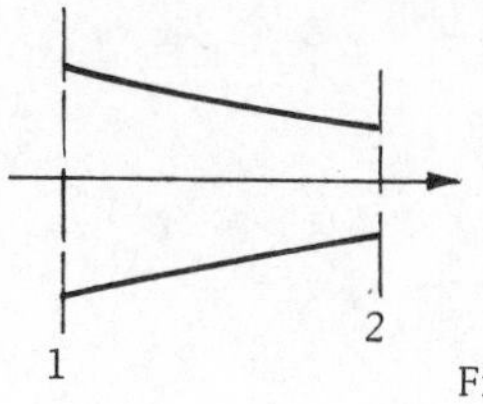

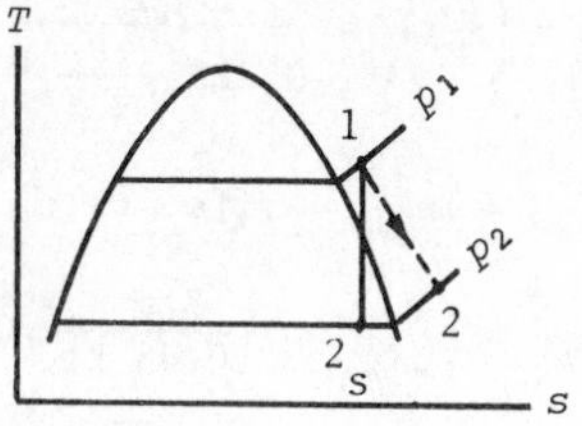

Figure 17.2

$$b_1 = h_1 - T_0 s_1 = 3256\ \frac{\text{kJ}}{\text{kg}} - 298\ \text{K}\left(7.268\ \frac{\text{kJ}}{\text{K kg}}\right) = 1090.1\ \frac{\text{kJ}}{\text{kg}}$$

$$s_1 = s_{2_s} = 7.268\ \frac{\text{kJ}}{\text{K kg}} \qquad \text{(values from page 7)}$$

$$x_{2_s} = \frac{7.268 - 1.303}{6.056} = 0.985$$

$$h_{2_s} = 417 + 0.985(2258) = 2641.1\ \frac{\text{kJ}}{\text{kg}} \qquad \text{(bottom of page 3)}$$

$$\eta\left(h_1 - h_{2_s}\right) = h_1 - h_2 \qquad \text{(where } \eta \text{ is the nozzle efficiency)}$$

$$h_2 = h_1 - (h_1 - h_2) = 2702.6\ \frac{\text{kJ}}{\text{kg}}$$

$$s_2 = \frac{(2702.6 - 2676)}{(2777 - 2676)}(7.614 - 7.360) + 7.360 = 7.427\ \frac{\text{kJ}}{\text{K kg}}$$

Now in this case the kinetic energy is a significant term and has to be included in the available energy term by mere addition.

i.e. $b_2 = h_2 - T_0 s_2 + \frac{1}{2}u_2{}^2 = h_2 - T_0 s_2 + h_1 - h_2 = h_1 - T_0 s_2$

(since from the energy equation in steady flow $\frac{1}{2}u_2{}^2 = h_1 - h_2$)

Thus $b_2 = 3256\ \frac{\text{kJ}}{\text{kg}} - 298\ \text{K}\left(7.427\ \frac{\text{kJ}}{\text{K kg}}\right) = 1042.8\ \frac{\text{kJ}}{\text{kg}}$

and $b_1 - b_2 = 47.3\ \frac{\text{kJ}}{\text{kg}}$

or $\dfrac{b_1 - b_2}{b_1} = \dfrac{47.3}{1090.1} \times 100 = 4.3\%$

---

3. Two vessels A and B whose volumes are respectively 3 m³ and 2 m³ are connected by a pipe containing a valve. Initially the valve is shut, vessel A containing air at 5 bar, 500 K whilst there is a vacuum in B.

Assuming that after the valve is opened the flow is adiabatic and ignoring the volume of connecting pipe and valve calculate the loss in available energy.

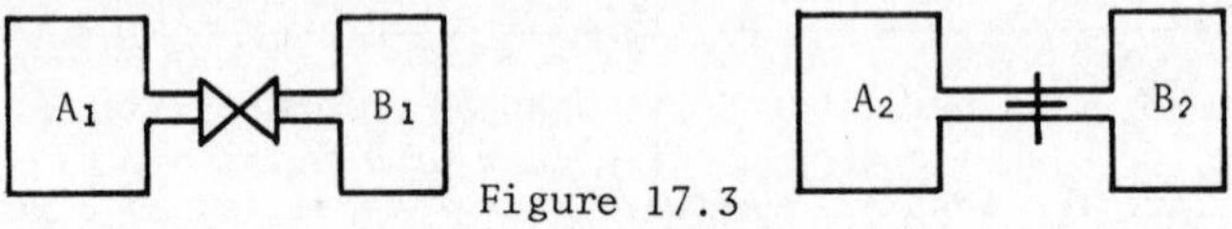

Figure 17.3

$$m = \left(\frac{pV}{RT}\right)_{\text{A}} = \frac{5\ \text{bar} \times 3\ \text{m}^3}{0.287\ \frac{\text{kJ}}{\text{kg K}} \times 500\ \text{K}} \frac{[100\ \text{kN}]}{[\text{bar m}^2]} = 10.45\ \text{kg}$$

$$A_{\text{A}_1} = ma_{\text{A}_1} = m[(e - T_0 s) - (e_0 - T_0 s_0) + p_0(v - v_0)]_{\text{A}_1}$$

$$v_{\text{A}_1} = \left(\frac{V}{m}\right)_{\text{A}_1} = \frac{3\ \text{m}^3}{10.45\ \text{kg}} = 0.287\ \frac{\text{m}^3}{\text{kg}}$$

$$v_0 = \frac{RT_0}{p_0} = \frac{0.287\ \frac{\text{kJ}}{\text{kg K}} \times 298\ \text{K}}{101.3\ \frac{\text{kN}}{\text{m}^2}} = 0.844\ \frac{\text{m}^3}{\text{kg}}$$

$$A_{\text{A}_1} = m\left[c_v(T - T_0) - T_0\left(c_p \ln\frac{T}{T_0} - R\ln\frac{p}{p_0}\right) + p_0(v - v_0)\right]_{\text{A}_1}$$

$$= 10.45\ \text{kg}\left[0.718\ \frac{\text{kJ}}{\text{kg K}}(500 - 298)\ \text{K} - 298\ \text{K}\left(1.005\ \frac{\text{kJ}}{\text{kg K}} \ln\frac{500}{298} - 0.287\ \frac{\text{kJ}}{\text{kg K}} \ln\frac{5}{1.013}\right) + 101.3\ \frac{\text{kN}}{\text{m}^2}(0.287 - 0.844)\ \frac{\text{m}^3}{\text{kg}}\right]$$

$$A_{A_1} = 732.8 \text{ kJ}$$

After the valve opens the new volume for the same mass of air is

$$V_{A_2+B_2} = 3 + 2 = 5 \text{ m}^3$$

$$v_{A_2+B_2} = \frac{V_{A_2+B_2}}{m} = \frac{5 \text{ m}^3}{10.46 \text{ kg}} = 0.478 \frac{\text{m}^3}{\text{kg}} = \frac{RT_2}{p_2}$$

Energy Equation

$$_1Q_2 = {_1W_2} + E_2 - E_1$$

and $_1Q_2 = {_1W_2} = 0$

or $E_2 = E_1$

i.e. $T_2 = T_1$ (since the fluid is a perfect gas)

$$p_2 = \frac{RT_2}{v_2} = \frac{RT_1}{v_2} = \frac{0.287 \times 500}{0.478} \frac{\text{kJ}}{\text{kg K}} \text{ K } \frac{\text{kg}}{\text{m}^3} = 299.9 \frac{\text{kN}}{\text{m}^2}$$

Thus

$$A_{A_2+B_2} = 10.45\left[0.718(500 - 298) - 298\left(1.005 \ln \frac{500}{298} - 0.287 \ln \frac{299.9}{101.3}\right) + 101.3(0.478 - 0.844)\right]$$

$$= 476.7 \text{ kJ} \quad \text{(in a similar manner to that above)}$$

Loss in availability is thus

$$A_1 - A_2 = 732.8 - 476.7 = 256.1 \text{ kJ}$$

Note that although no mass has left the system of vessels, and only a redistribution of mass and energy has occurred due to the opening of the valve, nevertheless some 35% of availability has been lost.

4. An internal combustion engine is started by means of two 12 volt batteries each of capacity 60 amp hours.

It is desired to use compressed air from a receiver as an alternative, equivalent means of starting. If the air is stored at 14 bar, 25 °C when the atmosphere is at 1 bar, 25 °C, calculate the receiver volume to give the same ideal available energy as the batteries.

Note that here we have to take p_0 as 1 bar (not 1.013 bar)

Specific availability of air at 14 bar, 25 °C

$$a = (e - e_0) - T_0(s - s_0) + p_0(v - v_0)$$

Now

$$v = \frac{RT}{p} = \frac{0.287 \times 298}{1400} \frac{\text{kJ}}{\text{kg K}} \text{ K } \frac{\text{m}^2}{\text{kN}} = 0.061 \frac{\text{m}^3}{\text{kg}}$$

and

$$v_0 = \frac{RT_0}{p_0} = \frac{0.287 \times 298}{100} = 0.855 \frac{\text{m}^3}{\text{kg}}$$

Thus

$$a = c_v(T - T_0) - T_0\left(c_p \ln \frac{T}{T_0} - R \ln \frac{p}{p_0}\right) + p_0(v - v_0)$$

$$= 0 + T_0 R \ln \frac{p}{p_0} + p_0(v - v_0) \quad \text{(since } T = T_0\text{)}$$

$$= \left(298 \text{ K} \times 0.287 \frac{\text{kJ}}{\text{kg K}} \ln 14\right) + \left[100 \frac{\text{kN}}{\text{m}^2}(0.061 - 0.855) \frac{\text{m}^3}{\text{kg}}\right]$$

$$= 225.7 - 79.4$$

$$= 146.3 \frac{\text{kJ}}{\text{kg}}$$

Now the available energy from the batteries is given by

$$A = 2 \times 12 \times 60 \text{ Wh} \left[\frac{\text{kW}}{10^3 \text{ W}}\right]\left[\frac{3600 \text{ s}}{\text{h}}\right]\left[\frac{\text{kJ}}{\text{kW s}}\right]$$

$$= 5184 \text{ kJ}$$

Thus for an equivalent available energy, the mass of air in the receiver is given by

$$m = \frac{A}{a} = \frac{5184 \text{ kJ}}{146.3 \frac{\text{kJ}}{\text{kg}}} = 35.43 \text{ kg}$$

and the receiver volume is given by

$$V = \frac{mRT}{p} = \frac{35.43 \text{ kg} \times 0.287 \frac{\text{kJ}}{\text{kg K}} \times 298 \text{ K}}{1400 \frac{\text{kN}}{\text{m}^2}}$$

$$V = 2.165 \text{ m}^3$$

5. A rigid, perfectly insulated vessel is divided into two parts by a non-permeable membrane.

In one part is a volume of 0.05 m^3 of nitrogen at 7 bar and 90 °C and in the other a volume of 0.075 m^3 of oxygen at 14 bar and 45 °C.

The membrane is completely shattered by a solenoid-operated needle.

Calculate the irreversibility when the two gases mix.

Assume that both gases are perfect and that the values for c_p are 1.04 kJ/kg K and 0.92 kJ/kg K for nitrogen and oxygen respectively.

Figure 17.5

Let the initial nitrogen state be denoted by subscript A, the original oxygen state by subscript B and the final mixed state by subscript C.

Energy Equation

$$E_A + E_B = E_C \qquad (1) \text{ (all other terms zero)}$$

Mass Continuity Equation

$$m_A + m_B = m_C \qquad (2)$$

Availability

$$m_A a_A + m_B a_B - m_C a_C = I \quad (3) \quad (\text{where } a = e - T_0 s + p_0 v)$$

From these three equations we may write

$$I = (E_A - T_0 S_A + p_0 V_A) + (E_B - T_0 S_B + p_0 V_B) - (E_C - T_0 S_C + p_0 V_C)$$

$$= T_0 [S_C - (S_A + S_B)] + p_0 (V_A + V_B - V_C)$$

$$= T_0 [m_C s_C - m_A s_A - m_B s_B] \quad (\text{since the volumes cancel out})$$

(Note that this expression conforms to that for I given before)

$$I = T_0 \left(\Delta S_{\text{system}} + \Delta S_{\text{surroundings}} \right)$$

since the above expression gives the product of T_0 and the entropy change of the system, the entropy change of the surroundings being zero because the vessel is perfectly insulated.)

Thus $I = T_0 [(m_A + m_B)(s_C) - m_A s_A - m_B s_B]$

$$= T_0 [m_A (s_C - s_A) + m_B (s_C - s_B)]$$

$$= T_0 \left[m_A \left(c_{v_A} \ln \frac{T_C}{T_A} + R_A \ln \frac{V_C}{V_A} \right) + m_B \left(c_{v_B} \ln \frac{T_C}{T_B} + R_B \ln \frac{V_C}{V_B} \right) \right]$$

Now $R_{N_2} = \frac{R_0}{m_w} = \dfrac{8.3143 \frac{\text{kJ}}{\text{kg-mol K}}}{28 \frac{\text{kg}}{\text{kg-mol K}}} = 0.297 \frac{\text{kJ}}{\text{kg K}}$

Also $R_{O_2} = \frac{8.3143}{32} = 0.260 \frac{\text{kJ}}{\text{kg K}}$

$$m_A = \left(\frac{pV}{RT} \right)_A = \frac{700 \times 0.05}{0.297 \times 318} \frac{\text{kN}}{\text{m}^2} \frac{\text{m}^3}{\text{kg}} \frac{\text{kg K}}{\text{kJ}} \frac{1}{\text{K}} = 0.325 \text{ kg}$$

$$m_B = \frac{1400 \times 0.075}{0.26 \times 318} = 1.271 \text{ kg}$$

$$c_v\ (N_2) = (c_p - R) = 1.04 \frac{\text{kJ}}{\text{kg K}} - 0.297 \frac{\text{kJ}}{\text{kg K}} = 0.743 \frac{\text{kJ}}{\text{kg K}}$$

$$c_v\ (O_2) = 0.92 - 0.26 = 0.66 \frac{\text{kJ}}{\text{kg K}}$$

Now $E_C = E_A + E_B$

Thus $T_C = \dfrac{(mc_v T)_A + (mc_v T)_B}{(mc_v)_C} = \dfrac{(mc_v T)_A + (mc_v T)_B}{(mc_v)_A + (mc_v)_B}$

$$= \frac{(0.325 \times 0.743 \times 90) + (1.271 \times 0.66 \times 45)}{(0.325 \times 0.743) + (1.271 \times 0.66)}$$

$$= 55.1\ ^\circ\text{C}\ (328.1\ \text{K})$$

$$\text{Thus } I = 298 \text{ K}\left[0.325 \text{ kg}\left(0.743 \frac{\text{kJ}}{\text{kg K}} \ln \frac{328}{363} + 0.297 \frac{\text{kJ}}{\text{kg K}} \ln \frac{0.125}{0.050}\right)\right.$$

$$\left. + 1.271 \text{ kg}\left(0.66 \frac{\text{kJ}}{\text{kg K}} \ln \frac{328.1}{318} + 0.26 \frac{\text{kJ}}{\text{kg K}} \ln \frac{0.125}{0.075}\right)\right]$$

$$= 298[0.325(-0.0753 + 0.2721) + 1.271(0.0206 + 0.1328)] \text{ kJ}$$

$$I = 77.2 \text{ kJ}$$

6. Derive an expression for the availability of a fluid in steady flow having a specific enthalpy h, a specific entropy s and a velocity u, with respect to an environment at temperature T_0. Interpret graphically, on h/s coordinates, the expression derived.

In a steam-jet ejector the motive steam leaves the nozzle at the rate of 1.134 kg/s with a velocity of 1128 m/s, a pressure of 0.069 bar and a dryness of 0.84.

In the mixing chamber the motive steam mixes with saturated steam entering at right angles to the axis of the ejector, at the rate of 0.45 kg/s with a velocity of 91 m/s.

Mixing takes place adiabatically at constant pressure and with conservation of axial momentum.

Determine the rate of loss of availability in the mixing process with respect to the saturation temperature at 0.069 bar as the environment temperature. (London University Part III 1966)

The expression called for (which can be found in standard texts) is

$$b - b_0 = \left(h - T_0 s + \frac{u^2}{2}\right) - (h_0 - T_0 s_0)$$

where u has a significant value and the datum or reference state is given by h_0, s_0 and $u_0 = 0$.

The graphical interpretation on the h/s field is given below.

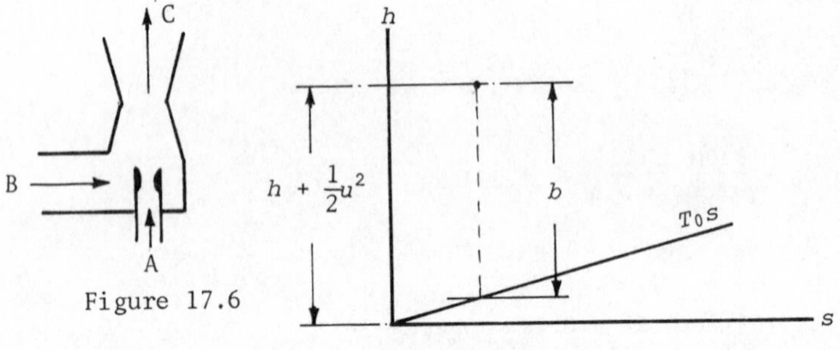

Figure 17.6

The value of b is given graphically by the vertical distance between the line which represents the quantity $T_0 s$ and the point representing the value $h + u^2/2$.

There are three conditions to be satisfied in this problem.

(1) Conservation of mass

(2) Conservation of axial momentum

(3) Conservation of energy

Additionally there must be a statement regarding irreversibility.

Let subscript A refer to the high-speed steam

Let subscript B refer to the saturated steam

Let subscript C refer to the emergent steam

Mass continuity

$$\dot{m}_A + \dot{m}_B = \dot{m}_C \qquad (1)$$

Momentum

$$\dot{m}_A u_A = \dot{m}_C u_C = \left(\dot{m}_A + \dot{m}_B\right) u_C \qquad (2) \qquad \dot{m}_B u_B = 0$$

Energy

$$\dot{m}_A\left(h_A + \frac{1}{2}u_A^2\right) + \dot{m}_B\left(h_B + \frac{1}{2}u_B^2\right) = \dot{m}_C\left(h_C + \frac{1}{2}u_C^2\right) \qquad (3)$$

Availability

$$\dot{I} = \dot{m}_A b_A + \dot{m}_B b_B - \dot{m}_C b_C \qquad (4)$$

and $b = h - T_0 s + \frac{1}{2}u^2$

Interpolating in the steam tables at 0.069 bar

$$h_A = 162 + 0.84(2409.6) = 2186.1 \ \frac{\text{kJ}}{\text{kg}}$$

$$s_A = 0.550 + 0.84(7.724) = 7.038 \ \frac{\text{kJ}}{\text{K kg}}$$

Also $h_B = 2572 \ \frac{\text{kJ}}{\text{kg}}$

(saturated steam)

and $s_B = 8.274 \ \frac{\text{kJ}}{\text{K kg}}$

From equation (2) we get

$$u_C = \frac{\dot{m}_A u_A}{\left(\dot{m}_A + \dot{m}_B\right)} = \frac{1.134 \times 1128}{1.584} = 807.5 \ \frac{\text{m}}{\text{s}}$$

Thus substituting in (3)

$$h_C = \frac{\dot{m}_A\left(h_A + \frac{1}{2}u_A^2\right) + \dot{m}_B\left(h_B + \frac{1}{2}u_B^2\right)}{\dot{m}_A + \dot{m}_B} - \frac{1}{2}u_C^2$$

$$\frac{1}{2}u_A^2 = \frac{1128}{2} \ \frac{\text{m}}{\text{s}} \ \frac{[\text{kJ}]}{[10^3 \text{ Nm}]} \frac{[\text{N s}^2]}{[\text{kg m}]} = 636.2 \ \frac{\text{kJ}}{\text{kg}}$$

$$\frac{1}{2}u_B^2 = \frac{91^2}{2000} = 4.1 \ \frac{\text{kJ}}{\text{kg}}$$

$$\frac{1}{2}u_C^2 = \frac{807.5^2}{2000} = 326 \ \frac{\text{kJ}}{\text{kg}}$$

Thus $h_C = \frac{1.134(2186.1 + 636.2) + 0.45(2572 + 4.1)}{1.584} = 2426.3 \ \frac{\text{kJ}}{\text{kg}}$

and $x_C = \frac{2426.3 - 162}{2409.6} = 0.94$

thus $s_C = 0.550 + 0.94(7.724) = 7.811 \ \frac{kJ}{K\ kg}$

Thus substituting in (4) we get

$$\dot{I} = 1.134 \ \frac{kg}{s}[2186.1 - (312)(7.038)] \ \frac{kJ}{kg}$$

$$+ 0.45 \ \frac{kg}{s}[2572 - (312)(8.274)] \ \frac{kJ}{kg}$$

$$- 1.584 \ \frac{kg}{s}[2426.3 - (312)(7.819)] \ \frac{kJ}{kg}$$

(since $T_0 = 39 + 273 = 312$ K from page 3 of tables)

$$\dot{I} = -10.55 - 4.3 + 16.96 = 2.1 \text{ kW}$$

Further Examples

7. A desuperheater is a device used in steam plant wherein a flow of water mixes with a flow of superheated steam such that the emergent stream is either saturated steam or wet steam.

In a given case 200 000 kg/h of water at 120 °C mix with 500 000 kg/h of steam at 7 bar and 300 °C under adiabatic conditions.

Calculate the loss in available energy expressed as a percentage of the original and referred to a datum temperature of 288 K.
(2.8%)

8. Referring again to example 15.9 and assuming additionally that the fluid leaving the condenser is saturated liquid, construct a table of values of h, s, $T_0 s$ and b for the principal state points 1 to 5 inclusive.

Hence calculate the irreversibilities of the two turbine sections, the condenser and the heat exchanger per kg passing through the boiler.
($i_{\text{HP Turbine}} = 33.1$ kJ/kg, $i_{\text{LP Turbine}} = 48.4$ kJ/kg,

$i_{\text{Condenser}} = 274$ kJ/kg, $i_{\text{Heat exchanger}} = 365.6$ kJ/kg)

9. A preheater is a device in which hot gases from a furnace are used to preheat the air to be used in combustion.

Given the following data, assuming no heat transfer with the environment and assuming air to be at low temperature with its properties given in the tables page 20 calculate the rate of irreversibility of the heat exchange process and also the effectiveness.

Data: $p_{gas} = p_{air} = p_0$

$\dot{m}_{gas} = 45000$ kg/h; $\dot{m}_{air} = 42000$ kg/h;

c_p (gas) = 1.09 kJ/(kg K); c_v (gas) = 0.872 kJ/(kg K);

Temperatures: Gas at entry 315 °C; Gas at exit 200 °C;
Air at entry 38 °C.

($\dot{I}$ = 0.364 MW, ε = 0.466)